Literature

EN 12: Texts and Contexts II

Edited by Frank Moliterno

Bedford/St. Martin's   BOSTON ◆ NEW YORK

Contents

CONTENTS

WILLIAM BLAKE   [1757–1827]

The Chimney Sweeper

William Blake (1757–1827) was born and raised in London. His only formal schooling was in art — he studied for a year at the Royal Academy and was apprenticed to an engraver. He later worked as a professional engraver, doing commissions and illustrations, assisted by his wife, Catherine Boucher. Blake, who had started writing poetry at the age of eleven, later engraved and handprinted his own poems, in very small batches, with his own illustrations. His early work was possessed of a strong social conscience, and his mature work turned increasingly mythic and prophetic.

When my mother died I was very young,
And my father sold me while yet my tongue
Could scarcely cry " 'weep! 'weep! 'weep! 'weep!"
So your chimneys I sweep, & in soot I sleep.

There's little Tom Dacre, who cried when his head   5
That curl'd like a lamb's back, was shav'd, so I said,
"Hush, Tom! never mind it, for when your head's bare,
You know that the soot cannot spoil your white hair."

And so he was quiet, & that very night,
As Tom was a-sleeping, he had such a sight!   10
That thousands of sweepers, Dick, Joe, Ned, & Jack,
Were all of them lock'd up in coffins of black;

And by came an Angel who had a bright key,
And he open'd the coffins & set them all free;
Then down a green plain, leaping, laughing, they run,   15
And wash in the river, and shine in the sun.

Then naked & white, all their bags left behind,
They rise upon clouds, and sport in the wind.
And the Angel told Tom, if he'd be a good boy,
He'd have God for his father & never want joy.   20

• • •

And so Tom awoke; and we rose in the dark,
And got with our bags & our brushes to work.
Tho' the morning was cold, Tom was happy & warm;
So if all do their duty, they need not fear harm.

[1789]

WILLIAM BLAKE [1757–1827]

The Garden of Love

William Blake (1757–1827) was born and raised in London. His only formal schooling was in art — he studied for a year at the Royal Academy and was apprenticed to an engraver. He later worked as a professional engraver, doing commissions and illustrations, assisted by his wife, Catherine Boucher. Blake, who had started writing poetry at the age of eleven, later engraved and handprinted his own poems, in very small batches, with his own illustrations. His early work was possessed of a strong social conscience, and his mature work turned increasingly mythic and prophetic.

I went to the Garden of Love,
And saw what I never had seen:
A Chapel was built in the midst,
Where I used to play on the green.

And the gates of this Chapel were shut,   5
And "Thou shalt not" writ over the door;
So I turn'd to the Garden of Love,
That so many sweet flowers bore,

And I saw it was filled with graves,
And tomb-stones where flowers should be;   10
And Priests in black gowns were walking their rounds,
And binding with briars my joys & desires.

[1794]

WILLIAM BLAKE [1757–1827]

The Lamb

William Blake (1757–1827) was born and raised in London. His only formal schooling was in art—he studied for a year at the Royal Academy and was apprenticed to an engraver. He later worked as a professional engraver, doing commissions and illustrations, assisted by his wife, Catherine Boucher. Blake, who had started writing poetry at the age of eleven, later engraved and handprinted his own poems, in very small batches, with his own illustrations. His early work was possessed of a strong social conscience, and his mature work turned increasingly mythic and prophetic.

Little Lamb, who made thee?
Dost thou know who made thee?
Gave thee life & bid thee feed,
By the stream & o'er the mead;
Gave thee clothing of delight, 5
Softest clothing wooly bright;
Gave thee such a tender voice,
Making all the vales rejoice!
   Little Lamb who made thee?
   Dost thou know who made thee? 10

Little Lamb I'll tell thee,
Little Lamb I'll tell thee!
He is callèd by thy name,
For he calls himself a Lamb:
He is meek & he is mild, 15
He became a little child:
I a child & thou a lamb,
We are callèd by his name.
   Little Lamb God bless thee.
   Little Lamb God bless thee. 20

[1789]

WILLIAM BLAKE   [1757–1827]

The Little Black Boy

William Blake (1757–1827) was born and raised in London. His only
formal schooling was in art — he studied for a year at the Royal Academy and was apprenticed to an engraver. He later worked as a professional engraver, doing commissions and illustrations, assisted by his
wife, Catherine Boucher. Blake, who had started writing poetry at the
age of eleven, later engraved and handprinted his own poems, in very
small batches, with his own illustrations. His early work was possessed of a strong social conscience, and his mature work turned increasingly mythic and prophetic.

My mother bore me in the southern wild,
And I am black, but O! my soul is white;
White as an angel is the English child,
But I am black as if bereav'd of light.

My mother taught me underneath a tree,   5
And sitting down before the heat of day,
She took me on her lap and kissèd me,
And pointing to the east, began to say:

"Look on the rising sun: there God does live
And gives his light, and gives his heat away;   10
And flowers and trees and beasts and men receive
Comfort in morning, joy in the noon day.

"And we are put on earth a little space,
That we may learn to bear the beams of love,
And these black bodies and this sun-burnt face   15
Is but a cloud, and like a shady grove.

"For when our souls have learn'd the heat to bear,
The cloud will vanish; we shall hear his voice,
Saying: 'Come out from the grove, my love & care,
And round my golden tent like lambs rejoice.'"   20

• • •

5

Thus did my mother say, and kissèd me;
And thus I say to little English boy:
When I from black and he from white cloud free,
And round the tent of God like lambs we joy,

I'll shade him from the heat till he can bear   25
To lean in joy upon our father's knee.
And then I'll stand and stroke his silver hair,
And be like him, and he will then love me.

[1789]

WILLIAM BLAKE [1757–1827]

London

William Blake (1757–1827) was born and raised in London. His only
formal schooling was in art—he studied for a year at the Royal Academy and was apprenticed to an engraver. He later worked as a professional engraver, doing commissions and illustrations, assisted by his
wife, Catherine Boucher. Blake, who had started writing poetry at the
age of eleven, later engraved and handprinted his own poems, in very
small batches, with his own illustrations. His early work was possessed of a strong social conscience, and his mature work turned increasingly mythic and prophetic.

I wander through each chartered street,
Near where the chartered Thames does flow,
And mark in every face I meet
Marks of weakness, marks of woe.

In every cry of every man,   5
In every infant's cry of fear,
In every voice, in every ban,
The mind-forged manacles I hear.

How the chimney-sweeper's cry
Every black'ning church appalls;   10
And the hapless soldier's sigh
Runs in blood down palace walls.

But most through midnight streets I hear
How the youthful harlot's curse
Blasts the new-born infant's tear,   15
And blights with plagues the marriage hearse.

[1794]

WILLIAM BLAKE [1757–1827]

A Poison Tree

William Blake (1757–1827) was born and raised in London. His only formal schooling was in art — he studied for a year at the Royal Academy and was apprenticed to an engraver. He later worked as a professional engraver, doing commissions and illustrations, assisted by his wife, Catherine Boucher. Blake, who had started writing poetry at the age of eleven, later engraved and handprinted his own poems, in very small batches, with his own illustrations. His early work was possessed of a strong social conscience, and his mature work turned increasingly mythic and prophetic.

I was angry with my friend:
I told my wrath, my wrath did end.
I was angry with my foe:
I told it not, my wrath did grow.

And I waterd it in fears,   5
Night & morning with my tears;
And I sunnèd it with smiles,
And with soft deceitful wiles.

And it grew both day and night,
Till it bore an apple bright.   10
And my foe beheld it shine,
And he knew that it was mine,

And into my garden stole,
When the night had veild the pole;
In the morning glad I see   15
My foe outstretchd beneath the tree.

[1794]

WILLIAM BLAKE   [1757–1827]

The Sick Rose

William Blake (1757–1827) was born and raised in London. His only formal schooling was in art — he studied for a year at the Royal Academy and was apprenticed to an engraver. He later worked as a professional engraver, doing commissions and illustrations, assisted by his wife, Catherine Boucher. Blake, who had started writing poetry at the age of eleven, later engraved and handprinted his own poems, in very small batches, with his own illustrations. His early work was possessed of a strong social conscience, and his mature work turned increasingly mythic and prophetic.

O Rose, thou art sick.
The invisible worm
That flies in the night
In the howling storm

Has found out thy bed   5
Of crimson joy,
And his dark secret love
Does thy life destroy.

[1794]

WILLIAM BLAKE [1757–1827]

The Tyger

William Blake (1757–1827) was born and raised in London. His only formal schooling was in art—he studied for a year at the Royal Academy and was apprenticed to an engraver. He later worked as a professional engraver, doing commissions and illustrations, assisted by his wife, Catherine Boucher. Blake, who had started writing poetry at the age of eleven, later engraved and handprinted his own poems, in very small batches, with his own illustrations. His early work was possessed of a strong social conscience, and his mature work turned increasingly mythic and prophetic.

Tyger, Tyger, burning bright
In the forests of the night,
What immortal hand or eye
Could frame thy fearful symmetry?

In what distant deeps or skies   5
Burnt the fire of thine eyes?
On what wings dare he aspire?
What the hand, dare seize the fire?

And what shoulder, & what art,
Could twist the sinews of thy heart?   10
And when thy heart began to beat,
What dread hand? & what dread feet?

What the hammer? what the chain?
In what furnace was thy brain?
What the anvil? what dread grasp   15
Dare its deadly terrors clasp?

When the stars threw down their spears
And water'd heaven with their tears,
Did he smile his work to see?
Did he who made the Lamb make thee?   20

Tyger, Tyger, burning bright
In the forests of the night,
What immortal hand or eye
Dare frame thy fearful symmetry?

[1794]

ROBERT BROWNING   [1812–1889]

My Last Duchess

Ferrara°

Robert Browning (1812–1889) was the son of a bank clerk in Camberwell, then a suburb of London. As an aspiring poet in 1844, Browning admired Elizabeth Barrett's poetry and began a correspondence with her that led to one of the world's most famous romances. His and Elizabeth's courtship lasted until 1846, when they were secretly wed and ran off to Italy, where they lived until Elizabeth's death in 1861. The years in Florence were among the happiest for both of them. To her he dedicated *Men and Women*, which contains his best poetry. Although she was the more popular poet during their time together, his reputation grew upon his return to London, after her death, assisted somewhat by public sympathy for him. The late 1860s were the peak of his career: he and Tennyson were mentioned together as the foremost poets of the age.

That's my last Duchess° painted on the wall,
Looking as if she were alive. I call
That piece a wonder, now: Frà Pandolf's° hands
Worked busily a day, and there she stands.
Will't please you sit and look at her? I said   5
"Frà Pandolf" by design, for never read
Strangers like you that pictured countenance,
The depth and passion of its earnest glance,
But to myself they turned (since none puts by
The curtain I have drawn for you, but I)   10
And seemed as they would ask me, if they durst,
How such a glance came there; so, not the first
Are you to turn and ask thus. Sir, 'twas not
Her husband's presence only, called that spot
Of joy into the Duchess' cheek: perhaps   15
Frà Pandolf chanced to say "Her mantle laps

Ferrara: The poem is based on events that occurred in the life of Alfonso II, duke of Ferrara in Italy, in the sixteenth century.
1. last Duchess: Ferrara's first wife, Lucrezia, died in 1561 at age seventeen after three years of marriage.
3. Frà Pandolf: Brother Pandolf, a fictional painter.

Over my lady's wrist too much," or "Paint
Must never hope to reproduce the faint
Half-flush that dies along her throat:" such stuff
Was courtesy, she thought, and cause enough   20
For calling up that spot of joy. She had
A heart—how shall I say?—too soon made glad,
Too easily impressed; she liked whate'er
She looked on, and her looks went everywhere.
Sir, 'twas all one! My favor at her breast,   25
The dropping of the daylight in the West,
The bough of cherries some officious fool
Broke in the orchard for her, the white mule
She rode with round the terrace—all and each
Would draw from her alike the approving speech,   30
Or blush, at least. She thanked men,—good! but thanked
Somehow—I know not how—as if she ranked
My gift of a nine-hundred-years-old name
With anybody's gift. Who'd stoop to blame
This sort of trifling? Even had you skill   35
In speech—(which I have not)—to make your will
Quite clear to such an one, and say, "Just this
Or that in you disgusts me; here you miss,
Or there exceed the mark"—and if she let
Herself be lessoned so, nor plainly set   40
Her wits to yours, forsooth, and made excuse,
—E'en then would be some stooping; and I choose
Never to stoop. Oh sir, she smiled, no doubt,
Whene'er I passed her; but who passed without
Much the same smile? This grew; I gave commands;   45
Then all smiles stopped together. There she stands
As if alive. Will't please you rise? We'll meet
The company below, then. I repeat,
The Count your master's known munificence
Is ample warrant that no just pretence   50
Of mine for dowry will be disallowed;
Though his fair daughter's self, as I avowed
At starting, is my object. Nay, we'll go
Together down, sir. Notice Neptune, though,
Taming a sea-horse, thought a rarity,   55
Which Claus of Innsbruck° cast in bronze for me!

                                                         [1842]

56. Claus of Innsbruck: A fictional sculptor.

ROBERT BROWNING   [1812–1889]

Porphyria's Lover

Robert Browning (1812–1889) was the son of a bank clerk in Camberwell, then a suburb of London. As an aspiring poet in 1844, Browning
admired Elizabeth Barrett's poetry and began a correspondence with
her that led to one of the world's most famous romances. His and Elizabeth's courtship lasted until 1846, when they were secretly wed and
ran off to Italy, where they lived until Elizabeth's death in 1861. The
years in Florence were among the happiest for both of them. To her he
dedicated *Men and Women*, which contains his best poetry. Although
she was the more popular poet during their time together, his reputation grew upon his return to London, after her death, assisted somewhat by public sympathy for him. The late 1860s were the peak of his
career: he and Tennyson were mentioned together as the foremost
poets of the age.

The rain set early in tonight,
   The sullen wind was soon awake,
It tore the elm-tops down for spite,
   And did its worst to vex the lake:
   I listened with heart fit to break.   5
When glided in Porphyria; straight
   She shut the cold out and the storm,
And kneeled and made the cheerless grate
   Blaze up, and all the cottage warm;
   Which done, she rose, and from her form   10
Withdrew the dripping cloak and shawl,
   And laid her soiled gloves by, untied
Her hat and let the damp hair fall,
   And, last, she sat down by my side
   And called me. When no voice replied,   15
She put my arm about her waist,
   And made her smooth white shoulder bare,
And all her yellow hair displaced,
   And, stooping, made my cheek lie there,
   And spread, o'er all, her yellow hair,   20
Murmuring how she loved me — she
   Too weak, for all her heart's endeavor,

To set its struggling passion free
   From pride, and vainer ties dissever,
   And give herself to me forever.   25
But passion sometimes would prevail,
   Nor could tonight's gay feast restrain
A sudden thought of one so pale
   For love of her, and all in vain:
   So, she was come through wind and rain.   30
Be sure I looked up at her eyes
   Happy and proud; at last I knew
Porphyria worshiped me: surprise
   Made my heart swell, and still it grew
   While I debated what to do.   35
That moment she was mine, mine, fair,
   Perfectly pure and good: I found
A thing to do, and all her hair
   In one long yellow string I wound
   Three times her little throat around,   40
And strangled her. No pain felt she;
   I am quite sure she felt no pain.
As a shut bud that holds a bee,
   I warily oped her lids: again
   Laughed the blue eyes without a stain.   45
And I untightened next the tress
   About her neck; her cheek once more
Blushed bright beneath my burning kiss:
   I propped her head up as before,
   Only, this time my shoulder bore   50
Her head, which droops upon it still:
   The smiling rosy little head,
So glad it has its utmost will,
   That all it scorned at once is fled,
   And I, its love, am gained instead!   55
Porphyria's love: she guessed not how
   Her darling one wish would be heard.
And thus we sit together now,
   And all night long we have not stirred,
   And yet God has not said a word!   60

[1836, 1842]

T. S. ELIOT [1888–1965]

The Love Song of
J. Alfred Prufrock

Born and raised in St. Louis, **T. S. [Thomas Stearns] Eliot** (1888–1965) went to prep school in Massachusetts and then to Harvard University, where he earned an M.A. in philosophy in 1910 and started his doctoral dissertation. He studied at the Sorbonne, in Paris, and then in Marburg, Germany, in 1914, when the war forced him to leave. Relocating to Oxford, he abandoned philosophy for poetry, and he married. After teaching and working in a bank, he became an editor at Faber and Faber and editor of the journal *Criterion* and was the dominant force in English poetry for several decades. He became a British citizen and a member of the Church of England in 1927. He won the Nobel Prize in literature in 1948. He also wrote plays and essays as well as a series of poems on cats that became the basis of a musical by Andrew Lloyd Weber. The Eliot poems included in this anthology show the poet's use of collage techniques to relate the fragmentation he saw in the culture and individual psyches of his day.

> *S'io credesse che mia risposta fosse*
> *A persona che mai tornasse al mondo,*
> *Questa fiamma staria senza piu scosse.*
> *Ma perciocche giammai di questo fondo*
> *Non torno vivo alcun, s'i'odo il vero,*
> *Senza tema d'infamia ti rispondo.*°

Let us go then, you and I,
When the evening is spread out against the sky
Like a patient etherised upon a table;

Epigraph: "If I thought that my answer were being made to someone who would ever return to earth, this flame would remain without further movement; but since no one has ever returned alive from this depth, if what I hear is true, I answer you without fear of infamy" (Dante, *Inferno* 27.61–66). Dante encounters Guido de Montefeltro in the eighth circle of hell, where souls are trapped within flames (tongues of fire) as punishment for giving evil counsel. Guido tells Dante details about his evil life only because he assumes that Dante is on his way to an even deeper circle in hell and will never return to earth and be able to repeat what he has heard.

Let us go, through certain half-deserted streets,
The muttering retreats   5
Of restless nights in one-night cheap hotels
And sawdust restaurants with oyster-shells:
Streets that follow like a tedious argument
Of insidious intent
To lead you to an overwhelming question . . .   10
Oh, do not ask, "What is it?"
Let us go and make our visit.

    In the room the women come and go
Talking of Michelangelo.

    The yellow fog that rubs its back upon the window-panes,   15
The yellow smoke that rubs its muzzle on the window-panes
Licked its tongue into the corners of the evening,
Lingered upon the pools that stand in drains,
Let fall upon its back the soot that falls from chimneys,
Slipped by the terrace, made a sudden leap,   20
And seeing that it was a soft October night,
Curled once about the house, and fell asleep.

    And indeed there will be time
For the yellow smoke that slides along the street,
Rubbing its back upon the window-panes;   25
There will be time, there will be time
To prepare a face to meet the faces that you meet;
There will be time to murder and create,
And time for all the works and days° of hands
That lift and drop a question on your plate;   30
Time for you and time for me,
And time yet for a hundred indecisions,
And for a hundred visions and revisions,
Before the taking of a toast and tea.

    In the room the women come and go   35
Talking of Michelangelo.

    And indeed there will be time
To wonder, "Do I dare?" and, "Do I dare?"
Time to turn back and descend the stair,

---

29. works and days: *Works and Days* is the title of a didactic poem about farming by the Greek poet Hesiod (eighth century B.C.E.) that includes instruction about doing each task at the proper time.

16

With a bald spot in the middle of my hair—   40
[They will say: "How his hair is growing thin!"]
My morning coat, my collar mounting firmly to the chin,
My necktie rich and modest, but asserted by a simple pin—
[They will say: "But how his arms and legs are thin!"]
Do I dare   45
Disturb the universe?
In a minute there is time
For decisions and revisions which a minute will reverse.

   For I have known them all already, known them all:—
Have known the evenings, mornings, afternoons,   50
I have measured out my life with coffee spoons;
I know the voices dying with a dying fall°
Beneath the music from a farther room.
   So how should I presume?

   And I have known the eyes already, known them all—   55
The eyes that fix you in a formulated phrase,
And when I am formulated, sprawling on a pin,
When I am pinned and wriggling on the wall,
Then how should I begin
To spit out all the butt-ends of my days and ways?   60
   And how should I presume?

   And I have known the arms already, known them all—
Arms that are braceleted and white and bare
[But in the lamplight, downed with light brown hair!]
Is it perfume from a dress   65
That makes me so digress?
Arms that lie along a table, or wrap about a shawl.
   And should I then presume?
   And how should I begin?

          •   •   •

Shall I say, I have gone at dusk through narrow streets   70
And watched the smoke that rises from the pipes
Of lonely men in shirt-sleeves, leaning out of windows? . . .

   I should have been a pair of ragged claws
Scuttling across the floors of silent seas.

---

52. a dying fall: An allusion to Shakespeare's *Twelfth Night* (1.1.4): "That strain [of music] again! It had a dying fall" (a cadence that falls away).

. . .

And the afternoon, the evening, sleeps so peacefully!   75
Smoothed by long fingers,
Asleep . . . tired . . . or it malingers,
Stretched on the floor, here beside you and me.
Should I, after tea and cakes and ices,
Have the strength to force the moment to its crisis?   80
But though I have wept and fasted, wept and prayed,
Though I have seen my head [grown slightly bald] brought in upon a
        platter,°
I am no prophet — and here's no great matter;
I have seen the moment of my greatness flicker,
And I have seen the eternal Footman hold my coat, and snicker,   85
And in short, I was afraid.

    And would it have been worth it, after all,
After the cups, the marmalade, the tea,
Among the porcelain, among some talk of you and me,
Would it have been worth while,   90
To have bitten off the matter with a smile,
To have squeezed the universe into a ball
To roll it toward some overwhelming question,
To say: "I am Lazarus,° come from the dead,
Come back to tell you all, I shall tell you all"—   95
If one, settling a pillow by her head,
    Should say: "That is not what I meant at all.
    That is not it, at all."

    And would it have been worth it, after all,
Would it have been worth while,   100
After the sunsets and the dooryards and the sprinkled streets,
After the novels, after the teacups, after the skirts that trail along the
        floor—
And this, and so much more?—
It is impossible to say just what I mean!
But as if a magic lantern threw the nerves in patterns on a screen: 105
Would it have been worth while
If one, settling a pillow or throwing off a shawl,

82. **head . . . platter:** As a reward for dancing before King Herod, Salome, his
stepdaughter, asked for the head of John the Baptist to be presented to her on a
platter (Matthew 14:1–12; Mark 6:17–28).
94. **Lazarus:** Either the beggar Lazarus, who in Luke 16:19–31 did not return
from the dead, or Jesus' friend Lazarus, who did (John 11:1–44).

And turning toward the window, should say:
  "That is not it at all,
  That is not what I meant, at all."   110

      • • •

No! I am not Prince Hamlet, nor was meant to be;
Am an attendant lord, one that will do
To swell a progress,° start a scene or two,
Advise the prince; no doubt, an easy tool,
Deferential, glad to be of use,   115
Politic, cautious, and meticulous;
Full of high sentence,° but a bit obtuse;   *sententiousness*
At times, indeed, almost ridiculous—
Almost, at times, the Fool.

  I grow old . . . I grow old . . .   120
I shall wear the bottoms of my trousers rolled.°   *turned up, with cuffs*

  Shall I part my hair behind? Do I dare to eat a peach?
I shall wear white flannel trousers, and walk upon the beach.
I have heard the mermaids singing, each to each.

  I do not think that they will sing to me.   125

  I have seen them riding seaward on the waves
Combing the white hair of the waves blown back
When the wind blows the water white and black.

  We have lingered in the chambers of the sea
By sea-girls wreathed with seaweed red and brown   130
Till human voices wake us, and we drown.

                                  [1917]

113. **progress:** Ceremonial journey made by a royal court.

THOMAS HARDY [1840–1928]

The Convergence of the Twain

Lines on the Loss of the Titanic°

Thomas Hardy (1840–1928) was born in a cottage in Higher Bock-hampton, Dorset, near the regional market town of Dorchester in southwestern England. Apprenticed at age sixteen to an architect, he spent most of the next twenty years restoring old churches. Having always had an interest in literature, he started writing novels in his thirties, publishing more than a dozen, including *Tess of the D'Urbervilles* (1891) and *Jude the Obscure* (1895). In 1896 Hardy gave up prose and turned to poetry, writing verse until his death at age eighty-eight. He had a consistently bleak, even pessimistic, outlook on life. Many of his works stress the dark effects of "hap" (happenstance, coincidence) in the world, a central motif in "The Convergence of the Twain."

1

In a solitude of the sea
Deep from human vanity,
And the Pride of Life that planned her, stilly couches she.

2

Steel chambers, late the pyres
Of her salamandrine° fires,   5
Cold currents thrid,° and turn to rhythmic tidal lyres.   *thread*

3

Over the mirrors meant
To glass the opulent
The sea-worm crawls—grotesque, slimed, dumb, indifferent.

5. salamandrine: Fierce, inextinguishable (the lizardlike salamander supposedly is able to resist or live in fire).

Titanic: A famous luxury ocean liner, largest of its time and considered unsinkable. It collided with an iceberg on its maiden voyage, 15 April 1912, and sank. Of some 2,200 people aboard, more than 1,500 were lost.

4

Jewels in joy designed   10
To ravish the sensuous mind
Lie lightless, all their sparkles bleared and black and blind.

5

Dim moon-eyed fishes near
Gaze at the gilded gear
And query: "What does this vaingloriousness down here?"   15

6

Well: while was fashioning
This creature of cleaving wing,
The Immanent Will that stirs and urges everything

7

Prepared a sinister mate
For her—so gaily great—   20
A Shape of Ice, for the time far and dissociate.

8

And as the smart ship grew
In stature, grace, and hue,
In shadowy silent distance grew the Iceberg too.

9

Alien they seemed to be: 25
No mortal eye could see
The intimate welding of their later history,

10

Or sign that they were bent
By paths coincident
On being anon twin halves of one august event,   30

11

Till the Spinner of the Years
Said "Now!" And each one hears,
And consummation comes, and jars two hemispheres.

[1912]

21

THOMAS HARDY [1840–1928]

The Ruined Maid

Thomas Hardy (1840–1928) was born in a cottage in Higher Bock-
hampton, Dorset, near the regional market town of Dorchester in
southwestern England. Apprenticed at age sixteen to an architect, he
spent most of the next twenty years restoring old churches. Having always had an interest in literature, he started writing novels in his thirties, publishing more than a dozen, including *Tess of the D'Urbervilles*
(1891) and *Jude the Obscure* (1895). In 1896 Hardy gave up prose and
turned to poetry, writing verse until his death at age eighty-eight. He
had a consistently bleak, even pessimistic, outlook on life.

"O 'Melia, my dear, this does everything crown!
Who could have supposed I should meet you in Town?
And whence such fair garments, such prosperi-ty?"—
"O didn't you know I'd been ruined?" said she.

—"You left us in tatters, without shoes or socks,   5
Tired of digging potatoes, and spudding up docks,
And now you've gay bracelets and bright feathers three!"—
"Yes: that's how we dress when we're ruined," said she.

—"At home in the barton you said 'thee' and 'thou,'
And 'thik oon,' and 'theäs oon,' and 't'other'; but now   10
Your talking quite fits 'ee for high compa-ny!"—
"Some polish is gained with one's ruin," said she.

—"Your hands were like paws then, your face blue and bleak
But now I'm bewitched by your delicate cheek,
And your little gloves fit as on any la-dy!"—   15
"We never do work when we're ruined," said she.

—"You used to call home-life a hag-ridden dream,
And you'd sigh, and you'd sock; but at present you seem
To know not of megrims or melancho-ly!"—
"True. One's pretty lively when ruined," said she.   20

• • •

22

—"I wish I had feathers, a fine sweeping gown,
And a delicate face, and could strut about Town!"—
"My dear—a raw country girl, such as you be,
Cannot quite expect that. You ain't ruined," said she.

[1901]

NATHANIEL HAWTHORNE [1804–1864]

Young Goodman Brown

Born in Salem, Massachusetts, into a family descended from the New England Puritans, **Nathaniel Hawthorne** (1804–1864) graduated from Bowdoin College, Maine, in 1825. For the next twelve years he lived in Salem in relative seclusion, reading, observing the New England landscape and people, and writing his first novel, *Fanshawe* (published anonymously in 1828), and the first series of *Twice-Told Tales* (1837). (The second series, published in 1842, was reviewed by Edgar Allan Poe and won some notice.) To support himself Hawthorne took a job in the Boston customhouse, resigning in 1841 to live at Brook Farm, a utopian community. The following year he left Brook Farm, married Sophia Peabody, and moved to Concord, Massachusetts, where his neighbors included Ralph Waldo Emerson and Henry David Thoreau. There he wrote the stories collected in *Mosses from an Old Manse* (1846). Returning to Salem, he took a position as a customs inspector and began full-time work on what was to become his most celebrated novel, *The Scarlet Letter* (1850). The novels *The House of the Seven Gables* (1851) and *The Blithedale Romance* (1852), based on his Brook Farm experience, quickly followed. Also in 1852, he wrote a campaign biography of Franklin Pierce, a former college friend who, on becoming president, appointed Hawthorne U.S. consul at Liverpool. Hawthorne's subsequent travels in Europe contributed to the novel *The Marble Faun* (1860), his last major work.

Young Goodman Brown came forth at sunset into the street at Salem village; but put his head back, after crossing the threshold, to exchange a parting kiss with his young wife. And Faith, as the wife was aptly named, thrust her own pretty head into the street, letting the wind play with the pink ribbons of her cap while she called to Goodman Brown.

"Dearest heart," whispered she, softly and rather sadly, when her lips were close to his ear, "prithee put off your journey until sunrise and sleep in your own bed to-night. A lone woman is troubled with such dreams and such thoughts that she's afeared of herself sometimes. Pray tarry with me this night, dear husband, of all nights in the year."

"My love and my Faith," replied young Goodman Brown, "of all nights in the year, this one night must I tarry away from thee. My journey, as

24

thou callest it, forth and back again, must needs be done 'twixt now and sunrise. What, my sweet, pretty wife, dost thou doubt me already, and we but three months married?"

"Then God bless you!" said Faith, with the pink ribbons, "and may you find all well when you come back."

"Amen!" cried Goodman Brown. "Say thy prayers, dear Faith, and go to bed at dusk, and no harm will come to thee."

So they parted; and the young man pursued his way until, being about to turn the corner by the meeting-house, he looked back and saw the head of Faith still peeping after him with a melancholy air, in spite of her pink ribbons.

"Poor little Faith!" thought he, for his heart smote him. "What a wretch am I to leave her on such an errand! She talks of dreams, too. Methought as she spoke there was trouble in her face, as if a dream had warned her what work is to be done to-night. But no, no; 't would kill her to think it. Well, she's a blessed angel on earth, and after this one night I'll cling to her skirts and follow her to heaven."

With this excellent resolve for the future, Goodman Brown felt himself justified in making more haste on his present evil purpose. He had taken a dreary road, darkened by all the gloomiest trees of the forest, which barely stood aside to let the narrow path creep through, and closed immediately behind. It was all as lonely as could be; and there is this peculiarity in such a solitude, that the traveller knows not who may be concealed by the innumerable trunks and the thick boughs overhead; so that with lonely footsteps he may yet be passing through an unseen multitude.

"There may be a devilish Indian behind every tree," said Goodman Brown to himself; and he glanced fearfully behind him as he added, "What if the devil himself should be at my very elbow!"

His head being turned back, he passed a crook of the road, and, looking forward again, beheld the figure of a man, in grave and decent attire, seated at the foot of an old tree. He arose at Goodman Brown's approach and walked onward side by side with him.

"You are late, Goodman Brown," said he. "The clock of the Old South was striking as I came through Boston, and that is full fifteen minutes agone."

"Faith kept me back a while," replied the young man, with a tremor in his voice, caused by the sudden appearance of his companion, though not wholly unexpected.

It was now deep dusk in the forest, and deepest in that part of it where these two were journeying. As nearly as could be discerned, the second traveller was about fifty years old, apparently in the same rank of life as Goodman Brown, and bearing a considerable resemblance to him,

25

though perhaps more in expression than features. Still they might have been taken for father and son. And yet, though the elder person was as simply clad as the younger, and as simple in manner too, he had an indescribable air of one who knew the world, and who would not have felt abashed at the governor's dinner table or in King William's court, were it possible that his affairs should call him thither. But the only thing about him that could be fixed upon as remarkable was his staff, which bore the likeness of a great black snake, so curiously wrought that it might almost be seen to twist and wriggle itself like a living serpent. This, of course, must have been an ocular deception, assisted by the uncertain light.

"Come, Goodman Brown," cried his fellow-traveller, "this is a dull pace for the beginning of a journey. Take my staff, if you are so soon weary."

"Friend," said the other, exchanging his slow pace for a full stop, "having kept covenant by meeting thee here, it is my purpose now to return whence I came. I have scruples touching the matter thou wot'st of."

"Sayest thou so?" replied he of the serpent, smiling apart. "Let us walk on, nevertheless, reasoning as we go; and if I convince thee not thou shalt turn back. We are but a little way in the forest yet."

"Too far! too far!" exclaimed the goodman, unconsciously resuming his walk. "My father never went into the woods on such an errand, nor his father before him. We have been a race of honest men and good Christians since the days of the martyrs; and shall I be the first of the name of Brown that ever took this path and kept"—

"Such company, thou wouldst say," observed the elder person, interpreting his pause. "Well said, Goodman Brown! I have been as well acquainted with your family as with ever a one among the Puritans; and that's no trifle to say. I helped your grandfather, the constable, when he lashed the Quaker woman so smartly through the streets of Salem; and it was I that brought your father a pitch-pine knot, kindled at my own hearth, to set fire to an Indian village, in King Philip's war.° They were my good friends, both; and many a pleasant walk have we had along this path, and returned merrily after midnight. I would fain be friends with you for their sake."

"If it be as thou sayest," replied Goodman Brown, "I marvel they never spoke of these matters; or, verily, I marvel not, seeing that the least rumor of the sort would have driven them from New England. We are a people of prayer, and good works to boot, and abide no such wickedness."

"Wickedness or not," said the traveller with the twisted staff, "I have a very general acquaintance here in New England. The deacons of many a

King Philip: Wampanoag chief who waged war against the New England colonists (1675–76).

26

church have drunk the communion wine with me; the selectmen of divers towns make me their chairman; and a majority of the Great and General Court are firm supporters of my interest. The governor and I, too—But these are state secrets."

"Can this be so?" cried Goodman Brown, with a stare of amazement at his undisturbed companion. "Howbeit, I have nothing to do with the governor and council; they have their own ways, and are no rule for a simple husbandman like me. But, were I to go on with thee, how should I meet the eye of that good old man, our minister, at Salem village? Oh, his voice would make me tremble both Sabbath day and lecture day."

Thus far the elder traveller had listened with due gravity; but now burst into a fit of irrepressible mirth, shaking himself so violently that his snake-like staff actually seemed to wriggle in sympathy.

"Ha! ha! ha!" shouted he again and again; then composing himself, "Well, go on, Goodman Brown, go on; but, prithee, don't kill me with laughing."

"Well, then, to end the matter at once," said Goodman Brown, considerably nettled, "there is my wife, Faith. It would break her dear little heart; and I'd rather break my own."

"Nay, if that be the case," answered the other, "e'en go thy ways, Goodman Brown. I would not for twenty old women like the one hobbling before us that Faith should come to any harm."

As he spoke he pointed his staff at a female figure on the path, in whom Goodman Brown recognized a very pious and exemplary dame, who had taught him his catechism in youth, and was still his moral and spiritual adviser, jointly with the minister and Deacon Gookin.

"A marvel, truly that Goody Cloyse should be so far in the wilderness at nightfall," said he. "But with your leave, friend, I shall take a cut through the woods until we have left this Christian woman behind. Being a stranger to you, she might ask whom I was consorting with and whither I was going."

"Be it so," said his fellow-traveller. "Betake you to the woods, and let me keep the path."

Accordingly the young man turned aside, but took care to watch his companion, who advanced softly along the road until he had come within a staff's length of the old dame. She, meanwhile, was making the best of her way, with singular speed for so aged a woman, and mumbling some indistinct words—a prayer, doubtless—as she went. The traveller put forth his staff and touched her withered neck with what seemed the serpent's tail.

"The devil!" screamed the pious old lady.

"Then Goody Cloyse knows her old friend?" observed the traveller, confronting her and leaning on his writhing stick.

"Ah, forsooth, and is it your worship indeed?" cried the good dame. "Yea, truly is it, and in the very image of my old gossip, Goodman Brown, the grandfather of the silly fellow that now is. But—would your worship believe it?—my broomstick hath strangely disappeared, stolen, as I suspect, by that unhanged witch, Goody Cory, and that, too, when I was all anointed with the juice of smallage, and cinquefoil, and wolf's bane"—

"Mingled with fine wheat and the fat of a new-born babe," said the shape of old Goodman Brown.

"Ah, your worship knows the recipe," cried the old lady, cackling aloud. "So, as I was saying, being all ready for the meeting, and no horse to ride on, I made up my mind to foot it; for they tell me there is a nice young man to be taken into communion to-night. But now your good worship will lend me your arm, and we shall be there in a twinkling."

"That can hardly be," answered her friend. "I may not spare you my arm, Goody Cloyse; but here is my staff, if you will."

So saying, he threw it down at her feet, where, perhaps, it assumed life, being one of the rods which its owner had formerly lent to the Egyptian magi. Of this fact, however, Goodman Brown could not take cognizance. He had cast up his eyes in astonishment, and, looking down again, beheld neither Goody Cloyse nor the serpentine staff, but his fellow-traveller alone, who waited for him as calmly as if nothing had happened.

"That old woman taught me my catechism," said the young man; and there was a world of meaning in this simple comment.

They continued to walk onward, while the elder traveller exhorted his companion to make good speed and persevere in the path, discoursing so aptly that his arguments seemed rather to spring up in the bosom of his auditor than to be suggested by himself. As they went, he plucked a branch of maple to serve for a walking stick, and began to strip it of the twigs and little boughs, which were wet with evening dew. The moment his fingers touched them they became strangely withered and dried up as with a week's sunshine. Thus the pair proceeded, at a good free pace, until suddenly, in a gloomy hollow of the road, Goodman Brown sat himself down on the stump of a tree and refused to go any farther.

"Friend," he said, stubbornly, "my mind is made up. Not another step will I budge on this errand. What if a wretched old woman do choose to go to the devil when I thought she was going to heaven: is that any reason why I should quit my dear Faith and go after her?"

"You will think better of this by and by," said his acquaintance, composedly. "Sit here and rest yourself a while; and when you feel like moving again, there is my staff to help you along."

Without more words, he threw his companion the maple stick, and was as speedily out of sight as if he had vanished into the deepening gloom. The young man sat a few moments by the roadside, applauding himself greatly, and thinking with how clear a conscience he should meet the minister in his morning walk, nor shrink from the eye of good old Deacon Gookin. And what calm sleep would be his that very night, which was to have been spent so wickedly, but so purely and sweetly now, in the arms of Faith! Amidst these pleasant and praiseworthy meditations, Goodman Brown heard the tramp of horses along the road, and deemed it advisable to conceal himself within the verge of the forest, conscious of the guilty purpose that had brought him thither, though now so happily turned from it.

On came the hoof tramps and the voices of the riders, two grave old voices, conversing soberly as they drew near. These mingled sounds appeared to pass along the road, within a few yards of the young man's hiding-place; but, owing doubtless to the depth of the gloom at that particular spot, neither the travellers nor their steeds were visible. Though their figures brushed the small boughs by the wayside, it could not be seen that they intercepted, even for a moment, the faint gleam from the strip of bright sky athwart which they must have passed. Goodman Brown alternately crouched and stood on tiptoe, pulling aside the branches and thrusting forth his head as far as he durst without discerning so much as a shadow. It vexed him the more, because he could have sworn, were such a thing possible, that he recognized the voices of the minister and Deacon Gookin, jogging along quietly, as they were wont to do, when bound to some ordination or ecclesiastical council. While yet within hearing, one of the riders stopped to pluck a switch.

"Of the two, reverend sir," said the voice like the deacon's, "I had rather miss an ordination dinner than to-night's meeting. They tell me that some of our community are to be here from Falmouth and beyond, and others from Connecticut and Rhode Island, besides several of the Indian powwows, who, after their fashion, know almost as much deviltry as the best of us. Moreover, there is a goodly young woman to be taken into communion."

"Mighty well, Deacon Gookin!" replied the solemn old tones of the minister. "Spur up, or we shall be late. Nothing can be done, you know, until I get on the ground."

The hoofs clattered again; and the voices, talking so strangely in the empty air, passed on through the forest, where no church had ever been gathered or solitary Christian prayed. Whither, then, could these holy men be journeying so deep into the heathen wilderness? Young Goodman Brown caught hold of a tree for support, being ready to sink down on the ground, faint and overburdened with the heavy sickness of his heart. He looked up to the sky, doubting whether there really was a heaven above him. Yet there was the blue arch, and the stars brightening in it.

"With heaven above and Faith below, I will yet stand firm against the devil!" cried Goodman Brown.

While he still gazed upward into the deep arch of the firmament and had lifted his hands to pray, a cloud, though no wind was stirring, hurried across the zenith and hid the brightening stars. The blue sky was still visible, except directly overhead, where this black mass of cloud was sweeping swiftly northward. Aloft in the air, as if from the depths of the cloud, came a confused and doubtful sound of voices. Once the listener fancied that he could distinguish the accents of towns-people of his own, men and women, both pious and ungodly, many of whom he had met at the communion table, and had seen others rioting at the tavern. The next moment, so indistinct were the sounds, he doubted whether he had heard aught but the murmur of the old forest, whispering without a wind. Then came a stronger swell of those familiar tones, heard daily in the sunshine at Salem village, but never until now from a cloud of night. There was one voice, of a young woman, uttering lamentations, yet with an uncertain sorrow, and entreating for some favor, which, perhaps, it would grieve her to obtain; and all the unseen multitude, both saints and sinners, seemed to encourage her onward.

"Faith!" shouted Goodman Brown, in a voice of agony and desperation; and the echoes of the forest mocked him, crying, "Faith! Faith!" as if bewildered wretches were seeking her all through the wilderness.

The cry of grief, rage, and terror was yet piercing the night, when the unhappy husband held his breath for a response. There was a scream, drowned immediately in a louder murmur of voices, fading into far-off laughter, as the dark cloud swept away, leaving the clear and silent sky above Goodman Brown. But something fluttered lightly down through the air and caught on the branch of a tree. The young man seized it, and beheld a pink ribbon.

"My Faith is gone!" cried he after one stupefied moment. "There is no good on earth; and sin is but a name. Come, devil; for to thee is this world given."

And, maddened with despair, so that he laughed loud and long, did Goodman Brown grasp his staff and set forth again, at such a rate that he seemed to fly along the forest path rather than to walk or run. The road grew wilder and drearier and more faintly traced, and vanished at length, leaving him in the heart of the dark wilderness, still rushing onward with the instinct that guides mortal man to evil. The whole forest was peopled with frightful sounds—the creaking of the trees, the howling of wild beasts, and the yell of Indians; while sometimes the wind tolled like a distant church bell, and sometimes gave a broad roar around the traveller, as if all Nature were laughing him to scorn. But he was himself the chief horror of the scene, and shrank not from its other horrors.

"Ha! ha! ha!" roared Goodman Brown when the wind laughed at him. "Let us hear which will laugh loudest. Think not to frighten me with your deviltry. Come witch, come wizard, come Indian powwow, come devil himself, and here comes Goodman Brown. You may as well fear him as he fear you."

In truth, all through the haunted forest there could be nothing more frightful than the figure of Goodman Brown. On he flew among the black pines, brandishing his staff with frenzied gestures, now giving vent to an inspiration of horrid blasphemy, and now shouting forth such laughter as set all the echoes of the forest laughing like demons around him. The fiend in his own shape is less hideous than when he rages in the breast of man. Thus sped the demoniac on his course, until, quivering among the trees, he saw a red light before him, as when the felled trunks and branches of a clearing have been set on fire, and throw up their lurid blaze against the sky, at the hour of midnight. He paused, in a lull of the tempest that had driven him onward, and heard the swell of what seemed a hymn, rolling solemnly from a distance with the weight of many voices. He knew the tune; it was a familiar one in the choir of the village meeting-house. The verse died heavily away, and was lengthened by a chorus, not of human voices, but of all the sounds of the benighted wilderness pealing in awful harmony together. Goodman Brown cried out, and his cry was lost to his own ear by its unison with the cry of the desert.

In the interval of silence he stole forward until the light glared full upon his eyes. At one extremity of an open space, hemmed in by the dark wall of the forest, arose a rock, bearing some rude, natural resemblance either to an altar or a pulpit, and surrounded by four blazing pines, their tops aflame, their stems untouched, like candles at an evening meeting. The mass of foliage that had overgrown the summit of the rock was all on fire, blazing high into the night and fitfully illuminating the whole field. Each pendent twig and leafy festoon was in a blaze. As the red light arose and fell, a numerous congregation alternately shone forth, then disappeared in shadow, and again grew, as it were, out of the darkness, peopling the heart of the solitary woods at once.

"A grave and dark-clad company," quoth Goodman Brown.

In truth they were such. Among them, quivering to and fro between gloom and splendor, appeared faces that would be seen next day at the council board of the province, and others which, Sabbath after Sabbath, looked devoutly heavenward, and benignantly over the crowded pews, from the holiest pulpits in the land. Some affirm that the lady of the governor was there. At least there were high dames well known to her, and wives of honored husbands, and widows, a great multitude, and ancient maidens, all of excellent repute, and fair young girls, who trembled lest their mothers should espy them. Either the sudden gleams of light flashing over the obscure field bedazzled Goodman Brown, or he recognized a score of the church members of Salem village famous for their especial sanctity. Good old Deacon Gookin had arrived, and waited at the skirts of that venerable saint, his revered pastor. But, irreverently consorting with these grave, reputable, and pious people, these elders of the church, these chaste dames and dewy virgins, there were men of dissolute lives and women of spotted fame, wretches given over to all mean and filthy vice, and suspected even of horrid crimes. It was strange to see that the good shrank not from the wicked, nor were the sinners abashed by the saints. Scattered also among their pale-faced enemies were the Indian priests, or powwows, who had often scared their native forest with more hideous incantations than any known to English witchcraft.

"But where is Faith?" thought Goodman Brown; and, as hope came into his heart, he trembled.

Another verse of the hymn arose, a slow and mournful strain, such as the pious love, but joined to words which expressed all that our nature can conceive of sin, and darkly hinted at far more. Unfathomable to mere mortals is the lore of fiends. Verse after verse was sung; and still the chorus of the desert swelled between like the deepest tone of a mighty organ; and with the final peal of that dreadful anthem there came a sound, as if the roaring wind, the rushing streams, the howling beasts, and every other voice of the unconcerted wilderness were mingling and according with the voice of guilty man in homage to the prince of all. The four blazing pines threw up a loftier flame, and obscurely discovered shapes and visages of horror on the smoke wreaths above the impious assembly. At the same moment the fire on the rock shot redly forth and formed a flowing arch above its base, where now appeared a figure. With reverence be it spoken, the figure bore no slight similitude, both in garb and manner, to some grave divine of the New England churches.

"Bring forth the converts!" cried a voice that echoed through the field and rolled into the forest.

At the word, Goodman Brown stepped forth from the shadow of the trees and approached the congregation, with whom he felt a loathful brotherhood by the sympathy of all that was wicked in his heart. He could have well-nigh sworn that the shape of his own dead father beckoned him to advance, looking downward from a smoke wreath, while a woman, with dim features of despair, threw out her hand to warn him back. Was it his mother? But he had no power to retreat one step, nor to resist, even in thought, when the minister and good old Deacon Gookin seized his arms and led him to the blazing rock. Thither came also the slender form of a veiled female, led between Goody Cloyse, that pious teacher of the catechism, and Martha Carrier, who had received the devil's promise to be queen of hell. A rampant hag was she. And there stood the proselytes beneath the canopy of fire.

"Welcome, my children," said the dark figure, "to the communion of your race. Ye have found thus young your nature and your destiny. My children, look behind you!"

They turned; and flashing forth, as it were, in a sheet of flame, the fiend worshippers were seen; the smile of welcome gleamed darkly on every visage.

"There," resumed the sable form, "are all whom ye have reverenced from youth. Ye deemed them holier than yourselves and shrank from your own sin, contrasting it with their lives of righteousness and prayerful aspirations heavenward. Yet here are they all in my worshipping assembly. This night it shall be granted you to know their secret deeds: how hoary-bearded elders of the church have whispered wanton words to the young maids of their households; how many a woman, eager for widows' weeds, has given her husband a drink at bedtime and let him sleep his last sleep in her bosom; how beardless youths have made haste to inherit their fathers' wealth; and how fair damsels—blush not, sweet ones—have dug little graves in the garden, and bidden me, the sole guest, to an infant's funeral. By the sympathy of your human hearts for sin ye shall scent out all the places—whether in church, bedchamber, street, field, or forest—where crime has been committed, and shall exult to behold the whole earth one stain of guilt, one mighty blood spot. Far more than this. It shall be yours to penetrate, in every bosom, the deep mystery of sin, the fountain of all wicked arts, and which inexhaustibly supplies more evil impulses than human power—than my power at its utmost—can make manifest in deeds. And now, my children, look upon each other."

They did so; and, by the blaze of the hell-kindled torches, the wretched man beheld his Faith, and the wife her husband, trembling before that unhallowed altar.

"Lo, there ye stand, my children," said the figure, in a deep and solemn tone, almost sad with its despairing awfulness, as if his once angelic nature could yet mourn for our miserable race. "Depending upon one another's hearts, ye had still hoped that virtue were not all a dream. Now are ye undeceived. Evil is the nature of mankind. Evil must be your only happiness. Welcome again, my children, to the communion of your race."

33

"Welcome," repeated the fiend worshippers, in one cry of despair and triumph.

And there they stood, the only pair, as it seemed, who were yet hesitating on the verge of wickedness in this dark world. A basin was hallowed, naturally, in the rock. Did it contain water, reddened by the lurid light? or was it blood? or, perchance, a liquid flame? Herein did the shape of evil dip his hand and prepare to lay the mark of baptism upon their foreheads, that they might be partakers of the mystery of sin, more conscious of the secret guilt of others, both in deed and thought, than they could now be of their own. The husband cast one look at his pale wife, and Faith at him. What polluted wretches would the next glance show them to each other, shuddering alike at what they disclosed and what they saw!

"Faith! Faith!" cried the husband, "look up to heaven, and resist the wicked one."

Whether Faith obeyed he knew not. Hardly had he spoken when he found himself amid calm night and solitude, listening to a roar of the wind which died heavily away through the forest. He staggered against the rock, and felt it chill and damp; while a hanging twig, that had been all on fire, besprinkled his cheek with the coldest dew.

The next morning young Goodman Brown came slowly into the street of Salem village, staring around him like a bewildered man. The good old minister was taking a walk along the graveyard to get an appetite for breakfast and meditate his sermon, and bestowed a blessing, as he passed, on Goodman Brown. He shrank from the venerable saint as if to avoid an anathema. Old Deacon Gookin was at domestic worship, and the holy words of his prayer were heard through the open window. "What God doth the wizard pray to?" quoth Goodman Brown. Goody Cloyse, that excellent old Christian, stood in the early sunshine at her own lattice, catechizing a little girl who had brought her a pint of morning's milk. Goodman Brown snatched away the child as from the grasp of the fiend himself. Turning the corner by the meeting-house, he spied the head of Faith, with the pink ribbons, gazing anxiously forth, and bursting into such joy at sight of him that she skipped along the street and almost kissed her husband before the whole village. But Goodman Brown looked sternly and sadly into her face, and passed on without a greeting.

Had Goodman Brown fallen asleep in the forest and only dreamed a wild dream of a witch meeting?

Be it so if you will; but, alas! it was a dream of evil omen for young Goodman Brown. A stern, a sad, a darkly meditative, a distrustful, if not a desperate man did he become from the night of that fearful dream. On the Sabbath day, when the congregation were singing a holy psalm, he could not listen because an anthem of sin rushed loudly upon his ear and drowned all the blessed strain. When the minister spoke from the pulpit with power and fervid eloquence, and, with his hand on the open Bible, of the sacred truths of our religion, and of saint-like lives and triumphant deaths, and of future bliss or misery unutterable, then did Goodman Brown turn pale, dreading lest the roof should thunder down upon the gray blasphemer and his hearers. Often, awaking suddenly at midnight, he shrank from the bosom of Faith; and at morning or eventide, when the family knelt down at prayer, he scowled and muttered to himself, and gazed sternly at his wife, and turned away. And when he had lived long, and was borne to his grave a hoary corpse, followed by Faith, an aged woman, and children and grandchildren, a goodly procession, besides neighbors not a few, they carved no hopeful verse upon his tombstone, for his dying hour was gloom.

[1835]

SEAMUS HEANEY   [b. 1939]

Digging

Raised on a small farm near Castledawson, County Derry, Northern Ireland, **Seamus Heaney** (b. 1939) was educated at St. Columb's College, a Catholic boarding school situated in the city of Derry, and then at Queen's University, Belfast. As a young English teacher in Belfast in the early 1960s, he joined a poetry workshop and began writing verse, subsequently becoming a major force in contemporary Irish literature. The author of many volumes of poetry and essays as well as at least one play, he is well-known at present for his best-selling verse translation of *Beowulf* (2000). He held the chair of professor of poetry at Oxford University from 1989 to 1994. A resident of Dublin since 1976, since 1981 Heaney has spent part of each year teaching at Harvard University. He was awarded the Nobel Prize in literature in 1995.

Between my finger and my thumb
The squat pen rests; snug as a gun.

Under my window, a clean rasping sound
When the spade sinks into gravelly ground:
My father, digging. I look down   5

Till his straining rump among the flowerbeds
Bends low, comes up twenty years away
Stooping in rhythm through potato drills
Where he was digging.

The coarse boot nestled on the lug, the shaft   10
Against the inside knee was levered firmly.
He rooted out tall tops, buried the bright edge deep
To scatter new potatoes that we picked
Loving their cool hardness in our hands.

By God, the old man could handle a spade.   15
Just like his old man.

My grandfather cut more turf in a day
Than any other man on Toner's bog.
Once I carried him milk in a bottle
Corked sloppily with paper. He straightened up   20
To drink it, then fell to right away
Nicking and slicing neatly, heaving sods
Over his shoulder, going down and down
For the good turf. Digging.

The cold smell of potato mould, the squelch and slap   25
Of soggy peat, the curt cuts of an edge
Through living roots awaken in my head.
But I've no spade to follow men like them.

Between my finger and my thumb
The squat pen rests.   30
I'll dig with it.

[1966]

GERARD MANLEY HOPKINS [1844–1889]

Spring and Fall

to a young child

Born in London, **Gerard Manley Hopkins** (1844–1889) was the eldest of eight children. His father was a ship insurer who also wrote a book of poetry. Hopkins studied at Balliol College, Oxford, and, after converting to Catholicism, taught in a school in Birmingham. In 1868 he became a Jesuit and burned all of his early poetry, considering it "secular" and worthless. He worked as a priest and teacher in working-class London, Glasgow, and Merseyside, and later as a professor of classics at University College, Dublin. Hopkins went on to write many poems on spiritual themes but published little during his lifetime. His poems, which convey a spiritual sensuality, celebrating the wonder of nature both in their language and in their rhythms, which Hopkins called "sprung rhythm," were not widely known until they were published by his friend Robert Bridges in 1918.

Márgarét, áre you gríeving
Over Goldengrove unleaving?
Leáves, líke the things of mán, you
With your fresh thoughts care for, can you?
Áh! ás the héart grows ólder   5
It will come to such sights colder
By and by, nor spare a sigh
Though worlds of wanwood leafmeal° lie;
And yet you *will* weep and know why.
Now no matter, child, the name: 10
Sórrow's spríngs áre the sáme.
Nor mouth had, no nor mind, expressed
What héart héard of, ghóst° guéssed: *spirit*
It ís the blíght man was bórn for,
It is Margaret you mourn for.   15

[*1880;* 1918]

A. E. HOUSMAN [1859–1936]

To an Athlete Dying Young

A. E. Housman (1859–1936) was born in Fockbury, Worcestershire. A promising student at Oxford University, he failed his final exams (because of emotional turmoil, possibly caused by his suppressed homosexual love for a fellow student) and spent the next ten years feverishly studying and writing scholarly articles while working as a clerk at the patent office. Housman was rewarded with the chair of Latin at University College, London, and later at Cambridge University. His poetry like his scholarship was meticulous, impersonal in tone, and limited in output, consisting of two slender volumes—*A Shropshire Lad* (1896) and *Last Poems* (1922)—published during his lifetime and a small book titled *More Poems* (1936) that appeared after his death. His poems often take up the theme of doomed youths acting out their brief lives in the context of agricultural communities and activities, especially the English countryside and traditions that the poet loved.

The time you won your town the race
We chaired you through the market-place;
Man and boy stood cheering by,
And home we brought you shoulder-high.

To-day, the road all runners come,   5
Shoulder-high we bring you home,
And set you at your threshold down,
Townsman of a stiller town.

Smart lad, to slip betimes away
From fields where glory does not stay   10
And early though the laurel grows
It withers quicker than the rose.

Eyes the shady night has shut
Cannot see the record cut,°   *broken*
And silence sounds no worse than cheers   15
After earth has stopped the ears:

Now you will not swell the rout
Of lads that wore their honours out,
Runners whom renown outran
And the name died before the man.   20

So set, before its echoes fade,
The fleet foot on the sill of shade,
And hold to the low lintel up
The still-defended challenge-cup.

And round that early-laurelled head   25
Will flock to gaze the strengthless dead,
And find unwithered on its curls
The garland briefer than a girl's.

[1896]

JAMES JOYCE [1882–1941]

Araby

Born in Dublin, Ireland, **James Joyce** (1882–1941) was educated at
Jesuit schools in preparation for the priesthood. But at an early age
he abandoned Catholicism and in 1904 left Dublin for what he felt
would be the broader horizons of continental Europe. Living in Paris,
Zurich, and Trieste over the next twenty-five years, he tried to support
himself and his family by teaching languages and singing. In 1912 he
returned to Dublin briefly to arrange for the publication of his short
stories. Because of the printers' fear of censorship or libel suits, the
edition was burned, and *Dubliners* did not appear until 1914 in England. During World War I Joyce lived in Zurich, where he wrote
Portrait of the Artist As a Young Man (1916), a partly autobiographical account of his adolescent years that introduced some of the experimental techniques found in his later novels. About this time Joyce
fell victim to glaucoma; for the rest of his life he suffered periods of
intense pain and near blindness. His masterpiece, the novel *Ulysses*
(1922), known for its "stream of consciousness" style, was written and
published in periodicals between 1914 and 1921. Book publication
was delayed because of obscenity charges. *Ulysses* finally was issued
by Shakespeare & Company, a Paris bookstore owned and operated by
Sylvia Beach, an American expatriate; U.S. publication was banned
until 1933. *Finnegans Wake* (1939), an equally experimental novel,
took seventeen years to write. Because of the controversy surrounding his work, Joyce earned little in royalties and often had to rely on
friends for support. He died after surgery for a perforated ulcer in
Zurich.

North Richmond Street, being blind, was a quiet street except at the
hour when the Christian Brothers' School set the boys free. An uninhab-
ited house of two storeys stood at the blind end, detached from its neigh-
bours in a square ground. The other houses of the street, conscious of
decent lives within them, gazed at one another with brown imperturb-
able faces.

The former tenant of our house, a priest, had died in the back draw-ing-room. Air, musty from having been long enclosed, hung in all the rooms, and the waste room behind the kitchen was littered with old use-less papers. Among these I found a few paper-covered books, the pages of which were curled and damp: *The Abbot*, by Walter Scott, *The Devout Communicant*, and *The Memoirs of Vidocq*. I liked the last best because its leaves were yellow. The wild garden behind the house contained a central apple-tree and a few straggling bushes under one of which I found the late tenant's rusty bicycle-pump. He had been a very charita-ble priest; in his will he had left all his money to institutions and the fur-niture of his house to his sister.

When the short days of winter came dusk fell before we had well eaten our dinners. When we met in the street the houses had grown sombre. The space of sky above us was the colour of ever-changing violet and towards it the lamps of the street lifted their feeble lanterns. The cold air stung us and we played till our bodies glowed. Our shouts echoed in the silent street. The career of our play brought us through the dark muddy lanes behind the houses where we ran the gauntlet of the rough tribes from the cottages, to the back doors of the dark dripping gardens where odours arose from the ashpits, to the dark odorous stables where a coachman smoothed and combed the horse or shook music from the buckled harness. When we returned to the street light from the kitchen windows had filled the areas. If my uncle was seen turning the corner we hid in the shadow until we had seen him safely housed. Or if Mangan's sister came out on the doorstep to call her brother in to his tea we watched her from our shadow peer up and down the street. We waited to see whether she would remain or go in and, if she remained, we left our shadow and walked up to Mangan's steps resignedly. She was waiting for us, her figure defined by the light from the half-opened door. Her brother always teased her before he obeyed and I stood by the railings looking at her. Her dress swung as she moved her body and the soft rope of her hair tossed from side to side.

Every morning I lay on the floor in the front parlour watching her door. The blind was pulled down to within an inch of the sash so that I could not be seen. When she came out on the doorstep my heart leaped. I ran to the hall, seized my books, and followed her. I kept her brown fig-ure always in my eye and, when we came near the point at which our ways diverged, I quickened my pace and passed her. This happened morning after morning. I had never spoken to her, except for a few casual words, and yet her name was like a summons to all my foolish blood.

Her image accompanied me even in places the most hostile to romance. On Saturday evenings when my aunt went marketing I had to go to carry some of the parcels. We walked through the flaring streets, jostled by drunken men and bargaining women, amid the curses of labourers, the shrill litanies of shop-boys who stood on guard by the barrel of pigs' cheeks, the nasal chanting of street-singers, who sang a *come-all-you* about O'Donovan Rossa,° or a ballad about the troubles in our native land. These noises converged in a single sensation of life for me: I imagined that I bore my chalice safely through a throng of foes. Her name sprang to my lips at moments in strange prayers and praises which I myself did not understand. My eyes were often full of tears (I could not tell why) and at times a flood from my heart seemed to pour itself out into my bosom. I thought little of the future. I did not know whether I would ever speak to her or not or, if I spoke to her, how I could tell her of my confused adoration. But my body was like a harp and her words and gestures were like fingers running upon the wires.

One evening I went into the back drawing-room in which the priest had died. It was a dark rainy evening and there was no sound in the house. Through one of the broken panes I heard the rain impinge upon the earth, the fine incessant needles of water playing in the sodden beds. Some distant lamp or lighted window gleamed below me. I was thankful that I could see so little. All my senses seemed to desire to veil themselves and, feeling that I was about to slip from them, I pressed the palms of my hands together until they trembled, murmuring: *"O love! O love!"* many times.

At last she spoke to me. When she addressed the first words to me I was so confused that I did not know what to answer. She asked me was I going to *Araby*. I forgot whether I answered yes or no. It would be a splendid bazaar, she said she would love to go.

"And why can't you?" I asked.

While she spoke she turned a silver bracelet round and round her wrist. She could not go, she said, because there would be a retreat that week in her convent. Her brother and two other boys were fighting for their caps and I was alone at the railings. She held one of the spikes, bowing her head towards me. The light from the lamp opposite our door caught the white curve of her neck, lit up her hair that rested there and, falling, lit up the hand upon the railing. It fell over one side of her dress and caught the white border of a petticoat, just visible as she stood at ease.

"It's well for you," she said.

"If I go," I said, "I will bring you something."

What innumerable follies laid waste my waking and sleeping thoughts after that evening! I wished to annihilate the tedious intervening days. I chafed against the work of school. At night in my bedroom and by day in

O'Donovan Rossa: Jeremiah O'Donovan (1831–1915) was nicknamed "Dynamite Rossa" for his militant pursuit of Irish independence.

the classroom her image came between me and the page I strove to read. The syllables of the word *Araby* were called to me through the silence in which my soul luxuriated and cast an Eastern enchantment over me. I asked for leave to go to the bazaar on Saturday night. My aunt was surprised and hoped it was not some Freemason affair. I answered few questions in class. I watched my master's face pass from amiability to sternness; he hoped I was not beginning to idle. I could not call my wandering thoughts together. I had hardly any patience with the serious work of life which, now that it stood between me and my desire, seemed to me child's play, ugly monotonous child's play.

On Saturday morning I reminded my uncle that I wished to go to the bazaar in the evening. He was fussing at the hallstand, looking for the hat-brush, and answered me curtly:

"Yes, boy, I know."

As he was in the hall I could not go into the front parlour and lie at the window. I left the house in bad humour and walked slowly towards the school. The air was pitilessly raw and already my heart misgave me.

When I came home to dinner my uncle had not yet been home. Still it was early. I sat staring at the clock for some time and, when its ticking began to irritate me, I left the room. I mounted the staircase and gained the upper part of the house. The high cold empty gloomy rooms liberated me and I went from room to room singing. From the front window I saw my companions playing below in the street. Their cries reached me weakened and indistinct and, leaning my forehead against the cool glass, I looked over at the dark house where she lived. I may have stood there for an hour, seeing nothing but the brown-clad figure cast by my imagination, touched discreetly by the lamplight at the curved neck, at the hand upon the railings and at the border below the dress.

When I came downstairs again I found Mrs. Mercer sitting at the fire. She was an old garrulous woman, a pawnbroker's widow, who collected used stamps for some pious purpose. I had to endure the gossip of the tea-table. The meal was prolonged beyond an hour and still my uncle did not come. Mrs. Mercer stood up to go: she was sorry she couldn't wait any longer, but it was after eight o'clock and she did not like to be out late, as the night air was bad for her. When she had gone I began to walk up and down the room, clenching my fists. My aunt said:

"I'm afraid you may put off your bazaar for this night of Our Lord."

At nine o'clock I heard my uncle's latchkey in the halldoor. I heard him talking to himself and heard the hallstand rocking when it had received the weight of his overcoat. I could interpret these signs. When he was midway through his dinner I asked him to give me the money to go to the bazaar. He had forgotten.

"The people are in bed and after their first sleep now," he said.

I did not smile. My aunt said to him energetically: "Can't you give him the money and let him go? You've kept him late enough as it is."

My uncle said he was very sorry he had forgotten. He said he believed in the old saying: "All work and no play makes Jack a dull boy." He asked me where I was going and, when I had told him a second time he asked me did I know *The Arab's Farewell to his Steed*. When I left the kitchen he was about to recite the opening lines of the piece to my aunt.

I held a florin° tightly in my hand as I strode down Buckingham Street towards the station. The sight of the streets thronged with buyers and glaring with gas recalled to me the purpose of my journey. I took my seat in a third-class carriage of a deserted train. After an intolerable delay the train moved out of the station slowly. It crept onward among ruinous houses and over the twinkling river. At Westland Row Station a crowd of people pressed to the carriage doors; but the porters moved them back, saying that it was a special train for the bazaar. I remained alone in the bare carriage. In a few minutes the train drew up beside an improvised wooden platform. I passed out on to the road and saw by the lighted dial of a clock that it was ten minutes to ten. In front of me was a large building which displayed the magical name.

I could not find any sixpenny entrance and, fearing that the bazaar would be closed, I passed in quickly through a turnstile, handing a shilling to a weary-looking man. I found myself in a big hall girdled at half its height by a gallery. Nearly all the stalls were closed and the greater part of the hall was in darkness. I recognised a silence like that which pervades a church after a service. I walked into the centre of the bazaar timidly. A few people were gathered about the stalls which were still open. Before a curtain, over which the words *Café Chantant* were written in coloured lamps, two men were counting money on a salver. I listened to the fall of the coins.

Remembering with difficulty why I had come I went over to one of the stalls and examined porcelain vases and flowered tea-sets. At the door of the stall a young lady was talking and laughing with two young gentlemen. I remarked their English accents and listened vaguely to their conversation.

"O, I never said such a thing!"

"O, but you did!"

"O, but I didn't!"

"Didn't she say that?"

"Yes. I heard her."

"O, there's a . . . fib!"

Florin: A silver coin worth two shillings.

45

Observing me the young lady came over and asked me did I wish to buy anything. The tone of her voice was not encouraging; she seemed to have spoken to me out of a sense of duty. I looked humbly at the great jars that stood like eastern guards at either side of the dark entrance to the stall and murmured:

"No, thank you."

The young lady changed the position of one of the vases and went back to the two young men. They began to talk of the same subject. Once or twice the young lady glanced at me over her shoulder.

I lingered before her stall, though I knew my stay was useless, to make my interest in her wares seem the more real. Then I turned away slowly and walked down the middle of the bazaar. I allowed the two pennies to fall against the sixpence in my pocket. I heard a voice call from one end of the gallery that the light was out. The upper part of the hall was now completely dark.

Gazing up into the darkness I saw myself as a creature driven and derided by vanity; and my eyes burned with anguish and anger.

[1914]

JAMES JOYCE [1882–1941]

Eveline

.

Born in Dublin, Ireland, **James Joyce** was educated at Jesuit schools in preparation for the priesthood. At an early age, however, he abandoned Catholicism and in 1904 left Dublin for continental Europe. Living in Paris, Zurich, and Trieste over the next twenty-five years, he tried to support himself and his family by teaching languages and singing. In 1912 he returned to Dublin briefly to arrange for the publication of his short stories. Because of the printers' fears of censorship the first edition was burned, and *Dubliners* did not appear until 1914 in England. During World War I Joyce lived in Zurich, where he wrote *Portrait of the Artist As a Young Man* (1916), a partly autobiographical account of his adolescent years that introduced some of the experimental techniques found in his later novels. At this time Joyce fell victim to glaucoma; for the rest of his life he suffered periods of intense pain and near blindness. His masterpiece, the novel *Ulysses* (1922), known for its stream-of-consciousness style, was written and published in periodicals between 1914 and 1921. Book publication was delayed because of obscenity charges. *Ulysses* finally was issued by the Paris bookstore Shakespeare & Company. U.S. publication was banned until 1933. *Finnegans Wake* (1939), an equally experimental novel, took seventeen years to write. Because of the controversy surrounding his work, Joyce earned little in royalties and often had to rely on friends for support. He died after surgery for a perforated ulcer in Zurich. First published in *The Irish Homestead* in September 1904, "Eveline" is an exploration of gender in early twentieth-century Ireland. It later appeared in *Dubliners* as the advent between Joyce's stories of childhood and adolescence.

She sat at the window watching the evening invade the avenue. Her head was leaned against the window curtains and in her nostrils was the odor of dusty cretonne. She was tired.

Few people passed. The man out of the last house passed on his way home; she heard his footsteps clacking along the concrete pavement and afterwards crunching on the cinder path before the new red houses. One time there used to be a field there in which they used to play every evening with other people's children. Then a man from Belfast bought the field and built houses in it — not like their little brown houses but

47

bright brick houses with shining roofs. The children of the avenue used to play together in that field—the Devines, the Waters, the Dunns, little Keogh the cripple, she and her brothers and sisters. Ernest, however, never played: he was too grown up. Her father used often to hunt them in out of the field with his blackthorn stick; but usually little Keogh used to keep *nix* and call out when he saw her father coming. Still they seemed to have been rather happy then. Her father was not so bad then; and besides, her mother was alive. That was a long time ago; she and her brothers and sisters were all grown up; her mother was dead. Tizzie Dunn was dead, too, and the Waters had gone back to England. Everything changes. Now she was going to go away like the others, to leave her home.

Home! She looked round the room, reviewing all its familiar objects which she had dusted once a week for so many years, wondering where on earth all the dust came from. Perhaps she would never see again those familiar objects from which she had never dreamed of being divided. And yet during all those years she had never found out the name of the priest whose yellowing photograph hung on the wall above the broken harmonium beside the colored print of the promises made to Blessed Margaret Mary Alacoque. He had been a school friend of her father. Whenever he showed the photograph to a visitor her father used to pass it with a casual word:

—He is in Melbourne now.

She had consented to go away, to leave her home. Was that wise? She 5 tried to weigh each side of the question. In her home anyway she had shelter and food; she had those whom she had known all her life about her. Of course she had to work hard both in the house and at business. What would they say of her in the Stores when they found out that she had run away with a fellow? Say she was a fool, perhaps; and her place would be filled up by advertisement. Miss Gavan would be glad. She had always had an edge on her, especially whenever there were people listening.

—Miss Hill, don't you see these ladies are waiting?

—Look lively, Miss Hill, please.

She would not cry many tears at leaving the Stores.

But in her new home, in a distant unknown country, it would not be like that. Then she would be married—she, Eveline. People would treat her with respect then. She would not be treated as her mother had been. Even now, though she was over nineteen, she sometimes felt herself in danger of her father's violence. She knew it was that that had given her the palpitations. When they were growing up he had never gone for her, like he used to go for Harry and Ernest, because she was a girl; but latterly he had begun to threaten her and say what he would do to her only for her dead mother's sake. And now she had nobody to protect her.

Ernest was dead and Harry, who was in the church decorating business, was nearly always down somewhere in the country. Besides, the invariable squabble for money on Saturday nights had begun to weary her unspeakably. She always gave her entire wages—seven shillings—and Harry always sent up what he could but the trouble was to get any money from her father. He said she used to squander the money, that she had no head, that he wasn't going to give her his hard-earned money to throw about the streets, and much more, for he was usually fairly bad of a Saturday night. In the end he would give her the money and ask her had she any intention of buying Sunday's dinner. Then she had to rush out as quickly as she could and do her marketing, holding her black leather purse tightly in her hand as she elbowed her way through the crowds and returning home late under her load of provisions. She had hard work to keep the house together and to see that the two young children who had been left to her charge went to school regularly and got their meals regularly. It was hard work—a hard life—but now that she was about to leave it she did not find it a wholly undesirable life.

She was about to explore another life with Frank. Frank was very 10 kind, manly, open-hearted. She was to go away with him by the night-boat to be his wife and to live with him in Buenos Aires where he had a home waiting for her. How well she remembered the first time she had seen him; he was lodging in a house on the main road where she used to visit. It seemed a few weeks ago. He was standing at the gate, his peaked cap pushed back on his head and his hair tumbled forward over a face of bronze. Then they had come to know each other. He used to meet her outside the Stores every evening and see her home. He took her to see *The Bohemian Girl* and she felt elated as she sat in an unaccustomed part of the theater with him. He was awfully fond of music and sang a little. People knew that they were courting and, when he sang about the lass that loves a sailor, she always felt pleasantly confused. He used to call her Poppens out of fun. First of all it had been an excitement for her to have a fellow and then she had begun to like him. He had tales of distant countries. He had started as a deck boy at a pound a month on a ship of the Allan Line going out to Canada. He told her the names of the ships he had been on and the names of the different services. He had sailed through the Straits of Magellan and he told her stories of the terrible Patagonians. He had fallen on his feet in Buenos Aires, he said, and had come over to the old country just for a holiday. Of course, her father had found out the affair and had forbidden her to have anything to say to him.

—I know these sailor chaps, he said.

One day he had quarreled with Frank and after that she had to meet her lover secretly.

The evening deepened in the avenue. The white of two letters in her lap grew indistinct. One was to Harry; the other was to her father. Ernest had been her favorite but she liked Harry too. Her father was becoming old lately, she noticed; he would miss her. Sometimes he could be very nice. Not long before, when she had been laid up for a day, he had read her out a ghost story and made toast for her at the fire. Another day, when their mother was alive, they had all gone for a picnic to the Hill of Howth. She remembered her father putting on her mother's bonnet to make the children laugh.

Her time was running out but she continued to sit by the window, leaning her head against the window curtain, inhaling the odor of dusty cretonne. Down far in the avenue she could hear a street organ playing. She knew the air. Strange that it should come that very night to remind her of the promise to her mother, her promise to keep the home together as long as she could. She remembered the last night of her mother's illness; she was again in the close dark room at the other side of the hall and outside she heard a melancholy air of Italy. The organ-player had been ordered to go away and given sixpence. She remembered her father strutting back into the sickroom saying:

—Damned Italians! coming over here!   15

As she mused the pitiful vision of her mother's life laid its spell on the very quick of her being—that life of commonplace sacrifices closing in final craziness. She trembled as she heard again her mother's voice saying constantly with foolish insistence:

—Derevaun Seraun! Derevaun Seraun!°

She stood up in a sudden impulse of terror. Escape! She must escape! Frank would save her. He would give her life, perhaps love, too. But she wanted to live. Why should she be unhappy? She had a right to happiness. Frank would take her in his arms, fold her in his arms. He would save her.

She stood among the swaying crowd in the station at the North Wall. He held her hand and she knew that he was speaking to her, saying something about the passage over and over again. The station was full of soldiers with brown baggages. Through the wide doors of the sheds she caught a glimpse of the black mass of the boat, lying in beside the quay wall, with illumined portholes. She answered nothing. She felt her cheek pale and cold and, out of a maze of distress, she prayed to God to direct her, to show her what was her duty. The boat blew a long mournful whistle into the mist. If she went, tomorrow she would be on the sea with Frank,

Derevaun Seraun!: "The end of pleasure is pain!" (Gaelic).

steaming toward Buenos Aires. Their passage had been booked. Could
she still draw back after all he had done for her? Her distress awoke a
nausea in her body and she kept moving her lips in silent fervent prayer.

A bell clanged upon her heart. She felt him seize her hand: 20
— Come!

All the seas of the world tumbled about her heart. He was drawing her
into them: he would drown her. She gripped with both hands at the iron
railing.
— Come!

No! No! No! It was impossible. Her hands clutched the iron in frenzy.
Amid the seas she sent a cry of anguish!·
— Eveline! Evvy!   25

He rushed beyond the barrier and called to her to follow. He was
shouted at to go on but he still called to her. She set her white face to
him, passive, like a helpless animal. Her eyes gave him no sign of love or
farewell or recognition.

[1904]

JOHN KEATS [1795–1821]

Ode on a Grecian Urn

John Keats (1795–1821) was born in London. His father, a worker at a livery stable who married his employer's daughter and inherited the business, was killed by a fall from a horse when Keats was eight. When his mother died of tuberculosis six years later, Keats and his siblings were entrusted to the care of a guardian, a practical-minded man who took Keats out of school at fifteen and apprenticed him to a doctor. But as soon as he qualified for medical practice, in 1815, Keats abandoned medicine for poetry, which he had begun writing two years earlier. In 1818, the year he himself contracted tuberculosis, he also fell madly in love with a pretty, vivacious young ·woman named Fanny Brawne whom he could not marry because of his poverty, illness, and devotion to poetry. In the midst of such stress and emotional turmoil, his masterpieces poured out, between January and September 1819: the great odes, a number of sonnets, and several longer lyric poems. In February 1820, his health failed rapidly; he went to Italy in the autumn, in the hope that the warmer climate would improve his health, and died there on February 23, 1821. His poems are rich with sensuous, lyrical beauty and emotional resonance, reflecting both his delight in life as well as his awareness of life's brevity and difficulty.

1

Thou still unravished bride of quietness,
   Thou foster child of silence and slow time,
Sylvan historian, who canst thus express
   A flowery tale more sweetly than our rhyme:
What leaf-fringed legend haunts about thy shape   5
   Of deities or mortals, or of both,
      In Tempe or the dales of Arcady?°
   What men or gods are these? What maidens loath?
What mad pursuit? What struggle to escape?
   What pipes and timbrels? What wild ecstasy?   10

---

7. **Tempe, Arcady:** Tempe, a valley in Greece, and Arcadia ("Arcady"), a region of ancient Greece, represent ideal pastoral landscapes.

2

Heard melodies are sweet, but those unheard
    Are sweeter; therefore, ye soft pipes, play on;
Not to the sensual ear,° but, more endeared,
    Pipe to the spirit ditties of no tone:
Fair youth, beneath the trees, thou canst not leave   15
    Thy song, nor ever can those trees be bare;
        Bold lover, never, never canst thou kiss,
Though winning near the goal—yet, do not grieve;
        She cannot fade, though thou hast not thy bliss,
    Forever wilt thou love, and she be fair!   20

3

Ah, happy, happy boughs! that cannot shed
    Your leaves, nor ever bid the spring adieu;
And, happy melodist, unwearièd,
    Forever piping songs forever new;
More happy love! more happy, happy love!   25
    Forever warm and still to be enjoyed,
        Forever panting, and forever young;
All breathing human passion far above,
        That leaves a heart high-sorrowful and cloyed,
        A burning forehead, and a parching tongue.   30

4

Who are these coming to the sacrifice?
    To what green altar, O mysterious priest,
Lead'st thou that heifer lowing at the skies,
    And all her silken flanks with garlands dressed?
What little town by river or sea shore,   35
    Or mountain-built with peaceful citadel,
        Is emptied of this folk, this pious morn?
And, little town, thy streets forevermore
    Will silent be; and not a soul to tell
        Why thou art desolate, can e'er return.   40

5

O Attic° shape! Fair attitude! with brede°
    Of marble men and maidens overwrought,

---

13. not . . . ear: Not to the ear of the senses, but to the imagination.
41. Attic: Greek, specifically Athenian; **brede:** Interwoven pattern.

With forest branches and the trodden weed;
  Thou, silent form, dost tease us out of thought
As doth eternity: Cold Pastoral!   45
    When old age shall this generation waste,
      Thou shalt remain, in midst of other woe
    Than ours, a friend to man, to whom thou say'st,
"Beauty is truth, truth beauty,"° — that is all
    Ye know on earth, and all ye need to know.   50

                                     [1820]

49. Beauty . . . beauty: The quotation marks around this phrase were found in its earliest printing, in an 1820 volume of poetry by Keats, but not in a printing later that year or in written transcripts. This discrepancy has led to considerable critical controversy concerning the last two lines. Critics disagree whether "Beauty is truth, truth beauty" is spoken by the urn (and thus perhaps expressing a limited perspective not to be taken at face value) or by the speaker in the poem, or whether the last two lines in their entirety are said by the urn (some recent editors enclose both lines in parentheses to make this explicit) or by the speaker.

JOHN KEATS   [1795–1821]

Ode to a Nightingale

John Keats (1795–1821) was born in London. His father, a worker at a livery stable who married his employer's daughter and inherited the business, was killed by a fall from a horse when Keats was eight. When his mother died of tuberculosis six years later, Keats and his siblings were entrusted to the care of a guardian, a practical-minded man who took Keats out of school at fifteen and apprenticed him to a doctor. But as soon as he qualified for medical practice, in 1815, Keats abandoned medicine for poetry, which he had begun writing two years earlier. In 1818, the year he himself contracted tuberculosis, he also fell madly in love with a pretty, vivacious young woman named Fanny Brawne whom he could not marry because of his poverty, illness, and devotion to poetry. In the midst of such stress and emotional turmoil, his masterpieces poured out, between January and September 1819: the great odes, a number of sonnets, and several longer lyric poems. In February 1820, his health failed rapidly; he went to Italy in the autumn, in the hope that the warmer climate would improve his health, and died there on February 23, 1821. His poems are rich with sensuous, lyrical beauty and emotional resonance, reflecting both his delight in life as well as his awareness of life's brevity and difficulty.

1

My heart aches, and a drowsy numbness pains
  My sense, as though of hemlock I had drunk,
Or emptied some dull opiate to the drains
  One minute past, and Lethe-wards had sunk:
'Tis not through envy of thy happy lot,   5
  But being too happy in thine happiness,—
    That thou, light-winged Dryad of the trees,
        In some melodious plot
Of beechen green, and shadows numberless,
  Singest of summer in full-throated ease.   10

2

O, for a draught of vintage! that hath been
    Cool'd a long age in the deep-delved earth,
Tasting of Flora and the country green,
    Dance, and Provençal song, and sunburnt mirth!
O for a beaker full of the warm South,   15
    Full of the true, the blushful Hippocrene,
        With beaded bubbles winking at the brim,
            And purple-stained mouth;
    That I might drink, and leave the world unseen,
        And with thee fade away into the forest dim: 20

3

Fade far away, dissolve, and quite forget
    What thou among the leaves hast never known,
The weariness, the fever, and the fret
    Here, where men sit and hear each other groan;
Where palsy shakes a few, sad, last gray hairs,   25
    Where youth grows pale, and spectre-thin, and dies;
        Where but to think is to be full of sorrow
            And leaden-eyed despairs,
    Where Beauty cannot keep her lustrous eyes,
        Or new Love pine at them beyond to-morrow.   30

4

Away! away! for I will fly to thee,
    Not charioted by Bacchus and his pards,
But on the viewless wings of Poesy,
    Though the dull brain perplexes and retards:
Already with thee! tender is the night,   35
    And haply the Queen-Moon is on her throne,
        Cluster'd around by all her starry Fays;
            But here there is no light,
    Save what from heaven is with the breezes blown
        Through verdurous glooms and winding mossy ways.   40

5

I cannot see what flowers are at my feet,
  Nor what soft incense hangs upon the boughs,
But, in embalmed darkness, guess each sweet
  Wherewith the seasonable mouth endows
The grass, the thicket, and the fruit-tree wild;   45
  White hawthorn, and the pastoral eglantine;
    Fast fading violets cover'd up in leaves;
      And mid-May's eldest child,
The coming musk-rose, full of dewy wine,
  The murmurous haunt of flies on summer eves.   50

6

Darkling I listen; and, for many a time
  I have been half in love with easeful Death,
Call'd him soft names in many a mused rhyme,
  To take into the air my quiet breath;
Now more than ever seems it rich to die,   55
  To cease upon the midnight with no pain,
    While thou art pouring forth thy soul abroad
      In such an ecstasy!
Still wouldst thou sing, and I have ears in vain—
  To thy high requiem become a sod.   60

7

Thou wast not born for death, immortal Bird!
  No hungry generations tread thee down;
The voice I hear this passing night was heard
  In ancient days by emperor and clown:
Perhaps the self-same song that found a path   65
  Through the sad heart of Ruth, when, sick for home,
    She stood in tears amid the alien corn,
      The same that oft-times hath
Charm'd magic casements, opening on the foam
  Of perilous seas, in faery lands forlorn.   70

8

Forlorn! the very word is like a bell
  To toll me back from thee to my sole self!
Adieu! the fancy cannot cheat so well
  As she is fam'd to do, deceiving elf.
Adieu! adieu! thy plaintive anthem fades   75
    Past the near meadows, over the still stream,
      Up the hill-side; and now 'tis buried deep
        In the next valley-glades:
  Was it a vision, or a waking dream?
    Fled is that music: — Do I wake or sleep?   80

[1819]

HERMAN MELVILLE [1819–1891]

Bartleby, the Scrivener

A Story of Wall Street

Born in New York City, the second son of well-established, affluent parents, **Herman Melville** (1819–1891) lived comfortably until he was eleven, when his father went bankrupt and moved the family to Albany. After his father's death in 1832, Melville left school to work. In 1839 he sailed as a merchant seaman to Liverpool, and in 1841 as a whaleman to the South Pacific. On his return to the United States in 1844, he began immediately to write about his sea adventures. He wrote at an extraordinary pace, producing seven novels in six years, beginning with *Typee* (1846) and *Omoo* (1847), about the South Seas, and including *Moby-Dick* (1851) and *Pierre* (1852). The early novels were well-received, but *Moby-Dick*, now recognized as a masterpiece, was misunderstood and *Pierre* was considered a total failure. During this period Melville had married Elizabeth Shaw, daughter of the chief justice of Massachusetts; in 1850 the couple bought a farm near Pittsfield, Massachusetts, where the writer became close friends with Nathaniel Hawthorne. Despite serious financial problems and a slight nervous breakdown, Melville published stories and sketches in magazines — several of the best, including "Bartleby, the Scrivener" and "Benito Cereno," were collected in *The Piazza Tales* (1856) — as well as the novels *Israel Potter* (1855) and *The Confidence Man* (1857) before turning almost exclusively to poetry for thirty years. Needing money, he sold the farm and worked as a customs inspector in New York City for twenty years; when his wife received a small inheritance he was able to retire. In his final years he wrote the novella *Billy Budd*, which was not published until 1924, thirty-three years after he died in poverty and obscurity. Many of his unpublished stories and journals were also published posthumously.

I am a rather elderly man. The nature of my avocations, for the last thirty years, has brought me into more than ordinary contact with what would seem an interesting and somewhat singular set of men, of whom, as yet, nothing, that I know of, has ever been written — I mean, the law-copyists, or scriveners. I have known very many of them, professionally and privately, and, if I pleased, could relate divers histories, at which good-natured gentlemen might smile, and sentimental souls might weep. But I waive the biographies of all other scriveners, for a few passages in the life of Bartleby, who was a scrivener, the strangest I ever saw, or heard of. While, of other law-copyists, I might write the complete life, of Bartleby nothing of that sort can be done. I believe that no materials exist, for a full and satisfactory biography of this man. It is an irreparable loss to literature. Bartleby was one of those beings of whom nothing is ascertainable, except from the original sources, and, in his case, those are very small. What my own astonished eyes saw of Bartleby, *that* is all I know of him, except, indeed, one vague report, which will appear in the sequel.

Ere introducing the scrivener, as he first appeared to me, it is fit I make some mention of myself, my *employés*, my business, my chambers, and general surroundings, because some such description is indispensable to an adequate understanding of the chief character about to be presented. Imprimis:° I am a man who, from his youth upwards, has been filled with a profound conviction that the easiest way of life is the best. Hence, though I belong to a profession proverbially energetic and nervous, even to turbulence, at times, yet nothing of that sort have I ever suffered to invade my peace. I am one of those unambitious lawyers who never address a jury, or in any way draw down public applause; but, in the cool tranquillity of a snug retreat, do a snug business among rich men's bonds, and mortgages, and title-deeds. All who know me, consider me an eminently *safe* man. The late John Jacob Astor, a personage little given to poetic enthusiasm, had no hesitation in pronouncing my first grand point to be prudence; my next, method. I do not speak it in vanity, but simply record the fact, that I was not unemployed in my profession by the late John Jacob Astor; a name which, I admit, I love to repeat; for it hath a rounded and orbicular sound to it, and rings like unto bullion. I will freely add, that I was not insensible to the late John Jacob Astor's good opinion.

Some time prior to the period at which this little history begins, my avocations had been largely increased. The good old office, now extinct in the State of New York, of a Master in Chancery, had been conferred upon me. It was not a very arduous office, but very pleasantly remunerative. I seldom lose my temper; much more seldom indulge in dangerous indignation at wrongs and outrages; but I must be permitted to be rash here and declare, that I consider the sudden and violent abrogation of the office of Master in Chancery, by the new Constitution, as a——premature act; inasmuch as I had counted upon a life-lease of the profits, whereas I only received those of a few short years. But this is by the way.

My chambers were up stairs, at No.—Wall Street. At one end, they

Imprimis: In the first place (Latin).

looked upon the white wall of the interior of a spacious skylight shaft, penetrating the building from top to bottom.

This view might have been considered rather tame than otherwise, deficient in what landscape painters call "life." But, if so, the view from the other end of my chambers offered, at least, a contrast, if nothing more. In that direction, my windows commanded an unobstructed view of a lofty brick wall, black by age and everlasting shade; which wall required no spy-glass to bring out its lurking beauties, but, for the benefit of all near-sighted spectators, was pushed up to within ten feet of my window-panes. Owing to the great height of the surrounding buildings, and my chambers being on the second floor, the interval between this wall and mine not a little resembled a huge square cistern.

At the period just preceding the advent of Bartleby, I had two persons as copyists in my employment, and a promising lad as an office-boy. First, Turkey; second, Nippers; third, Ginger Nut. These may seem names, the like of which are not usually found in the Directory. In truth, they were nicknames, mutually conferred upon each other by my three clerks, and were deemed expressive of their respective persons or characters. Turkey was a short, pursy Englishman, of about my own age — that is, somewhere not far from sixty. In the morning, one might say, his face was of a fine florid hue, but after twelve o'clock, meridian — his dinner hour — it blazed like a grate full of Christmas coals; and continued blazing — but, as it were, with a gradual wane — till six o'clock, P.M., or thereabouts; after which, I saw no more of the proprietor of the face, which, gaining its meridian with the sun, seemed to set with it, to rise, culminate, and decline the following day, with the like regularity and undiminished glory. There are many singular coincidences I have known in the course of my life, not the least among which was the fact, that, exactly when Turkey displayed his fullest beams from his red and radiant countenance, just then, too, at that critical moment, began the daily period when I considered his business capacities as seriously disturbed for the remainder of the twenty-four hours. Not that he was absolutely idle, or averse to business then; far from it. The difficulty was, he was apt to be altogether too energetic. There was a strange, inflamed, flurried, flighty recklessness of activity about him. He would be incautious in dipping his pen into his inkstand. All his blots upon my documents were dropped there after twelve o'clock, meridian. Indeed, not only would he be reckless, and sadly given to making blots in the afternoon, but, some days, he went further, and was rather noisy. At such times, too, his face flamed with augmented blazonry, as if cannel coal had been heaped on anthracite. He made an unpleasant racket with his chair; spilled his sand-box; in mending his pens, impatiently split them all to pieces, and threw them on the floor in a sudden passion; stood up, and leaned over his table, boxing his papers about in a most indecorous manner, very sad to behold in an elderly man like him. Nevertheless, as he was in many ways a most valuable person to me, and all the time before twelve o'clock, meridian, was the quickest, steadiest creature, too, accomplishing a great deal of work in a style not easily to be matched—for these reasons, I was willing to overlook his eccentricities, though, indeed, occasionally, I remonstrated with him. I did this very gently, however, because, though the civilest, nay, the blandest and most reverential of men in the morning, yet, in the afternoon, he was disposed, upon provocation, to be slightly rash with his tongue—in fact, insolent. Now, valuing his morning services as I did, and resolved not to lose them—yet, at the same time, made uncomfortable by his inflamed ways after twelve o'clock—and being a man of peace, unwilling by my admonitions to call forth unseemly retorts from him, I took upon me, one Saturday noon (he was always worse on Saturdays) to hint to him, very kindly, that, perhaps, now that he was growing old, it might be well to abridge his labors; in short, he need not come to my chambers after twelve o'clock, but, dinner over, had best go home to his lodgings, and rest himself till tea-time. But no; he insisted upon his afternoon devotions. His countenance became intolerably fervid, as he oratorically assured me—gesticulating with a long ruler at the other end of the room—that if his services in the morning were useful, how indispensable, then, in the afternoon?

"With submission, sir," said Turkey, on this occasion, "I consider myself your right-hand man. In the morning I but marshal and deploy my columns; but in the afternoon I put myself at their head, and gallantly charge the foe, thus"—and he made a violent thrust with the ruler.

"But the blots, Turkey," intimated I.

"True; but, with submission, sir, behold these hairs! I am getting old. Surely, sir, a blot or two of a warm afternoon is not to be severely urged against gray hairs. Old age—even if it blot the page—is honorable. With submission, sir, we *both* are getting old."

This appeal to my fellow-feeling was hardly to be resisted. At all events, I saw that go he would not. So, I made up my mind to let him stay, resolving, nevertheless, to see to it that, during the afternoon, he had to do with my less important papers.

Nippers, the second on my list, was a whiskered, sallow, and, upon the whole, rather piratical-looking young man, of about five-and-twenty. I always deemed him the victim of two evil powers—ambition and indigestion. The ambition was evinced by a certain impatience of the duties of a mere copyist, an unwarrantable usurpation of strictly professional affairs such as the original drawing up of legal documents. The indigestion seemed betokened in an occasional nervous testiness and grinning irritability, causing the teeth to audibly grind together over mistakes committed in copying; unnecessary maledictions, hissed, rather than spoken, in the heat of business; and especially by a continual discontent with the height of the table where he worked. Though of a very ingenious mechanical turn, Nippers could never get this table to suit him. He put chips under it, blocks of various sorts, bits of pasteboard, and at last went so far as to attempt an exquisite adjustment, by final pieces of folded blotting paper. But no invention would answer. If, for the sake of easing his back, he brought the table-lid at a sharp angle well up towards his chin, and wrote there like a man using the steep roof of a Dutch house for his desk, then he declared that it stopped the circulation in his arms. If now he lowered the table to his waistbands, and stooped over it in writing, then there was a sore aching in his back. In short, the truth of the matter was, Nippers knew not what he wanted. Or, if he wanted anything, it was to be rid of a scrivener's table altogether. Among the manifestations of his diseased ambition was a fondness he had for receiving visits from certain ambiguous-looking fellows in seedy coats, whom he called his clients. Indeed, I was aware that not only was he, at times, considerable of a ward-politician, but he occasionally did a little business at the justices' courts, and was not unknown on the steps of the Tombs.° I have good reason to believe, however, that one individual who called upon him at my chambers, and who, with a grand air, he insisted was his client, was no other than a dun, and the alleged title-deed, a bill. But, with all his failings, and the annoyances he caused me, Nippers, like his compatriot Turkey, was a very useful man to me; wrote a neat, swift hand; and, when he chose, was not deficient in a gentlemanly sort of deportment. Added to this, he always dressed in a gentlemanly sort of way; and so, incidentally, reflected credit upon my chambers. Whereas, with respect to Turkey, I had much ado to keep him from being a reproach to me. His clothes were apt to look oily, and smell of eating-houses. He wore his pantaloons very loose and baggy in summer. His coats were execrable, his hat not to be handled. But while the hat was a thing of indifference to me, inasmuch as his natural civility and deference, as a dependent Englishman, always led him to doff it the moment he entered the room, yet his coat was another matter. Concerning his coats, I reasoned with him; but with no effect. The truth was, I suppose, that a man with so small an income could not afford to sport such a lustrous face and a lustrous coat at one and the same time. As Nippers once observed, Turkey's money went chiefly for red ink. One winter day, I presented Turkey with a highly respectable-looking coat of my own—a padded gray coat, of a most comfortable warmth, and which buttoned straight

The Tombs: Nickname of the Manhattan House of Detention.

up from the knee to the neck. I thought Turkey would appreciate the favor, and abate his rashness and obstreperousness of afternoons. But no; I verily believe that buttoning himself up in so downy and blanket-like a coat had a pernicious effect upon him upon the same principle that too much oats are bad for horses. In fact, precisely as a rash, restive horse is said to feel his oats, so Turkey felt his coat. It made him insolent. He was a man whom prosperity harmed.

Though, concerning the self-indulgent habits of Turkey, I had my own private surmises, yet, touching Nippers, I was well persuaded that, whatever might be his faults in other respects, he was, at least, a temperate young man. But, indeed, nature herself seemed to have been his vintner, and, at his birth, charged him so thoroughly with an irritable, brandy-like disposition, that all subsequent potations were needless. When I consider how, amid the stillness of my chambers, Nippers would sometimes impatiently rise from his seat, and stooping over his table, spread his arms wide apart, seize the whole desk, and move it, and jerk it, with a grim, grinding motion on the floor, as if the table were a perverse voluntary agent, intent on thwarting and vexing him, I plainly perceive that, for Nippers, brandy-and-water were altogether superfluous.

It was fortunate for me that, owing to its peculiar cause—indigestion— the irritability and consequent nervousness of Nippers were mainly observable in the morning, while in the afternoon he was comparatively mild. So that, Turkey's paroxysms only coming on about twelve o'clock, I never had to do with their eccentricities at one time. Their fits relieved each other, like guards. When Nippers' was on, Turkey's was off; and *vice versa*. This was a good natural arrangement, under the circumstances.

Ginger Nut, the third on my list, was a lad, some twelve years old. His father was a carman, ambitious of seeing his son on the bench instead of a cart, before he died. So he sent him to my office, as student at law, errand-boy, cleaner, and sweeper, at the rate of one dollar a week. He had a little desk to himself, but he did not use it much. Upon inspection, the drawer exhibited a great array of the shells of various sorts of nuts. Indeed, to this quick-witted youth, the whole noble science of the law was contained in a nutshell. Not the least among the employments of Ginger Nut, as well as one which he discharged with the most alacrity, was his duty as cake and apple purveyor for Turkey and Nippers. Copying lawpapers being proverbially a dry, husky sort of business, my two scriveners were fain to moisten their mouths very often with Spitzenbergs, to be had at the numerous stalls nigh the Custom House and Post Office. Also, they sent Ginger Nut very frequently for that peculiar cake—small, flat, round, and very spicy—after which he had been named by them. Of a cold morning, when business was but dull, Turkey would gobble up scores of these cakes, as if they were mere wafers—

indeed, they sell them at the rate of six or eight for a penny—the scrape of his pen blending with the crunching of the crisp particles in his mouth. Of all the fiery afternoon blunders and flurried rashness of Turkey, was his once moistening a ginger-cake between his lips, and clapping it on to a mortgage, for a seal. I came within an ace of dismissing him then. But he mollified me by making an oriental bow, and saying—

"With submission, sir, it was generous of me to find you in stationery on my own account."

Now my original business—that of a conveyancer and title hunter, and drawer-up of recondite documents of all sorts—was considerably increased by receiving the Master's office. There was now great work for scriveners. Not only must I push the clerks already with me, but I must have additional help.

In answer to my advertisement, a motionless young man one morning stood upon my office threshold, the door being open, for it was summer. I can see that figure now—pallidly neat, pitiably respectable, incurably forlorn! It was Bartleby.

After a few words touching his qualifications, I engaged him, glad to have among my corps of copyists a man of so singularly sedate an aspect, which I thought might operate beneficially upon the flighty temper of Turkey, and the fiery one of Nippers.

I should have stated before that ground-glass folding-doors divided my premises into two parts, one of which was occupied by my scriveners, the other by myself. According to my humor, I threw open these doors, or closed them. I resolved to assign Bartleby a corner by the folding-doors, but on my side of them, so as to have this quiet man within easy call, in case any trifling thing was to be done. I placed his desk close up to a small side-window in that part of the room, a window which originally had afforded a lateral view of certain grimy brickyards and bricks, but which, owing to subsequent erections, commanded at present no view at all, though it gave some light. Within three feet of the panes was a wall, and the light came down from far above, between two lofty buildings, as from a very small opening in a dome. Still further to a satisfactory arrangement, I procured a high green folding screen, which might entirely isolate Bartleby from my sight, though not remove him from my voice. And thus, in a manner, privacy and society were conjoined.

At first, Bartleby did an extraordinary quantity of writing. As if long famishing for something to copy, he seemed to gorge himself on my documents. There was no pause for digestion. He ran a day and night line, copying by sun-light and by candle-light. I should have been quite delighted with his application, had he been cheerfully industrious. But he wrote on silently, palely, mechanically.

It is, of course, an indispensable part of a scrivener's business to verify the accuracy of his copy, word by word. Where there are two or more scriveners in an office, they assist each other in this examination, one reading from the copy, the other holding the original. It is a very dull, wearisome, and lethargic affair. I can readily imagine that, to some sanguine temperaments, it would be altogether intolerable. For example, I cannot credit that the mettlesome poet, Byron, would have contentedly sat down with Bartleby to examine a law document of, say five hundred pages, closely written in a crimpy hand.

Now and then, in the haste of business, it had been my habit to assist in comparing some brief document myself, calling Turkey or Nippers for this purpose. One object I had, in placing Bartleby so handy to me behind the screen, was, to avail myself of his services on such trivial occasions. It was on the third day, I think, of his being with me, and before any necessity had arisen for having his own writing examined, that, being much hurried to complete a small affair I had in hand, I abruptly called to Bartleby. In my haste and natural expectancy of instant compliance, I sat with my head bent over the original on my desk, and my right hand sideways, and somewhat nervously extended with the copy, so that, immediately upon emerging from his retreat, Bartleby might snatch it and proceed to business without the least delay.

In this very attitude did I sit when I called to him, rapidly stating what it was I wanted him to do—namely, to examine a small paper with me. Imagine my surprise, nay, my consternation, when, without moving from his privacy, Bartleby, in a singularly mild, firm voice, replied, "I would prefer not to."

I sat awhile in perfect silence, rallying my stunned faculties. Immediately it occurred to me that my ears had deceived me, or Bartleby had entirely misunderstood my meaning. I repeated my request in the clearest tone I could assume; but in quite as clear a one came the previous reply, "I would prefer not to."

"Prefer not to," echoed I, rising in high excitement, and crossing the room with a stride. "What do you mean? Are you moonstruck? I want you to help me compare this sheet here—take it," and I thrust it towards him.

"I would prefer not to," said he.

I looked at him steadfastly. His face was leanly composed; his gray eye dimly calm. Not a wrinkle of agitation rippled him. Had there been the least uneasiness, anger, impatience, or impertinence in his manner; in other words, had there been anything ordinarily human about him, doubtless I should have violently dismissed him from the premises. But as it was, I should have as soon thought of turning my pale plaster-of-paris bust of Cicero out of doors. I stood gazing at him awhile, as he went on with his own writing, and then reseated myself at my desk. This is very strange, thought I. What had one best do? But my business hurried me. I concluded to forget the matter for the present, reserving it for my future leisure. So, calling Nippers from the other room, the paper was speedily examined.

A few days after this, Bartleby concluded four lengthy documents, being quadruplicates of a week's testimony taken before me in my High Court of Chancery. It became necessary to examine them. It was an important suit, and great accuracy was imperative. Having all things arranged, I called Turkey, Nippers, and Ginger Nut, from the next room, meaning to place the four copies in the hands of my four clerks, while I should read from the original. Accordingly, Turkey, Nippers, and Ginger Nut had taken their seats in a row, each with his document in his hand, when I called to Bartleby to join this interesting group.

"Bartleby! quick, I am waiting."

I heard a slow scrape of his chair legs on the uncarpeted floor, and soon he appeared standing at the entrance of his hermitage.

"What is wanted?" said he, mildly.

"The copies, the copies," said I, hurriedly. "We are going to examine them. There"—and I held towards him the fourth quadruplicate.

"I would prefer not to," he said, and gently disappeared behind the screen.

For a few moments I was turned into a pillar of salt, standing at the head of my seated column of clerks. Recovering myself, I advanced towards the screen, and demanded the reason for such extraordinary conduct.

"*Why* do you refuse?"

"I would prefer not to."

With any other man I should have flown outright into a dreadful passion, scorned all further words, and thrust him ignominiously from my presence. But there was something about Bartleby that not only strangely disarmed me, but, in a wonderful manner, touched and disconcerted me. I began to reason with him.

"These are your own copies we are about to examine. It is labor saving to you, because one examination will answer for your four papers. It is common usage. Every copyist is bound to help examine his copy. Is it not so? Will you not speak? Answer!"

"I prefer not to," he replied in a flute-like tone. It seemed to me that, while I had been addressing him, he carefully revolved every statement that I made; fully comprehended the meaning; could not gainsay the irresistible conclusion; but, at the same time, some paramount consideration prevailed with him to reply as he did.

"You are decided, then, not to comply with my request—a request made according to common usage and common sense?"

He briefly gave me to understand, that on that point my judgment was sound. Yes: his decision was irreversible.

It is not seldom the case that, when a man is browbeaten in some unprecedented and violently unreasonable way, he begins to stagger in his own plainest faith. He begins, as it were, vaguely to surmise that, wonderful as it may be, all the justice and all the reason is on the other side. Accordingly, if any disinterested persons are present, he turns to them for some reinforcement for his own faltering mind.

"Turkey," said I, "what do you think of this? Am I not right?"

"With submission, sir," said Turkey, in his blandest tone, "I think that you are."

"Nippers," said I, "what do *you* think of it?"

"I think I should kick him out of the office."

(The reader of nice perceptions will have perceived that, it being morning, Turkey's answer is couched in polite and tranquil terms, but Nippers replies in ill-tempered ones. Or, to repeat a previous sentence, Nippers' ugly mood was on duty, and Turkey's off.)

"Ginger Nut," said I, willing to enlist the smallest suffrage in my behalf, "what do *you* think of it?"

"I think, sir, he's a little *luny*," replied Ginger Nut, with a grin.

"You hear what they say," said I, turning towards the screen, "come forth and do your duty."

But he vouchsafed no reply. I pondered a moment in sore perplexity. But once more business hurried me. I determined again to postpone the consideration of this dilemma to my future leisure. With a little trouble we made out to examine the papers without Bartleby, though at every page or two Turkey deferentially dropped his opinion, that this proceeding was quite out of the common; while Nippers, twitching in his chair with a dyspeptic nervousness, ground out, between his set teeth, occasional hissing maledictions against the stubborn oaf behind the screen. And for his (Nippers') part, this was the first and the last time he would do another man's business without pay.

Meanwhile Bartleby sat in his hermitage, oblivious to everything but his own peculiar business there.

Some days passed, the scrivener being employed upon another lengthy work. His late remarkable conduct led me to regard his ways narrowly. I observed that he never went to dinner; indeed, that he never went anywhere. As yet I had never, of my personal knowledge, known him to be outside of my office. He was a perpetual sentry in the corner. At about eleven o'clock though, in the morning, I noticed that Ginger Nut would advance towards the opening in Bartleby's screen, as if silently beckoned thither by a gesture invisible to me where I sat. The boy would then leave the office, jingling a few pence, and reappear with a handful of ginger-nuts, which he delivered in the hermitage, receiving two of the cakes for his trouble.

He lives, then, on ginger-nuts, thought I; never eats a dinner, properly speaking; he must be a vegetarian, then, but no; he never eats even vegetables, he eats nothing but ginger-nuts. My mind then ran on in reveries concerning the probable effects upon the human constitution of living entirely on ginger-nuts. Ginger-nuts are so called, because they contain ginger as one of their peculiar constituents, and the final flavoring one. Now, what was ginger? A hot, spicy thing. Was Bartleby hot and spicy? Not at all. Ginger, then, had no effect upon Bartleby. Probably he preferred it should have none.

Nothing so aggravates an earnest person as a passive resistance. If the individual so resisted be of a not inhumane temper, and the resisting one perfectly harmless in his passivity, then, in the better moods of the former, he will endeavor charitably to construe to his imagination what proves impossible to be solved by his judgment. Even so, for the most part, I regarded Bartleby and his ways. Poor fellow! thought I, he means no mischief; it is plain he intends no insolence; his aspect sufficiently evinces that his eccentricities are involuntary. He is useful to me. I can get along with him. If I turn him away, the chances are he will fall in with some less indulgent employer, and then he will be rudely treated, and perhaps driven forth miserably to starve. Yes. Here I can cheaply purchase a delicious self-approval. To befriend Bartleby; to humor him in his strange wilfulness, will cost me little or nothing, while I lay up in my soul what will eventually prove a sweet morsel for my conscience. But this mood was not invariable with me. The passiveness of Bartleby sometimes irritated me. I felt strangely goaded on to encounter him in new opposition — to elicit some angry spark from him answerable to my own. But, indeed, I might as well have essayed to strike fire with my knuckles against a bit of Windsor soap. But one afternoon the evil impulse in me mastered me, and the following little scene ensued:

"Bartleby," said I, "when those papers are all copied, I will compare them with you."

"I would prefer not to."

"How? Surely you do not mean to persist in that mulish vagary?"

No answer.

I threw open the folding-doors nearby, and turning upon Turkey and Nippers, exclaimed:

"Bartleby a second time says, he won't examine his papers. What do you think of it, Turkey?"

It was afternoon, be it remembered. Turkey sat glowing like a brass boiler; his bald head steaming; his hands reeling among his blotted papers.

"Think of it?" roared Turkey. "I think I'll just step behind his screen, and black his eyes for him!"

So saying, Turkey rose to his feet and threw his arms into a pugilistic position. He was hurrying away to make good his promise, when I detained him, alarmed at the effect of incautiously rousing Turkey's combativeness after dinner.

"Sit down, Turkey," said I, "and hear what Nippers has to say. What do you think of it, Nippers? Would I not be justified in immediately dismissing Bartleby?"

"Excuse me, that is for you to decide, sir. I think his conduct quite unusual, and, indeed, unjust, as regards Turkey and myself. But it may only be a passing whim."

"Ah," exclaimed I, "you have strangely changed your mind, then—you speak very gently of him now."

"All beer," cried Turkey; "gentleness is effects of beer—Nippers and I dined together to-day. You see how gentle *I* am, sir. Shall I go and black his eyes?"

"You refer to Bartleby, I suppose. No, not to-day, Turkey," I replied; "pray, put up your fists."

I closed the doors, and again advanced towards Bartleby. I felt additional incentives tempting me to my fate. I burned to be rebelled against again. I remembered that Bartleby never left the office.

"Bartleby," said I, "Ginger Nut is away; just step around to the Post Office, won't you?" (it was but a three minutes' walk) "and see if there is anything for me."

"I would prefer not to."

"You *will* not?"

"I *prefer* not."

I staggered to my desk, and sat there in a deep study. My blind inveteracy returned. Was there any other thing in which I could procure myself to be ignominiously repulsed by this lean, penniless wight? my hired clerk? What added thing is there, perfectly reasonable, that he will be sure to refuse to do?

"Bartleby!"

No answer.

"Bartleby," in a louder tone.

No answer.

"Bartleby," I roared.

Like a very ghost, agreeably to the laws of magical invocation, at the third summons, he appeared at the entrance of his hermitage.

"Go to the next room, and tell Nippers to come to me."

"I would prefer not to," he respectfully and slowly said, and mildly disappeared.

"Very good, Bartleby," said I, in a quiet sort of serenely-severe self-possessed tone, intimating the unalterable purpose of some terrible retribution very close at hand. At the moment I half intended something of the kind. But upon the whole, as it was drawing towards my dinner-hour, I thought it best to put on my hat and walk home for the day, suffering much from perplexity and distress of mind.

Shall I acknowledge it? The conclusion of this whole business was, that it soon became a fixed fact of my chambers, that a pale young scrivener, by the name of Bartleby, had a desk there; that he copied for me at the usual rate of four cents a folio (one hundred words); but he was permanently exempt from examining the work done by him, that duty being transferred to Turkey and Nippers, out of compliment, doubtless, to their superior acuteness; moreover, said Bartleby was never, on any account, to be dispatched on the most trivial errand of any sort; and that even if entreated to take upon him such a matter, it was generally understood that he would "prefer not to"—in other words, that he would refuse point blank.

As days passed on, I became considerably reconciled to Bartleby. His steadiness, his freedom from all dissipation, his incessant industry (except when he chose to throw himself into a standing revery behind his screen), his great stillness, his unalterableness of demeanor under all circumstances, made him a valuable acquisition. One prime thing was this—*he was always there*—first in the morning, continually through the day, and the last at night. I had a singular confidence in his honesty. I felt my most precious papers perfectly safe in his hands. Sometimes, to be sure, I could not, for the very soul of me, avoid falling into sudden spasmodic passions with him. For it was exceeding difficult to bear in mind all the time those strange peculiarities, privileges, and unheard-of exemptions, forming the tacit stipulations on Bartleby's part under which he remained in my office. Now and then, in the eagerness of dispatching pressing business, I would inadvertently summon Bartleby, in a short, rapid tone, to put his finger, say, on the incipient tie of a bit of red tape with which I was about compressing some papers. Of course, from behind the screen the usual answer, "I prefer not to," was sure to come; and then, how could a human creature, with the common infirmities of our nature, refrain from bitterly exclaiming upon such perverseness—such unreasonableness? However, every added repulse of this sort which I received only tended to lessen the probability of my repeating the inadvertence.

Here it must be said, that, according to the custom of most legal gentlemen occupying chambers in densely populated law buildings, there were several keys to my door. One was kept by a woman residing in the attic, which person weekly scrubbed and daily swept and dusted my apartments. Another was kept by Turkey for convenience sake. The third I sometimes carried in my own pocket. The fourth I knew not who had.

Now, one Sunday morning I happened to go to Trinity Church, to hear a celebrated preacher, and finding myself rather early on the ground I thought I would walk round to my chambers for a while. Luckily I had my key with me; but upon applying it to the lock, I found it resisted by something inserted from the inside. Quite surprised, I called out; when to my consternation a key was turned from within; and thrusting his lean visage at me, and holding the door ajar, the apparition of Bartleby appeared, in his shirt-sleeves, and otherwise in a strangely tattered *deshabille*, saying quietly that he was sorry, but he was deeply engaged just then, and preferred not admitting me at present. In a brief word or two, he moreover added, that perhaps I had better walk round the block two or three times, and by that time he would probably have concluded his affairs.

Now, the utterly unsurmised appearance of Bartleby, tenanting my law-chambers of a Sunday morning, with his cadaverously gentlemanly *nonchalance*, yet withal firm and self-possessed, had such a strange effect upon me, that incontinently I slunk away from my own door, and did as desired. But not without sundry twinges of impotent rebellion against the mild effrontery of this unaccountable scrivener. Indeed, it was his wonderful mildness chiefly, which not only disarmed me, but unmanned me, as it were. For I consider that one, for the time, is sort of unmanned when he tranquilly permits his hired clerk to dictate to him, and order him away from his own premises. Furthermore, I was full of uneasiness as to what Bartleby could possibly be doing in my office in his shirt-sleeves, and in an otherwise dismantled condition on a Sunday morning. Was anything amiss going on? Nay, that was out of the question. It was not to be thought of for a moment that Bartleby was an immoral person. But what could he be doing there?—copying? Nay again, whatever might be his eccentricities, Bartleby was an eminently decorous person. He would be the last man to sit down to his desk in any state approaching to nudity. Besides, it was Sunday; and there was something about Bartleby that forbade the supposition that he would by any secular occupation violate the proprieties of the day.

Nevertheless, my mind was not pacified; and full of a restless curiosity, at last I returned to the door. Without hindrance I inserted my key, opened it, and entered. Bartleby was not to be seen. I looked round anxiously, peeped behind his screen; but it was very plain that he was gone. Upon more closely examining the place, I surmised that for an indefinite period Bartleby must have ate, dressed, and slept in my office, and that too without plate, mirror, or bed. The cushioned seat of a rickety old sofa in one corner bore the faint impress of a lean, reclining form.

Rolled away under his desk, I found a blanket; under the empty grate, a blacking box and brush; on a chair, a tin basin, with soap and a ragged towel; in a newspaper a few crumbs of ginger-nuts and a morsel of cheese. Yes, thought I, it is evident enough that Bartleby has been making his home here, keeping bachelor's hall all by himself. Immediately then the thought came sweeping across me, what miserable friendlessness and loneliness are here revealed! His poverty is great; but his solitude, how horrible! Think of it. Of a Sunday, Wall Street is deserted as Petra;° and every night of every day it is an emptiness. This building, too, which of week-days hums with industry and life, at nightfall echoes with sheer vacancy, and all through Sunday is forlorn. And here Bartleby makes his home; sole spectator of a solitude which he has seen all populous—a sort of innocent and transformed Marius° brooding among the ruins of Carthage!

For the first time in my life a feeling of overpowering stinging melancholy seized me. Before, I had never experienced aught but a not unpleasing sadness. The bond of a common humanity now drew me irresistibly to gloom. A fraternal melancholy! For both I and Bartleby were sons of Adam. I remembered the bright silks and sparkling faces I had seen that day, in gala trim, swan-like sailing down the Mississippi of Broadway; and I contrasted them with the pallid copyist, and thought to myself, Ah, happiness courts the light, so we deem the world is gay; but misery hides aloof, so we deem that misery there is none. These sad fancyings—chimeras, doubtless, of a sick and silly brain—led on to other and more special thoughts, concerning the eccentricities of Bartleby. Presentiments of strange discoveries hovered round me. The scrivener's pale form appeared to me laid out, among uncaring strangers, in its shivering winding-sheet.

Suddenly I was attracted by Bartleby's closed desk, the key in open sight left in the lock.

I mean no mischief, seek the gratification of no heartless curiosity, thought I; besides, the desk is mine, and its contents, too, so I will make bold to look within. Everything was methodically arranged, the papers smoothly placed. The pigeon-holes were deep, and removing the files of documents, I groped into their recesses. Presently I felt something there, and dragged it out. It was an old bandanna handkerchief, heavy and knotted. I opened it, and saw it was a saving's bank.

I now recalled all the quiet mysteries which I had noted in the man. I

Petra: A Middle Eastern city, deserted for more than ten centuries until its rediscovery by explorers in 1812.
Marius: Gaius Marius (157?–86 B.C.E.), Roman general and consul who was banished and fled to Africa, scene of his greatest military triumphs.

remembered that he never spoke but to answer; that, though at intervals he had considerable time to himself, yet I had never seen him reading— no, not even a newspaper; that for long periods he would stand looking out, at his pale window behind the screen, upon the dead brick wall; I was quite sure he never visited any refectory or eating-house; while his pale face clearly indicated that he never drank beer like Turkey; or tea and coffee even, like other men; that he never went anywhere in particular that I could learn; never went out for a walk, unless, indeed, that was the case at present; that he had declined telling who he was, or whence he came, or whether he had any relatives in the world; that though so thin and pale, he never complained of ill-health. And more than all, I remembered a certain unconscious air of pallid—how shall I call it?—of pallid haughtiness, say, or rather an austere reserve about him, which has positively awed me into my tame compliance with his eccentricities, when I had feared to ask him to do the slightest incidental thing for me, even though I might know, from his long-continued motionlessness, that behind his screen he must be standing in one of those dead-wall reveries of his.

Revolving all these things, and coupling them with the recently discovered fact, that he made my office his constant abiding place and home, and not forgetful of his morbid moodiness; revolving all these things, a prudential feeling began to steal over me. My first emotions had been those of pure melancholy and sincerest pity; but just in proportion as the forlornness of Bartleby grew and grew to my imagination, did that same melancholy merge into fear, that pity into repulsion. So true it is, and so terrible, too, that up to a certain point the thought or sight of misery enlists our best affections; but, in certain special cases, beyond that point it does not. They err who would assert that invariably this is owing to the inherent selfishness of the human heart. It rather proceeds from a certain hopelessness of remedying excessive and organic ill. To a sensitive being, pity is not seldom pain. And when at last it is perceived that such pity cannot lead to effectual succor, common sense bids the soul be rid of it. What I saw that morning persuaded me that the scrivener was the victim of innate and incurable disorder. I might give alms to his body; but his body did not pain him; it was his soul that suffered, and his soul I could not reach.

I did not accomplish the purpose of going to Trinity Church that morning. Somehow, the things I had seen disqualified me for the time from church-going. I walked homeward, thinking what I would do with Bartleby. Finally, I resolved upon this —I would put certain calm questions to him the next morning, touching his history, etc., and if he declined to answer them openly and unreservedly (and I supposed he would prefer not), then to give him a twenty dollar bill over and above whatever I might owe him, and tell him his services were no longer

74

required; but that if in any other way I could assist him, I would be happy to do so, especially if he desired to return to his native place, wherever that might be, I would willingly help to defray the expenses. Moreover, if, after reaching home, he found himself at any time in want of aid, a letter from him would be sure of a reply.

The next morning came.

"Bartleby," said I, gently calling to him behind his screen.

No reply.

"Bartleby," said I, in a still gentler tone, "come here; I am not going to ask you to do anything you would prefer not to do—I simply wish to speak to you."

Upon this he noiselessly slid into view.

"Will you tell me, Bartleby, where you were born?"

"I would prefer not to."

"Will you tell me *anything* about yourself?"

"I would prefer not to."

"But what reasonable objection can you have to speak to me? I feel friendly towards you."

He did not look at me while I spoke, but kept his glance fixed upon my bust of Cicero, which, as I then sat, was directly behind me, some six inches above my head.

"What is your answer, Bartleby?" said I, after waiting a considerable time for a reply, during which his countenance remained immovable, only there was the faintest conceivable tremor of the white attenuated mouth.

"At present I prefer to give no answer," he said, and retired into his hermitage.

It was rather weak in me I confess, but his manner, on this occasion, nettled me. Not only did there seem to lurk in it a certain calm disdain, but his perverseness seemed ungrateful, considering the undeniable good usage and indulgence he had received from me.

Again I sat ruminating what I should do. Mortified as I was at his behavior, and resolved as I had been to dismiss him when I entered my office, nevertheless I strangely felt something superstitious knocking at my heart, and forbidding me to carry out my purpose, and denouncing me for a villain if I dared to breathe one bitter word against this for-lornest of mankind. At last, familiarly drawing my chair behind his screen, I sat down and said: "Bartleby, never mind, then, about revealing your history; but let me entreat you, as a friend, to comply as far as may be with the usages of this office. Say now, you will help to examine papers tomorrow or next day: in short, say now, that in a day or two you will begin to be a little reasonable:—say so, Bartleby."

"At present I would prefer not to be a little reasonable," was his mildly cadaverous reply.

Just then the folding-doors opened, and Nippers approached. He seemed suffering from an unusually bad night's rest, induced by severer indigestion than common. He overheard those final words of Bartleby.

"*Prefer not*, eh?" gritted Nippers—"I'd *prefer* him, if I were you, sir," addressing me—"I'd *prefer* him; I'd give him preferences, the stubborn mule! What is it, sir, pray, that he *prefers* not to do now?"

Bartleby moved not a limb.

"Mr. Nippers," said I, "I'd prefer that you would withdraw for the present."

Somehow, of late, I had got into the way of involuntarily using this word "prefer" upon all sorts of not exactly suitable occasions. And I trembled to think that my contact with the scrivener had already and seriously affected me in a mental way. And what further and deeper aberration might it not yet produce? This apprehension had not been without efficacy in determining me to summary measures.

As Nippers, looking very sour and sulky, was departing, Turkey blandly and deferentially approached.

"With submission, sir," said he, "yesterday I was thinking about Bartleby here, and I think that if he would but prefer to take a quart of good ale every day, it would do much towards mending him, and enabling him to assist in examining his papers."

"So you have got the word, too," said I, slightly excited.

"With submission, what word, sir?" asked Turkey, respectfully crowding himself into the contracted space behind the screen, and by so doing, making me jostle the scrivener. "What word, sir?"

"I would prefer to be left alone here," said Bartleby, as if offended at being mobbed in his privacy.

"*That's* the word, Turkey," said I—"*that's* it."

"Oh, *prefer*? oh yes—queer word. I never use it myself. But, sir, as I was saying, if he would but prefer—"

"Turkey," interrupted I, "you will please withdraw."

"Oh certainly, sir, if you prefer that I should."

As he opened the folding-door to retire, Nippers at his desk caught a glimpse of me, and asked whether I would prefer to have a certain paper copied on blue paper or white. He did not in the least roguishly accent the word "prefer." It was plain that it involuntarily rolled from his tongue. I thought to myself, surely I must get rid of a demented man, who already has in some degree turned the tongues, if not the heads of myself and clerks. But I thought it prudent not to break the dismission at once.

The next day I noticed that Bartleby did nothing but stand at his window in his dead-wall revery. Upon asking him why he did not write, he said that he had decided upon doing no more writing.

"Why, how now? what next?" exclaimed I, "do no more writing?"

"No more."

"And what is the reason?"

"Do you not see the reason for yourself?" he indifferently replied.

I looked steadfastly at him, and perceived that his eyes looked dull and glazed. Instantly it occurred to me, that his unexampled diligence in copying by his dim window for the first few weeks of his stay with me might have temporarily impaired his vision.

I was touched. I said something in condolence with him. I hinted that of course he did wisely in abstaining from writing for a while; and urged him to embrace that opportunity of taking wholesome exercise in the open air. This, however, he did not do. A few days after this, my other clerks being absent, and being in a great hurry to dispatch certain letters by the mail, I thought that, having nothing else earthly to do, Bartleby would surely be less inflexible than usual, and carry these letters to the Post Office. But he blankly declined. So, much to my inconvenience, I went myself.

Still added days went by. Whether Bartleby's eyes improved or not, I could not say. To all appearance, I thought they did. But when I asked him if they did he vouchsafed no answer. At all events, he would do no copying. At last, in replying to my urgings, he informed me that he had permanently given up copying.

"What!" exclaimed I; "suppose your eyes should get entirely well— better than ever before—would you not copy then?"

"I have given up copying," he answered, and slid aside.

He remained as ever, a fixture in my chamber. Nay—if that were possible—he became still more of a fixture than before. What was to be done? He would do nothing in the office; why should he stay there? In plain fact, he had now become a millstone to me, not only useless as a necklace, but afflictive to bear. Yet I was sorry for him. I speak less than truth when I say that, on his own account, he occasioned me uneasiness. If he would but have named a single relative or friend, I would instantly have written, and urged their taking the poor fellow away to some convenient retreat. But he seemed alone, absolutely alone in the universe. A bit of wreck in the mid-Atlantic. At length, necessities connected with my business tyrannized over all other considerations. Decently as I could, I told Bartleby that in six days' time he must unconditionally leave the office. I warned him to take measures, in the interval, for procuring some other abode. I offered to assist him in this endeavor, if he himself would but take the first step towards a removal. "And when you finally quit me, Bartleby," added I, "I shall see that you go not away entirely unprovided. Six days from this hour, remember."

At the expiration of that period, I peeped behind the screen, and lo! Bartleby was there.

I buttoned up my coat, balanced myself; advanced slowly towards him, touched his shoulder, and said, "The time has come; you must quit this place; I am sorry for you; here is money; but you must go."

"I would prefer not," he replied, with his back still towards me.

"You *must.*"

He remained silent.

Now I had an unbounded confidence in this man's common honesty. He had frequently restored to me sixpences and shillings carelessly dropped upon the floor, for I am apt to be very reckless in such shirt-button affairs. The proceeding, then, which followed will not be deemed extraordinary.

"Bartleby," said I, "I owe you twelve dollars on account; here are thirty-two; the odd twenty are yours—Will you take it?" and I handed the bills towards him.

But he made no motion.

"I will leave them here, then," putting them under a weight on the table. Then taking my hat and cane and going to the door, I tranquilly turned and added—"After you have removed your things from these offices, Bartleby, you will of course lock the door—since every one is now gone for the day but you—and if you please, slip your key underneath the mat, so that I may have it in the morning. I shall not see you again; so good-bye to you. If, hereafter, in your new place of abode, I can be of any service to you, do not fail to advise me by letter. Good-bye, Bartleby, and fare you well."

But he answered not a word; like the last column of some ruined temple, he remained standing mute and solitary in the middle of the otherwise deserted room.

As I walked home in a pensive mood, my vanity got the better of my pity. I could not but highly plume myself on my masterly management in getting rid of Bartleby. Masterly I call it, and such it must appear to any dispassionate thinker. The beauty of my procedure seemed to consist in its perfect quietness. There was no vulgar bullying, no bravado of any sort, no choleric hectoring, and striding to and fro across the apartment, jerking out vehement commands for Bartleby to bundle himself off with his beggarly traps. Nothing of the kind. Without loudly bidding Bartleby depart—as an inferior genius might have done—I *assumed* the ground that depart he must; and upon that assumption built all I had to say. The more I thought over my procedure, the more I was charmed with it. Nevertheless, next morning, upon awakening, I had my doubts—I had somehow slept off the fumes of vanity. One of the coolest and wisest hours a man has, is just after he awakes in the morning. My procedure seemed as sagacious as ever—but only in theory. How it would prove in practice—there was the rub. It was truly a beautiful thought to have assumed Bartleby's departure; but, after all, that assumption was simply my own, and none of Bartleby's. The great point was, not whether I had assumed that he would quit me, but whether he would prefer to do so. He was more a man of preferences than assumptions.

After breakfast, I walked down town, arguing the probabilities *pro* and *con.* One moment I thought it would prove a miserable failure, and Bartleby would be found all alive at my office as usual; the next moment it seemed certain that I should find his chair empty. And so I kept veering about. At the corner of Broadway and Canal Street, I saw quite an excited group of people standing in earnest conversation.

"I'll take odds he doesn't," said a voice as I passed.

"Doesn't go?—done!" said I, "put up your money."

I was instinctively putting my hand in my pocket to produce my own, when I remembered that this was an election day. The words I had over-heard bore no reference to Bartleby, but to the success or non-success of some candidate for the mayoralty. In my intent frame of mind, I had, as it were, imagined that all Broadway shared in my excitement, and were debating the same question with me. I passed on, very thankful that the uproar of the street screened my momentary absent-mindedness.

As I had intended, I was earlier than usual at my office door. I stood listening for a moment. All was still. He must be gone. I tried the knob. The door was locked. Yes, my procedure had worked to a charm; he indeed must be vanished. Yet a certain melancholy mixed with this: I was almost sorry for my brilliant success. I was fumbling under the door mat for the key, which Bartleby was to have left there for me, when acci-dentally my knee knocked against a panel, producing a summoning sound, and in response a voice came to me from within—"Not yet; I am occupied."

It was Bartleby.

I was thunderstruck. For an instant I stood like the man who, pipe in mouth, was killed one cloudless afternoon long ago in Virginia, by summer lightning; at his own warm open window he was killed, and remained leaning out there upon the dreamy afternoon, till someone touched him, when he fell.

"Not gone!" I murmured at last. But again obeying that wondrous ascendancy which the inscrutable scrivener had over me, and from which ascendancy, for all my chafing, I could not completely escape, I slowly went down stairs and out into the street, and while walking round the block, considered what I should next do in this unheard-of perplex-ity. Turn the man out by an actual thrusting I could not; to drive him away by calling him hard names would not do; calling in the police was an unpleasant idea; and yet, permit him to enjoy his cadaverous triumph over me—this, too, I could not think of. What was to be done? or, if nothing could be done, was there anything further that I could *assume* in the matter? Yes, as before I had prospectively assumed that Bartleby would depart, so now I might retrospectively assume that departed he was. In the legitimate carrying out of this assumption, I might enter my office in a great hurry, and pretending not to see Bartleby at all, walk straight against him as if he were air. Such a proceeding would in a singular degree have the appearance of a home-thrust. It was hardly possible that Bartleby could withstand such an application of the doctrine of assumption. But upon second thoughts the success of the plan seemed rather dubious. I resolved to argue the matter over with him again.

"Bartleby," said I, entering the office, with a quietly severe expression, "I am seriously displeased. I am pained, Bartleby. I had thought better of you. I had imagined you of such a gentlemanly organization, that in any delicate dilemma a slight hint would suffice—in short, an assumption. But it appears I am deceived. Why," I added, unaffectedly starting, "you have not even touched that money yet," pointing to it, just where I had left it the evening previous.

He answered nothing.

"Will you, or will you not, quit me?" I now demanded in a sudden passion, advancing close to him.

"I would prefer *not* to quit you," he replied, gently emphasizing the *not*.

"What earthly right have you to stay here? Do you pay any rent? Do you pay my taxes? Or is this property yours?"

He answered nothing.

"Are you ready to go on and write now? Are your eyes recovered? Could you copy a small paper for me this morning? or help examine a few lines? or step round to the Post Office? In a word, will you do anything at all, to give a coloring to your refusal to depart the premises?"

He silently retired into his hermitage.

I was now in such a state of nervous resentment that I thought it but prudent to check myself at present from further demonstrations. Bartleby and I were alone. I remembered the tragedy of the unfortunate Adams and the still more unfortunate Colt in the solitary office of the latter; and how poor Colt,° being dreadfully incensed by Adams, and imprudently permitting himself to get wildly excited, was at unawares hurried into his fatal act—an act which certainly no man could possibly deplore more than the actor himself. Often it had occurred to me in my ponderings upon the subject that had that altercation taken place in the public street, or at a private residence, it would not have terminated as it did.

Colt: John C. Colt, who murdered the printer Samuel Adams in a fit of rage in January 1842, committed suicide a half-hour before he was to be hanged for the crime.

It was the circumstance of being alone in a solitary office, up stairs, of a building entirely unhallowed by humanizing domestic associations—an uncarpeted office, doubtless, of a dusty, haggard sort of appearance—this it must have been, which greatly helped to enhance the irritable desperation of the hapless Colt.

But when this old Adam of resentment rose in me and tempted me concerning Bartleby, I grappled him and threw him. How? Why, simply by recalling the divine injunction: "A new commandment give I unto you, that ye love one another." Yes, this it was that saved me. Aside from higher considerations, charity often operates as a vastly wise and prudent principle—a great safeguard to its possessor. Men have committed murder for jealousy's sake, and anger's sake, and hatred's sake, and self-ishness' sake, and spiritual pride's sake; but no man, that ever I heard of, ever committed a diabolical murder for sweet charity's sake. Mere self-interest, then, if no better motive can be enlisted, should, especially with high-tempered men, prompt all beings to charity and philanthropy. At any rate, upon the occasion in question, I strove to drown my exasperated feelings towards the scrivener by benevolently construing his conduct. Poor fellow, poor fellow! thought I, he don't mean anything; and besides, he has seen hard times, and ought to be indulged.

I endeavored, also, immediately to occupy myself, and at the same time to comfort my despondency. I tried to fancy, that in the course of the morning, at such time as might prove agreeable to him, Bartleby, of his own free accord, would emerge from his hermitage and take up some decided line of march in the direction of the door. But no. Half-past twelve o'clock came; Turkey began to glow in the face, overturn his ink-stand, and become generally obstreperous; Nippers abated down into quietude and courtesy; Ginger Nut munched his noon apple; and Bartleby remained standing at his window in one of his profoundest dead-wall reveries. Will it be credited? Ought I to acknowledge it? That afternoon I left the office without saying one further word to him.

Some days now passed, during which, at leisure intervals I looked a little into "Edwards on the Will," and "Priestley° on Necessity." Under the circumstances, those books induced a salutary feeling. Gradually I slid into the persuasion that these troubles of mine, touching the scrivener, had been all predestined from eternity, and Bartleby was billeted upon me for some mysterious purpose of an all-wise Providence, which it was not for a mere mortal like me to fathom. Yes, Bartleby, stay

Edwards ... Priestley: Jonathan Edwards (1703–1758), American theologian and author of the Calvinist *Freedom of the Will* (1754), and Joseph Priestley (1733–1804), English scientist, clergyman, and author of *The Doctrine of Philosophical Necessity* (1777).

there behind your screen, thought I; I shall persecute you no more; you are harmless and noiseless as any of these old chairs; in short, I never feel so private as when I know you are here. At last I see it, I feel it; I penetrate to the predestined purpose of my life. I am content. Others may have loftier parts to enact; but my mission in this world, Bartleby, is to furnish you with office-room for such period as you may see fit to remain.

I believe that this wise and blessed frame of mind would have continued with me, had it not been for the unsolicited and uncharitable remarks obtruded upon me by my professional friends who visited the rooms. But thus it often is, that the constant friction of illiberal minds wears out at last the best resolves of the more generous. Though to be sure, when I reflected upon it, it was not strange that people entering my office should be struck by the peculiar aspect of the unaccountable Bartleby, and so be tempted to throw out some sinister observations concerning him. Sometimes an attorney, having business with me, and calling at my office, and finding no one but the scrivener there, would undertake to obtain some sort of precise information from him touching my whereabouts; but without heeding his idle talk, Bartleby would remain standing immovable in the middle of the room. So after contemplating him in that position for a time, the attorney would depart, no wiser than he came.

Also, when a reference was going on, and the room full of lawyers and witnesses, and business driving fast, some deeply-occupied legal gentleman present, seeing Bartleby wholly unemployed, would request him to run round to his (the legal gentleman's) office and fetch some papers for him. Thereupon, Bartleby would tranquilly decline, and yet remain idle as before. Then the lawyer would give a great stare, and turn to me. And what could I say? At last I was made aware that all through the circle of my professional acquaintance, a whisper of wonder was running round, having reference to the strange creature I kept at my office. This worried me very much. And as the idea came upon me of his possibly turning out a long-lived man, and keeping occupying my chambers, and denying my authority; and perplexing my visitors; and scandalizing my professional reputation; and casting a general gloom over the premises; keeping soul and body together to the last upon his savings (for doubtless he spent but half a dime a day), and in the end perhaps outlive me, and claim possession of my office by right of his perpetual occupancy: as all these dark anticipations crowded upon me more and more, and my friends continually intruded their relentless remarks upon the apparition in my room, a great change was wrought in me. I resolved to gather all my faculties together, and forever rid me of this intolerable incubus.

Ere revolving any complicated project, however, adapted to this end, I first simply suggested to Bartleby the propriety of his permanent departure. In a calm and serious tone, I commended the idea to his careful and mature consideration. But, having taken three days to meditate upon it, he apprised me, that his original determination remained the same; in short, that he still preferred to abide with me.

What shall I do? I now said to myself, buttoning up my coat to the last button. What shall I do? what ought I to do? what does conscience say I *should* do with this man, or, rather, ghost. Rid myself of him, I must; go, he shall. But how? You will not thrust him, the poor, pale, passive mortal—you will not thrust such a helpless creature out of your door? you will not dishonor yourself by such cruelty? No, I will not, I cannot do that. Rather would I let him live and die here, and then mason up his remains in the wall. What, then, will you do? For all your coaxing, he will not budge. Bribes he leaves under your own paper-weight on your table; in short, it is quite plain that he prefers to cling to you.

Then something severe, something unusual must be done. What! surely you will not have him collared by a constable, and commit his innocent pallor to the common jail? And upon what ground could you procure such a thing to be done?—a vagrant, is he? What! he a vagrant, a wanderer, who refuses to budge? It is because he will not be a vagrant, then, that you seek to count him *as* a vagrant. That is too absurd. No visible means of support: there I have him. Wrong again: for indubitably he *does* support himself, and that is the only unanswerable proof that any man can show of his possessing the means so to do. No more, then. Since he will not quit me, I must quit him. I will change my offices; I will move elsewhere, and give him fair notice, that if I find him on my new premises I will then proceed against him as a common trespasser.

Acting accordingly, next day I thus addressed him: "I find these chambers too far from the City Hall; the air is unwholesome. In a word, I propose to remove my offices next week, and shall no longer require your services. I tell you this now, in order that you may seek another place."

He made no reply, and nothing more was said.

On the appointed day I engaged carts and men, proceeded to my chambers, and, having but little furniture, everything was removed in a few hours. Throughout, the scrivener remained standing behind the screen, which I directed to be removed the last thing. It was withdrawn; and, being folded up like a huge folio, left him the motionless occupant of a naked room. I stood in the entry watching him a moment, while something from within me upbraided me.

I re-entered, with my hand in my pocket—and—and my heart in my mouth.

"Good-bye, Bartleby; I am going—good-bye, and God some way bless you; and take that," slipping something in his hand. But it dropped upon the floor, and then—strange to say—I tore myself from him whom I had so longed to be rid of.

Established in my new quarters, for a day or two I kept the door locked, and started at every footfall in the passages. When I returned to my rooms, after any little absence, I would pause at the threshold for an instant, and attentively listen, ere applying my key. But these fears were needless. Bartleby never came nigh me.

I thought all was going well, when a perturbed-looking stranger visited me, inquiring whether I was the person who had recently occupied rooms at No.—Wall Street.

Full of forebodings, I replied that I was.

"Then, sir," said the stranger, who proved a lawyer, "you are responsible for the man you left there. He refuses to do any copying; he refuses to do anything; he says he prefers not to; and he refuses to quit the premises."

"I am very sorry, sir," said I, with assumed tranquillity, but an inward tremor, "but, really, the man you allude to is nothing to me—he is no relation or apprentice of mine, that you should hold me responsible for him."

"In mercy's name, who is he?"

"I certainly cannot inform you. I know nothing about him. Formerly I employed him as a copyist; but he has done nothing for me now for some time past."

"I shall settle him, then—good morning, sir."

Several days passed, and I heard nothing more; and, though I often felt a charitable prompting to call at the place and see poor Bartleby, yet a certain squeamishness, of I know not what, withheld me.

All is over with him, by this time, thought I, at last, when, through another week, no further intelligence reached me. But, coming to my room the day after, I found several persons waiting at my door in a high state of nervous excitement.

"That's the man—here he comes," cried the foremost one, whom I recognized as the lawyer who had previously called upon me alone.

"You must take him away, sir, at once," cried a portly person among them, advancing upon me, and whom I knew to be the landlord of No.—Wall Street. "These gentlemen, my tenants, cannot stand it any longer; Mr. B——" pointing to the lawyer, "has turned him out of his room, and he now persists in haunting the building generally, sitting upon the banisters of the stairs by day, and sleeping in the entry by night. Everybody is concerned; clients are leaving the offices; some fears are entertained of a mob; something you must do, and that without delay."

Aghast at this torrent, I fell back before it, and would fain have locked myself in my new quarters. In vain I persisted that Bartleby was nothing to me—no more than to any one else. In vain—I was the last person known to have anything to do with him, and they held me to the terrible account. Fearful, then, of being exposed in the papers (as one person present obscurely threatened), I considered the matter, and, at length, said, that if the lawyer would give me a confidential interview with the scrivener, in his (the lawyer's) own room, I would, that afternoon, strive my best to rid them of the nuisance they complained of.

Going up stairs to my old haunt, there was Bartleby silently sitting upon the banister at the landing.

"What are you doing here, Bartleby?" said I.

"Sitting upon the banister," he mildly replied.

I motioned him into the lawyer's room, who then left us.

"Bartleby," said I, "are you aware that you are the cause of great tribulation to me, by persisting in occupying the entry after being dismissed from the office?"

No answer.

"Now one of two things must take place. Either you must do something, or something must be done to you. Now what sort of business would you like to engage in? Would you like to re-engage in copying for some one?"

"No; I would prefer not to make any change."

"Would you like a clerkship in a dry-goods store?"

"There is too much confinement about that. No, I would not like a clerkship; but I am not particular."

"Too much confinement," I cried, "why, you keep yourself confined all the time!"

"I would prefer not to take a clerkship," he rejoined, as if to settle that little item at once.

"How would a bar-tender's business suit you? There is no trying of the eye-sight in that."

"I would not like it at all; though, as I said before, I am not particular."

His unwonted wordiness inspirited me. I returned to the charge.

"Well, then, would you like to travel through the country collecting bills for the merchants? That would improve your health."

"No, I would prefer to be doing something else."

"How, then, would going as a companion to Europe, to entertain some young gentleman with your conversation—how would that suit you?"

"Not at all. It does not strike me that there is anything definite about that. I like to be stationary. But I am not particular."

"Stationary you shall be, then," I cried, now losing all patience, and, for the first time in all my exasperating connections with him, fairly flying into a passion. "If you do not go away from these premises before night, I shall feel bound—indeed, I *am* bound—to—to—to quit the premises myself!" I rather absurdly concluded, knowing not with what possible threat to try to frighten his immobility into compliance. Despairing of all further efforts, I was precipitately leaving him, when a final thought occurred to me—one which had not been wholly unindulged before.

"Bartleby," said I, in the kindest tone I could assume under such exciting circumstances, "will you go home with me now not to my office, but my dwelling—and remain there till we can conclude upon some convenient arrangement for you at our leisure? Come, let us start now, right away."

"No: at present I would prefer not to make any change at all."

I answered nothing; but, effectually dodging every one by the suddenness and rapidity of my flight, rushed from the building, ran up Wall Street towards Broadway, and, jumping into the first omnibus, was soon removed from pursuit. As soon as tranquillity returned, I distinctly perceived that I had now done all that I possibly could, both in respect to the demands of the landlord and his tenants, and with regard to my own desire and sense of duty, to benefit Bartleby, and shield him from rude persecution. I now strove to be entirely care-free and quiescent; and my conscience justified me in the attempt; though, indeed, it was not so successful as I could have wished. So fearful was I of being again hunted out by the incensed landlord and his exasperated tenants, that, surrendering my business to Nippers, for a few days, I drove about the upper part of the town and through the suburbs, in my rockaway; crossed over to Jersey City and Hoboken, and paid fugitive visits to Manhattanville and Astoria. In fact, I almost lived in my rockaway for the time.

When again I entered my office, lo, a note from the landlord lay upon the desk. I opened it with trembling hands. It informed me that the writer had sent to the police, and had Bartleby removed to the Tombs as a vagrant. Moreover, since I knew more about him than any one else, he wished me to appear at that place, and make a suitable statement of the facts. These tidings had a conflicting effect upon me. At first I was indignant; but, at last, almost approved. The landlord's energetic, summary disposition, had led him to adopt a procedure which I do not think I would have decided upon myself; and yet, as a last resort, under such peculiar circumstances, it seemed the only plan.

As I afterwards learned, the poor scrivener, when told that he must be conducted to the Tombs, offered not the slightest obstacle, but, in his pale, unmoving way, silently acquiesced.

Some of the compassionate and curious bystanders joined the party; and headed by one of the constables arm-in-arm with Bartleby, the silent procession filed its way through all the noise, and heat, and joy of the roaring thoroughfares at noon.

The same day I received the note, I went to the Tombs, or, to speak more properly, the Halls of Justice. Seeking the right officer, I stated the purpose of my call, and was informed that the individual I described was, indeed, within. I then assured the functionary that Bartleby was a perfectly honest man, and greatly to be compassionated, however unaccountably eccentric. I narrated all I knew, and closed by suggesting the idea of letting him remain in as indulgent confinement as possible, till something less harsh might be done—though, indeed, I hardly knew what. At all events, if nothing else could be decided upon, the almshouse must receive him. I then begged to have an interview.

Being under no disgraceful charge, and quite serene and harmless in all his ways, they had permitted him freely to wander about the prison, and, especially, in the inclosed grass-platted yards thereof. And so I found him there, standing all alone in the quietest of the yards, his face towards a high wall, while all around, from the narrow slits of the jail windows, I thought I saw peering out upon him the eyes of murderers and thieves.

"Bartleby!"

"I know you," he said, without looking round—"and I want nothing to say to you."

"It was not I that brought you here, Bartleby," said I, keenly pained at his implied suspicion. "And to you, this should not be so vile a place. Nothing reproachful attaches to you by being here. And see, it is not so sad a place as one might think. Look, there is the sky, and here is the grass."

"I know where I am," he replied, but would say nothing more, and so I left him.

As I entered the corridor again, a broad meat-like man, in an apron, accosted me, and, jerking his thumb over my shoulder, said "Is that your friend?"

"Yes."

"Does he want to starve? If he does, let him live on the prison fare, that's all."

"Who are you?" asked I, not knowing what to make of such an unofficially speaking person in such a place.

"I am the grub-man. Such gentlemen as have friends here, hire me to provide them with something good to eat."

"Is this so?" said I, turning to the turnkey.

He said it was.

"Well, then," said I, slipping some silver into the grub-man's hands (for so they called him), "I want you to give particular attention to my friend there; let him have the best dinner you can get. And you must be as polite to him as possible."

"Introduce me, will you?" said the grub-man, looking at me with an expression which seemed to say he was all impatience for an opportunity to give a specimen of his breeding.

Thinking it would prove of benefit to the scrivener, I acquiesced; and, asking the grub-man his name, went up with him to Bartleby.

"Bartleby, this is a friend; you will find him very useful to you."

"Your sarvant, sir, your sarvant," said the grub-man, making a low salutation behind his apron. "Hope you find it pleasant here, sir; nice grounds — cool apartments — hope you'll stay with us some time — try to make it agreeable. What will you have for dinner to-day?"

"I prefer not to dine to-day," said Bartleby, turning away. "It would disagree with me; I am unused to dinners." So saying, he slowly moved to the other side of the inclosure, and took up a position fronting the dead-wall.

"How's this?" said the grub-man, addressing me with a stare of astonishment. "He's odd, ain't he?"

"I think he is a little deranged," said I, sadly.

"Deranged? deranged is it? Well, now, upon my word, I thought that friend of yourn was a gentleman forger; they are always pale and genteel-like, them forgers. I can't help pity 'em — can't help it, sir. Did you know Monroe Edwards?" he added, touchingly, and paused. Then, laying his hand piteously on my shoulder, sighed, "he died of consumption at Sing-Sing. So you weren't acquainted with Monroe?"

"No, I was never socially acquainted with any forgers. But I cannot stop longer. Look to my friend yonder. You will not lose by it. I will see you again."

Some few days after this, I again obtained admission to the Tombs, and went through the corridors in quest of Bartleby; but without finding him.

"I saw him coming from his cell not long ago," said a turnkey, "may be he's gone to loiter in the yards."

So I went in that direction.

"Are you looking for the silent man?" said another turnkey, passing me. "Yonder he lies — sleeping in the yard there. 'Tis not twenty minutes since I saw him lie down."

The yard was entirely quiet. It was not accessible to the common prisoners. The surrounding walls, of amazing thickness, kept off all sounds behind them. The Egyptian character of the masonry weighed upon me with its gloom. But a soft imprisoned turf grew under foot. The heart of the eternal pyramids, it seemed, wherein, by some strange magic, through the clefts, grass-seed, dropped by birds, had sprung.

Strangely huddled at the base of the wall, his knees drawn up, and lying on his side, his head touching the cold stones, I saw the wasted

Bartleby. But nothing stirred. I paused; then went close up to him; stooped over, and saw that his dim eyes were open; otherwise he seemed profoundly sleeping. Something prompted me to touch him. I felt his hand, when a tingling shiver ran up my arm and down my spine to my feet.

The round face of the grub-man peered upon me now. "His dinner is ready. Won't he dine to-day, either? Or does he live without dining?"

"Lives without dining," said I, and closed the eyes.

"Eh!—He's asleep, ain't he?"

"With kings and counselors,"° murmured I.

There would seem little need for proceeding further in this history. Imagination will readily supply the meagre recital of poor Bartleby's interment. But, ere parting with the reader, let me say, that if this little narrative has sufficiently interested him, to awaken curiosity as to who Bartleby was, and what manner of life he led prior to the present narrator's making his acquaintance, I can only reply, that in such curiosity I fully share, but am wholly unable to gratify it. Yet here I hardly know whether I should divulge one little item of rumor, which came to my ear a few months after the scrivener's decease. Upon what basis it rested, I could never ascertain; and hence, how true it is I cannot now tell. But, inasmuch as this vague report has not been without a certain suggestive interest to me, however sad, it may prove the same with some others; and so I will briefly mention it. The report was this: that Bartleby had been a subordinate clerk in the Dead Letter Office at Washington, from which he had been suddenly removed by a change in the administration. When I think over this rumor, hardly can I express the emotions which seize me. Dead letters! does it not sound like dead men? Conceive a man by nature and misfortune prone to a pallid hopelessness, can any business seem more fitted to heighten it than that of continually handling these dead letters, and assorting them for the flames? For by the cartload they are annually burned. Sometimes from out the folded paper the pale clerk takes a ring—the finger it was meant for, perhaps, moulders in the grave; a bank-note sent in swiftest charity—he whom it would relieve, nor eats nor hungers any more; pardon for those who died despairing; hope for those who died unhoping; good tidings for those who died stifled by unrelieved calamities. On errands of life, these letters speed to death.

Ah, Bartleby! Ah, humanity!

[1853]

With kings and counselors: A reference to the biblical book of Job, 3:13–14: "then had I been at rest with kings and counselors of the earth, which built desolate places for themselves."

WILLIAM SHAKESPEARE [1564–1616]

Hamlet, Prince of Denmark

William Shakespeare (1564–1616) was born in Stratford-upon-Avon, England, where his father was a glovemaker and bailiff, and he presumably went to grammar school there. He married Anne Hathaway in 1582 and sometime before 1592 left for London to work as a playwright and actor. Shakespeare joined the Lord Chamberlain's Men (later the King's Men), an acting company for which he wrote thirty-seven plays—comedies, tragedies, histories, and romances—upon which his reputation as the finest dramatist in the English language is based. He was also arguably the finest lyric poet of his day, as exemplified by songs scattered throughout his plays, two early nondramatic poems (*Venus and Adonis* and *The Rape of Lucrece*), and the sonnet sequence expected of all noteworthy writers in the Elizabethan age. Shakespeare's sonnets were probably written in the 1590s, although they were not published until 1609. Shakespeare retired to Stratford around 1612, and by the time he died at the age of fifty-two, he was acknowledged as a leading light of the Elizabethan stage and had become successful enough to have purchased a coat of arms for his family home.

[Dramatis Personae
CLAUDIUS, *King of Denmark*
HAMLET, *son to the late King Hamlet, and nephew to the present King*
POLONIUS, *Lord Chamberlain*
HORATIO, *friend to Hamlet*
LAERTES, *son to Polonius*
VOLTIMAND,
CORNELIUS,
ROSENCRANTZ,
GUILDENSTERN, } *courtiers*
OSRIC,
GENTLEMAN,

Note: The text of *Hamlet* has come down to us in different versions—such as the first quarto, the second quarto, and the first Folio. The copy of the text used here is largely drawn from the second quarto. Passages enclosed in square brackets are taken from one of the other versions, in most cases the first Folio.

Hamlet, Prince of Denmark. Footnotes from *Hamlet* from *The Complete Works of Shakespeare,* Fourth Edition, by David Bevington. Copyright © 1992 by HarperCollins Publishers. Reprinted by permission of Pearson Education, Inc.

PRIEST, OR DOCTOR OF DIVINITY
MARCELLUS, ⎱ *officers*
BERNARDO, ⎰
FRANCISCO, *a solider*
REYNALDO, *servant to Polonius*
PLAYERS
TWO CLOWNS, *grave-diggers*
FORTINBRAS, *Prince of Norway*
CAPTAIN
ENGLISH AMBASSADORS

GERTRUDE, *Queen of Denmark, mother to Hamlet*
OPHELIA, *daughter to Polonius*

LORDS, LADIES, OFFICERS, SOLDIERS, SAILORS, MESSENGERS, AND OTHER
    ATTENDANTS
GHOST *of Hamlet's father*

Scene: *Denmark.*]

{ACT I   *Scene 1*}°

(*Enter Bernardo and Francisco, two sentinels, [meeting].*)

BERNARDO: Who's there?
FRANCISCO: Nay, answer me.° Stand and unfold yourself.
BERNARDO: Long live the King!
FRANCISCO: Bernardo?
BERNARDO: He.   5
FRANCISCO: You come most carefully upon your hour.
BERNARDO: 'Tis now struck twelve. Get thee to bed, Francisco.
FRANCISCO: For this relief much thanks. 'Tis bitter cold,
    And I am sick at heart.
BERNARDO: Have you had quiet guard?
FRANCISCO: Not a mouse stirring.   10
BERNARDO: Well, good night.
    If you do meet Horatio and Marcellus,
    The rivals° of my watch, bid them make haste.

(*Enter Horatio and Marcellus.*)

FRANCISCO: I think I hear them. Stand, ho! Who is there?
HORATIO: Friends to this ground.

I, I. Location: Elsinore castle. A guard platform.   **2. me:** Francisco emphasizes
that *he* is the sentry currently on watch.   **13. rivals:** Partners.

MARCELLUS:	And liegemen to the Dane.°	15

FRANCISCO: Give you° good night.
MARCELLUS: O, farewell, honest soldier.
  Who hath relieved you?
FRANCISCO: Bernardo hath my place.
  Give you good night.   (*Exit Francisco.*)
MARCELLUS: Holla, Bernardo!
BERNARDO: Say,
  What, is Horatio there?
HORATIO: A piece of him.
BERNARDO: Welcome, Horatio. Welcome, good Marcellus.   20
HORATIO: What, has this thing appear'd again tonight?
BERNARDO: I have seen nothing.
MARCELLUS: Horatio says 'tis but our fantasy,
  And will not let belief take hold of him
  Touching this dreaded sight, twice seen of us.   25
  Therefore I have entreated him along
  With us to watch the minutes of this night,
  That if again this apparition come
  He may approve° our eyes and speak to it.
HORATIO: Tush, tush, 'twill not appear.
BERNARDO: Sit down awhile,   30
  And let us once again assail your ears,
  That are so fortified against our story,
  What we have two nights seen.
HORATIO: Well, sit we down,
  And let us hear Bernardo speak of this.
BERNARDO: Last night of all,   35
  When yond same star that's westward from the pole°
  Had made his° course t' illume that part of heaven
  Where now it burns, Marcellus and myself,
  The bell then beating one —

(*Enter Ghost.*)

MARCELLUS: Peace, break thee off! Look where it comes again!   40
BERNARDO: In the same figure, like the King that's dead.
MARCELLUS: Thou art a scholar.° Speak to it, Horatio.
BERNARDO: Looks 'a° not like the King? Mark it, Horatio.

---

15. liegemen to the Dane: Men sworn to serve the Danish king.   **16. Give you:**
God give you.   **29. approve:** Corroborate.   **36. pole:** Polestar.   **37. his:** Its.
42. scholar: One learned in Latin and able to address spirits.   **43. 'a:** He.

HORATIO: Most like. It harrows me with fear and wonder.
BERNARDO: It would be spoke to.
MARCELLUS: Speak to it,° Horatio.   45
HORATIO: What art thou that usurp'st this time of night,
   Together with that fair and warlike form
   In which the majesty of buried Denmark°
   Did sometimes° march? By heaven I charge thee speak!
MARCELLUS: It is offended.
BERNARDO: See, it stalks away.   50
HORATIO: Stay! Speak, speak. I charge thee, speak.

                                              (*Exit Ghost.*)

MARCELLUS: 'Tis gone, and will not answer.
BERNARDO: How now, Horatio? You tremble and look pale.
   Is not this something more than fantasy?
   What think you on 't?   55
HORATIO: Before my God, I might not this believe
   Without the sensible° and true avouch
   Of mine own eyes.
MARCELLUS: Is it not like the King?
HORATIO: As thou art to thyself.
   Such was the very armor he had on   60
   When he the ambitious Norway° combated.
   So frown'd he once when, in an angry parle,°
   He smote the sledded° Polacks° on the ice.
   'Tis strange.
MARCELLUS: Thus twice before, and jump° at this dead hour,   65
   With martial stalk hath he gone by our watch.
HORATIO: In what particular thought to work I know not,
   But, in the gross and scope° of mine opinion,
   This bodes some strange eruption to our state.
MARCELLUS: Good now,° sit down, and tell me, he that knows,   70
   Why this same strict and most observant watch
   So nightly toils° the subject° of the land,
   And why such daily cast° of brazen cannon,

---

45. It . . . it: A ghost could not speak until spoken to.   **48. buried Denmark:** The buried king of Denmark.   **49. sometimes:** Formerly.   **57. sensible:** Confirmed by the senses.   **61. Norway:** King of Norway.   **62. parle:** Parley.   **63. sledded:** Traveling on sleds.   **Polacks:** Poles.   **65. jump:** Exactly.   **68. gross and scope:** General view.   **70. Good now:** An expression denoting entreaty or expostulation. **72. toils:** Causes to toil.   **subject:** Subjects.   **73. cast:** Casting.

And foreign mart° for implements of war,
Why such impress° of shipwrights, whose sore task   75
Does not divide the Sunday from the week.
What might be toward,° that this sweaty haste
Doth make the night joint-laborer with the day?
Who is 't that can inform me?
HORATIO: That can I,
At least, the whisper goes so. Our last king,   80
Whose image even but now appear'd to us,
Was, as you know, by Fortinbras of Norway,
Thereto prick'd on° by a most emulate° pride,
Dar'd to the combat; in which our valiant Hamlet—
For so this side of our known world esteem'd him—   85
Did slay this Fortinbras; who, by a seal'd compact,
Well ratified by law and heraldry,
Did forfeit, with his life, all those his lands
Which he stood seiz'd° of, to the conqueror;
Against the° which a moi'ty competent°   90
Was gaged° by our king, which had return'd
To the inheritance of Fortinbras
Had he been vanquisher, as, by the same comart°
And carriage° of the article design'd,
His fell to Hamlet. Now, sir, young Fortinbras,   95
Of unimproved° mettle hot and full,
Hath in the skirts° of Norway here and there
Shark'd up° a list of lawless resolutes°
For food and diet° to some enterprise
That hath a stomach° in 't, which is no other—   100
As it doth well appear unto our state—
But to recover of us, by strong hand
And terms compulsatory, those foresaid lands
So by his father lost. And this, I take it,
Is the main motive of our preparations,   105

---

74. **mart:** Buying and selling.   75. **impress:** Impressment, conscription.
77. **toward:** In preparation.   83. **prick'd on:** Incited.   **emulate:** Ambitious.
89. **seiz'd:** Possessed.   90. **Against the:** In return for. . . .   **moi'ty competent:**
Sufficient portion.   91. **gaged:** Engaged, pledged.   93. **comart:** Joint bargain
(?).   94. **carriage:** Import, bearing.   96. **unimproved:** Not turned to account
(?) or untested (?).   97. **skirts:** Outlying regions, outskirts.   98. **Shark'd up:**
Got together in haphazard fashion.   **resolutes:** Desperadoes.   99. **food and
diet:** No pay but their keep.   100. **stomach:** Relish of danger.

The source of this our watch, and the chief head°
Of this post-haste and romage° in the land.
BERNARDO: I think it be no other but e'en so.
Well may it sort° that this portentous figure
Comes armed through our watch so like the King   110
That was and is the question of these wars.
HORATIO: A mote° it is to trouble the mind's eye.
In the most high and palmy° state of Rome,
A little ere the mightiest Julius fell,
The graves stood tenantless and the sheeted° dead   115
Did squeak and gibber in the Roman streets;
As° stars with trains of fire and dews of blood,
Disasters° in the sun; and the moist star°
Upon whose influence Neptune's° empire stands°
Was sick almost to doomsday° with eclipse.   120
And even the like precurse° of fear'd events,
As harbingers° preceding still° the fates
And prologue to the omen° coming on,
Have heaven and earth together demonstrated   )
Unto our climatures° and countrymen.   125

(*Enter Ghost.*)

But soft, behold! Lo where it comes again!
I'll cross° it, though it blast me. Stay, illusion!
If thou hast any sound, or use of voice,
Speak to me!   (*It spreads his arms.*)
If there be any good thing to be done   130
That may to thee do ease and grace to me,
Speak to me!
If thou art privy to thy country's fate,
Which, happily,° foreknowing may avoid,
O, speak!   135
Or if thou hast uphoarded in thy life

---

106. head: Source.   107. romage: Bustle, commotion.   109. sort: Suit.
112. mote: Speck of dust.   113. palmy: Flourishing.   115. sheeted: Shrouded.
117. As: This abrupt transition suggests that matter is possibly omitted between
lines 116 and 117.   118. Disasters: Unfavorable signs or aspects. moist star:
Moon, governing tides.   119. Neptune: God of the sea. stands: Depends.
120. sick . . . doomsday: See Matt. 24:29 and Rev. 6:12.   121. precurse: Heralding,
foreshadowing.   122. harbingers: Forerunners. still: Continually.   123. omen:
Calamitous event.   125. climatures: Regions.   127. cross: Meet, face directly.
134. happily: Haply, perchance.

Extorted treasure in the womb of earth,
For which, they say, you spirits oft walk in death,

(*The cock crows.*)

Speak of it. Stay, and speak! Stop it, Marcellus.
MARCELLUS: Shall I strike at it with my partisan?°   140
HORATIO: Do, if it will not stand.   [*They strike at it.*]
BERNARDO: 'Tis here!
HORATIO: 'Tis here!
MARCELLUS: 'Tis gone.   [*Exit Ghost.*]
     We do it wrong, being so majestical,
     To offer it the show of violence;
     For it is, as the air, invulnerable,   145
     And our vain blows malicious mockery.
BERNARDO: It was about to speak when the cock crew.
HORATIO: And then it started like a guilty thing
     Upon a fearful summons. I have heard,
     The cock, that is the trumpet to the morn,   150
     Doth with his lofty and shrill-sounding throat
     Awake the god of day, and, at his warning,
     Whether in sea or fire, in earth or air,
     Th' extravagant and erring° spirit hies
     To his confine; and of the truth herein   155
     This present object made probation.°
MARCELLUS: It faded on the crowing of the cock.
     Some say that ever 'gainst° that season comes
     Wherein our Savior's birth is celebrated,
     The bird of dawning singeth all night long,   160
     And then, they say, no spirit dare stir abroad;
     The nights are wholesome, then no planets strike,°
     No fairy takes,° nor witch hath power to charm,
     So hallowed and so gracious° is that time.
HORATIO: So have I heard and do in part believe it.   165
     But, look, the morn, in russet mantle clad,
     Walks o'er the dew of yon high eastward hill.
     Break we our watch up, and by my advice
     Let us impart what we have seen tonight
     Unto young Hamlet; for, upon my life,   170

140. **partisan:** Long-handled spear.   154. **extravagant and erring:** Wandering. (The words have similar meaning.)   156. **probation:** Proof.   158. **'gainst:** Just before.   162. **strike:** Exert evil influence.   163. **takes:** Bewitches.   164. **gracious:** Full of goodness.

This spirit, dumb to us, will speak to him.
Do you consent we shall acquaint him with it,
As needful in our loves, fitting our duty?
MARCELLUS: Let's do 't, I pray, and I this morning know
Where we shall find him most conveniently.   175

                                        .   (*Exeunt.*)°

                               {*Scene II*}°

(*Flourish. Enter Claudius, King of Denmark, Gertrude the Queen, Councilors,
Polonius and his son Laertes, Hamlet, cum aliis°* [*including Voltimand and
Cornelius*].)

KING: Though yet of Hamlet our dear brother's death
     The memory be green, and that it us befitted
     To bear our hearts in grief and our whole kingdom
     To be contracted in one brow of woe,
     Yet so far hath discretion fought with nature   5
     That we with wisest sorrow think on him,
     Together with remembrance of ourselves.
     Therefore our sometime sister, now our queen,
     Th' imperial jointress° to this warlike state,
     Have we, as 'twere with a defeated joy—   10
     With an auspicious and a dropping eye,
     With mirth in funeral and with dirge in marriage,
     In equal scale weighing delight and dole—
     Taken to wife. Nor have we herein barr'd
     Your better wisdoms, which have freely gone   15
     With this affair along. For all, our thanks.
     Now follows that you know° young Fortinbras,
     Holding a weak supposal° of our worth,
     Or thinking by our late dear brother's death
     Our state to be disjoint and out of frame,   20
     Colleagued with° this dream of his advantage,°
     He hath not fail'd to pester us with message
     Importing° the surrender of those lands

[S.D.] *Exeunt:* Latin for "they go out."   I, II. Location: The castle.   [S.D.] *cum
aliis:* With others.   9. jointress: Woman possessed of a joint tenancy of an
estate.   17. know: Be informed (that).   18. weak supposal: Low estimate.
21. Colleagued with: Joined to, allied with.   dream . . . advantage: Illusory
hope of success.   23. Importing: Pertaining to.

Lost by his father, with all bands° of law,
To our most valiant brother. So much for him.   25
Now for ourself and for this time of meeting.
Thus much the business is: we have here writ
To Norway, uncle of young Fortinbras—
Who, impotent and bed-rid, scarcely hears
Of this his nephew's purpose—to suppress   30
His° further gait° herein, in that the levies,
The lists, and full proportions are all made
Out of his subject;° and we here dispatch
You, good Cornelius, and you, Voltimand,
For bearers of this greeting to old Norway,   35
Giving to you no further personal power
To business with the King, more than the scope
Of these delated° articles allow.   [*Gives a paper.*]
Farewell, and let your haste commend your duty.
CORNELIUS, VOLTIMAND: In that, and all things, will we show our duty.   40
KING: We doubt it nothing. Heartily farewell.

                                 [*Exit Voltimand and Cornelius.*]

And now, Laertes, what's the news with you?
You told us of some suit; what is 't, Laertes?
You cannot speak of reason to the Dane°
And lose your voice.° What wouldst thou beg, Laertes,   45
That shall not be my offer, not thy asking?
The head is not more native° to the heart,
The hand more instrumental° to the mouth,
Than is the throne of Denmark to thy father.
What wouldst thou have, Laertes?
LAERTES: My dread lord,   50
Your leave and favor to return to France,
From whence though willingly I came to Denmark
To show my duty in your coronation,
Yet now I must confess, that duty done,
My thoughts and wishes bend again toward France   55
And bow them to your gracious leave and pardon.°

---

24. bands: Contracts.   **31. His:** Fortinbras's.   **gait:** Proceeding.   **31–33. in that . . . subject:** Since the levying of troops and supplies is drawn entirely from the King of Norway's own subjects.   **38. delated:** Detailed. (Variant of *dilated.*)   **44. the Dane:** The Danish king.   **45. lose your voice:** Waste your speech.   **47. native:** Closely connected, related.   **48. instrumental:** Serviceable.   **56. leave and pardon:** Permission to depart.

KING: Have you your father's leave? What says Polonius?
POLONIUS: H'ath, my lord, wrung from me my slow leave
  By laborsome petition, and at last
  Upon his will I seal'd my hard° consent.   60
  I do beseech you, give him leave to go.
KING: Take thy fair hour, Laertes. Time be thine,
  And thy best graces spend it at thy will!
  But now, my cousin° Hamlet, and my son—
HAMLET: A little more than kin, and less than kind.°   65
KING: How is it that the clouds still hang on you?
HAMLET: Not so, my lord. I am too much in the sun.°
QUEEN: Good Hamlet, cast thy nighted color off,
  And let thine eye look like a friend on Denmark.
  Do not forever with thy veiled° lids   70
  Seek for thy noble father in the dust.
  Thou know'st 'tis common,° all that lives must die,
  Passing through nature to eternity.
HAMLET: Ay, madam, it is common.
QUEEN: If it be,
  Why seems it so particular with thee?   75
HAMLET: Seems, madam! Nay, it is. I know not "seems."
  'Tis not alone my inky cloak, good mother,
  Nor customary suits of solemn black,
  Nor windy suspiration of forc'd breath,
  No, nor the fruitful° river in the eye,   80
  Nor the dejected havior of the visage,
  Together with all forms, moods, shapes of grief,
  That can denote me truly. These indeed seem,
  For they are actions that a man might play.
  But I have that within which passes show;   85
  These but the trappings and the suits of woe.
KING: 'Tis sweet and commendable in your nature, Hamlet,
  To give these mourning duties to your father.
  But you must know your father lost a father,
  That father lost, lost his, and the survivor bound   90

---

60. hard: Reluctant. **64. cousin:** Any kin not of the immediate family. **65. A little . . . kind:** Closer than an ordinary nephew (since I am stepson), and yet more separated in natural feeling (with pun on *kind,* meaning affectionate and natural, lawful). This line is often read as an aside, but it need not be. **67. sun:** The sunshine of the King's royal favor (with pun on *son*). **70. veiled:** Downcast. **72. common:** Of universal occurrence. (But Hamlet plays on the sense of *vulgar* in line 74.) **80. fruitful:** Abundant.

In filial obligation for some term
To do obsequious° sorrow. But to persever°
In obstinate condolement° is a course
Of impious stubbornness. 'Tis unmanly grief.
It shows a will most incorrect to heaven,   95
A heart unfortified, a mind impatient,
An understanding simple and unschool'd.
For what we know must be and is as common
As any the most vulgar thing to sense,°
Why should we in our peevish opposition   100
Take it to heart? Fie, 'tis a fault to heaven,
A fault against the dead, a fault to nature,
To reason most absurd, whose common theme
Is death of fathers, and who still hath cried,
From the first corse° till he that died today,   105
"This must be so." We pray you, throw to earth
This unprevailing° woe, and think of us
As of a father; for let the world take note,
You are the most immediate° to our throne,
And with no less nobility of love   110
Than that which dearest father bears his son
Do I impart toward you. For your intent
In going back to school in Wittenberg,°
It is most retrograde° to our desire,
And we beseech you, bend you° to remain   115
Here in the cheer and comfort of our eye,
Our chiefest courtier, cousin, and our son.
QUEEN: Let not thy mother lose her prayers, Hamlet.
    I pray thee stay with us, go not to Wittenberg.
HAMLET: I shall in all my best obey you, madam.   120
KING: Why, 'tis a loving and a fair reply.
    Be as ourself in Denmark. Madam, come.
    This gentle and unforc'd accord of Hamlet
    Sits smiling to my heart, in grace whereof
    No jocund° health that Denmark drinks today   125
    But the great cannon to the clouds shall tell,

92. **obsequious:** Suited to obsequies or funerals. **persever:** Persevere.
93. **condolement:** Sorrowing. 99. **As . . . sense:** As the most ordinary experience. 105. **corse:** Corpse. 107. **unprevailing:** Unavailing. 109. **most immediate:** Next in succession. 113. **Wittenberg:** Famous German university founded in 1502. 114. **retrograde:** Contrary. 115. **bend you:** Incline yourself. 125. **jocund:** Merry.

100

And the King's rouse° the heaven shall bruit again,°
Respeaking earthly thunder.° Come away.

(*Flourish. Exeunt all but Hamlet.*)

HAMLET: O, that this too too sullied° flesh would melt,
Thaw, and resolve itself into a dew!   130
Or that the Everlasting had not fix'd
His canon° 'gainst self-slaughter! O God, God,
How weary, stale, flat, and unprofitable
Seem to me all the uses of this world!
Fie on 't, ah, fie! 'Tis an unweeded garden   135
That grows to seed. Things rank and gross in nature
Possess it merely.° That it should come to this!
But two months dead—nay, not so much, not two.
So excellent a king, that was to° this
Hyperion° to a satyr; so loving to my mother   140
That he might not beteem° the winds of heaven
Visit her face too roughly. Heaven and earth,
Must I remember? Why, she would hang on him
As if increase of appetite had grown
By what it fed on, and yet, within a month—   145
Let me not think on 't. Frailty, thy name is woman!—
A little month, or ere those shoes were old
With which she followed my poor father's body,
Like Niobe,° all tears, why she, even she—
O God, a beast, that wants discourse of reason,°   150
Would have mourn'd longer—married with my uncle,
My father's brother, but no more like my father
Than I to Hercules. Within a month,
Ere yet the salt of most unrighteous tears
Had left the flushing in her galled° eyes,   155
She married. O, most wicked speed, to post

127. **rouse:** Draft of liquor. **bruit again:** Loudly echo. 128. **thunder:** Of trumpet and kettledrum sounded when the King drinks, see I, IV, 8–12. 129. **sullied:** Defiled. (The early quartos read *sallied*, the Folio *solid*.) 132. **canon:** Law. 137. **merely:** Completely. 139. **to:** In comparison to. 140. **Hyperion:** Titan sun-god, father of Helios. 141. **beteem:** Allow. 149. **Niobe:** Tantalus's daughter, Queen of Thebes, who boasted that she had more sons and daughters than Leto; for this, Apollo and Artemis, children of Leto, slew her fourteen children. She was turned by Zeus into a stone that continually dropped tears. 150. **wants . . . reason:** Lacks the faculty of reason. 155. **galled:** Irritated, inflamed.

With such dexterity to incestuous° sheets!
It is not nor it cannot come to good.
But break, my heart, for I must hold my tongue.

(*Enter Horatio, Marcellus, and Bernardo.*)

HORATIO: Hail to your lordship!
HAMLET: I am glad to see you well.   160
   Horatio! — or I do forget myself.
HORATIO: The same, my lord, and your poor servant ever.
HAMLET: Sir, my good friend; I'll change° that name with you.
   And what make° you from Wittenberg, Horatio?
   Marcellus?   165
MARCELLUS: My good lord.
HAMLET: I am very glad to see you. [*To Bernardo.*] Good even, sir. —
   But what, in faith, make you from Wittenberg?
HORATIO: A truant disposition, good my lord.
HAMLET: I would not hear your enemy say so,   170
   Nor shall you do my ear that violence
   To make it truster of your own report
   Against yourself. I know you are no truant.
   But what is your affair in Elsinore?
   We'll teach you to drink deep ere you depart.   175
HORATIO: My lord, I came to see your father's funeral.
HAMLET: I prithee do not mock me, fellow student;
   I think it was to see my mother's wedding.
HORATIO: Indeed, my lord, it followed hard° upon.
HAMLET: Thrift, thrift, Horatio! The funeral bak'd meats   180
   Did coldly furnish forth the marriage tables.
   Would I had met my dearest° foe in heaven
   Or° ever I had seen that day, Horatio!
   My father! — Methinks I see my father.
HORATIO: Where, my lord?
HAMLET: In my mind's eye, Horatio.   185
HORATIO: I saw him once. 'A° was a goodly king.
HAMLET: 'A was a man, take him for all in all,
   I shall not look upon his like again.
HORATIO: My lord, I think I saw him yesternight.
HAMLET: Saw? Who?   190

---

157. **incestuous:** In Shakespeare's day, the marriage of a man like Claudius to his deceased brother's wife was considered incestuous.   163. **change:** Exchange (i.e., the name of friend).   164. **make:** Do.   179. **hard:** Close.   182. **dearest:** Direst.   183. **Or:** Ere, before.   186. **'A:** He.

HORATIO: My lord, the King your father.
HAMLET: The King my father?
HORATIO: Season your admiration° for a while
    With an attent° ear, till I may deliver,
    Upon the witness of these gentlemen,
    This marvel to you.
HAMLET: For God's love, let me hear!   195
HORATIO: Two nights together had these gentlemen,
    Marcellus and Bernardo, on their watch,
    In the dead waste and middle of the night,
    Been thus encount'red. A figure like your father,
    Armed at point° exactly, cap-a-pe,°   200
    Appears before them, and with solemn march
    Goes slow and stately by them. Thrice he walk'd
    By their oppress'd and fear-surprised eyes
    Within his truncheon's° length, whilst they, distill'd
    Almost to jelly with the act° of fear,   205
    Stand dumb and speak not to him. This to me
    In dreadful secrecy impart they did,
    And I with them the third night kept the watch,
    Where, as they had delivered, both in time,
    Form of the thing, each word made true and good,   210
    The apparition comes. I knew your father;
    These hands are not more like.
HAMLET: But where was this?
MARCELLUS: My lord, upon the platform where we watch.
HAMLET: Did you not speak to it?
HORATIO: My lord, I did,
    But answer made it none. Yet once methought   215
    It lifted up it° head and did address
    Itself to motion, like as it would speak;
    But even then the morning cock crew loud,
    And at the sound it shrunk in haste away,
    And vanish'd from our sight.
HAMLET: 'Tis very strange.   220
HORATIO: As I do live, my honor'd lord, 'tis true,
    And we did think it writ down in our duty
    To let you know of it.

---

192. Season your admiration: Restrain your astonishment.   193. attent: Attentive.   200. at point: Completely.   cap-a-pe: From head to foot.   204. truncheon: Officer's staff.   205. act: Action, operation.   216. it: Its.

HAMLET: Indeed, indeed, sirs. But this troubles me.
  Hold you the watch tonight?
ALL: We do, my lord.   225
HAMLET: Arm'd, say you?
ALL: Arm'd, my lord.
HAMLET: From top to toe?
ALL: My lord, from head to foot.
HAMLET: Then saw you not his face?
HORATIO: O, yes, my lord. He wore his beaver° up.   230
HAMLET: What, looked he frowningly?
HORATIO: A countenance more
  In sorrow than in anger.
HAMLET: Pale or red?
HORATIO: Nay, very pale.
HAMLET: And fix'd his eyes upon you?
HORATIO: Most constantly.
HAMLET: I would I had been there.
HORATIO: It would have much amaz'd you.   235
HAMLET: Very like, very like. Stay'd it long?
HORATIO: While one with moderate haste might tell° a hundred.
MARCELLUS, BERNARDO: Longer, longer.
HORATIO: Not when I saw 't.
HAMLET: His beard was grizzl'd,—no?
HORATIO: It was, as I have seen it in his life,   240
  A sable silver'd.°
HAMLET: I will watch tonight.
  Perchance 'twill walk again.
HORATIO: I warr'nt it will.
HAMLET: If it assume my noble father's person,
  I'll speak to it, though hell itself should gape
  And bid me hold my peace. I pray you all,   245
  If you have hitherto conceal'd this sight,
  Let it be tenable° in your silence still,
  And whatsomever else shall hap tonight,
  Give it an understanding, but no tongue.
  I will requite your loves. So, fare you well.   250
  Upon the platform, 'twixt eleven and twelve,
  I'll visit you.

---

230. beaver: Visor on the helmet.   **237. tell:** Count.   **241. sable silver'd:** Black
mixed with white.   **247. tenable:** Held tightly.

ALL: Our duty to your honor.
HAMLET: Your loves, as mine to you. Farewell.

                                              (*Exeunt [all but Hamlet*].)

My father's spirit in arms! All is not well.
I doubt° some foul play. Would the night were come!   255
Till then sit still, my soul. Foul deeds will rise,
Though all the earth o'erwhelm them, to men's eyes.

                                                            (*Exit.*)

                          {*Scene III*}°

(*Enter Laertes and Ophelia, his sister.*)

LAERTES: My necessaries are embark'd. Farewell.
    And, sister, as the winds give benefit
    And convoy is assistant,° do not sleep
    But let me hear from you.
OPHELIA: Do you doubt that?
LAERTES: For Hamlet, and the trifling of his favor,   5
    Hold it a fashion and a toy in blood,°
    A violet in the youth of primy° nature,
    Forward,° not permanent, sweet, not lasting,
    The perfume and suppliance° of a minute—
    No more.
OPHELIA: No more but so?
LAERTES: Think it no more.   10
    For nature crescent° does not grow alone
    In thews° and bulk, but, as this temple° waxes,
    The inward service of the mind and soul
    Grows wide withal.° Perhaps he loves you now,
    And now no soil° nor cautel° doth besmirch   15
    The virtue of his will;° but you must fear,
    His greatness weigh'd,° his will is not his own.

255. **doubt:** Suspect.   **I, III. Location:** Polonius's chambers.   **3. convoy is assis-tant:** Means of conveyance are available.   **6. toy in blood:** Passing amorous fancy.   **7. primy:** In its prime, springtime.   **8. Forward:** Precocious.   **9. sup-pliance:** Supply, filler.   **11. crescent:** Growing, waxing.   **12. thews:** Bodily strength.   **temple:** Body.   **14. Grows wide withal:** Grows along with it.   **15. soil:** Blemish.   **cautel:** Deceit.   **16. will:** Desire.   **17. greatness weigh'd:** High posi-tion considered.

[For he himself is subject to his birth.]
He may not, as unvalued persons do,
Carve° for himself; for on his choice depends   20
The safety and health of this whole state,
And therefore must his choice be circumscrib'd
Unto the voice and yielding° of that body
Whereof he is the head. Then if he says he loves you,
It fits your wisdom so far to believe it   25
As he in his particular act and place
May give his saying deed,° which is no further
Than the main voice of Denmark goes withal.
Then weigh what loss your honor may sustain
If with too credent° ear you list° his songs,   30
Or lose your heart, or your chaste treasure open
To his unmaster'd importunity.
Fear it, Ophelia, fear it, my dear sister,
And keep you in the rear of your affection,
Out of the shot° and danger of desire.   35
The chariest° maid is prodigal enough
If she unmask her beauty to the moon.
Virtue itself scapes not calumnious strokes.
The canker galls° the infants of the spring
Too oft before their buttons° be disclos'd,°   40
And in the morn and liquid dew° of youth
Contagious blastments° are most imminent.
Be wary then; best safety lies in fear.
Youth to itself rebels, though none else near.
OPHELIA: I shall the effect of this good lesson keep   45
As watchman to my heart. But, good my brother,
Do not, as some ungracious pastors do,
Show me the steep and thorny way to heaven,
Whiles, like a puff'd° and reckless libertine,
Himself the primrose path of dalliance treads,   50
And recks° not his own rede.°

(*Enter Polonius.*)

---

20. Carve: Choose pleasure. **23. voice and yielding:** Assent, approval.
27. deed: Effect. **30. credent:** Credulous. **list:** Listen to. **35. shot:** Range.
36. chariest: Most scrupulously modest. **39. canker galls:** Cankerworm destroys. **40. buttons:** Buds. **disclos'd:** Opened. **41. liquid dew:** Time when dew is fresh. **42. blastments:** Blights. **49. puff'd:** Bloated. **51. recks:** Heeds. **rede:** Counsel.

LAERTES: O, fear me not.
I stay too long. But here my father comes.
A double blessing is a double° grace;
Occasion° smiles upon a second leave.
POLONIUS: Yet here, Laertes? Aboard, aboard, for shame!   55
The wind sits in the shoulder of your sail,
And you are stay'd for. There—my blessing with thee!
And these few precepts in thy memory
Look thou character.° Give thy thoughts no tongue
Nor any unproportion'd thought his° act.   60
Be thou familiar,° but by no means vulgar.°
Those friends thou hast, and their adoption tried,°
Grapple them to thy soul with hoops of steel,
But do not dull thy palm with entertainment
Of each new-hatch'd, unfledg'd courage.° Beware   65
Of entrance to a quarrel, but, being in,
Bear't that° th' opposed may beware of thee.
Give every man thy ear, but few thy voice;
Take each man's censure,° but reserve thy judgment.
Costly thy habit as thy purse can buy,   70
But not express'd in fancy; rich, not gaudy,
For the apparel oft proclaims the man,
And they in France of the best rank and station
Are of a most select and generous chief° in that.
Neither a borrower nor a lender be,   75
For loan oft loses both itself and friend,
And borrowing dulleth edge of husbandry.°
This above all: to thine own self be true,
And it must follow, as the night the day,
Thou canst not then be false to any man.   80
Farewell. My blessing season° this in thee!
LAERTES: Most humbly do I take my leave, my lord.
POLONIUS: The time invests° you. Go, your servants tend.°
LAERTES: Farewell, Ophelia, and remember well
What I have said to you.   85

53. double: I.e., Laertes has already bidden his father good-bye.   54. Occasion:
Opportunity.   59. character: Inscribe.   60. his: Its.   61. familiar: Sociable.
vulgar: Common.   62. tried: Tested.   65. courage: Young man of spirit.
67. Bear't that: Manage it so that.   69. censure: Opinion, judgment.   74. generous chief: Noble eminence (?).   77. husbandry: Thrift.   81. season: Mature.
83. invests: Besieges, impresses upon.   tend: Attend, wait.

OPHELIA: 'Tis in my memory lock'd,
And you yourself shall keep the key of it.
LAERTES: Farewell.   (*Exit Laertes.*)
POLONIUS: What is 't, Ophelia, he hath said to you?
OPHELIA: So please you, something touching the Lord Hamlet.   90
POLONIUS: Marry,° well bethought.
   'Tis told me he hath very oft of late
   Given private time to you, and you yourself
   Have of your audience been most free and bounteous.
   If it be so—as so 'tis put on° me,   95
   And that in way of caution—I must tell you
   You do not understand yourself so clearly
   As it behooves my daughter and your honor.
   What is between you? Give me up the truth.
OPHELIA: He hath, my lord, of late made many tenders°   100
   Of his affection to me.
POLONIUS: Affection? Pooh! You speak like a green girl,
   Unsifted° in such perilous circumstance.
   Do you believe his tenders, as you call them?
OPHELIA: I do not know, my lord, what I should think.   105
POLONIUS: Marry, I will teach you. Think yourself a baby
   That you have ta'en these tenders° for true pay,
   Which are not sterling.° Tender° yourself more dearly,
   Or—not to crack the wind° of the poor phrase,
   Running it thus—you'll tender me a fool.°   110
OPHELIA: My lord, he hath importun'd me with love
   In honorable fashion.
POLONIUS: Ay, fashion° you may call it. Go to, go to.
OPHELIA: And hath given countenance° to his speech, my lord,
   With almost all the holy vows of heaven.   115
POLONIUS: Ay, springes° to catch woodcocks.° I do know,
   When the blood burns, how prodigal the soul
   Lends the tongue vows. These blazes, daughter,
   Giving more light than heat, extinct in both

---

91. Marry: By the Virgin Mary (a mild oath).   **95. put on:** Impressed on, told to.
100. tenders: Offers.   **103. Unsifted:** Untried.   **107. tenders:** With added
meaning here of *promises to pay.*   **108. sterling:** Legal currency.   **Tender:**
Hold.   **109. crack the wind:** Run it until it is broken, winded.   **110. tender me
a fool:** (1) Show yourself to me as a fool, (2) show me up as a fool, (3) present me
with a grandchild (*fool* was a term of endearment for a child).   **113. fashion:**
Mere form, pretense.   **114. countenance:** Credit, support.   **116. springes:**
Snares.   **woodcocks:** Birds easily caught; here used to connote gullibility.

Even in their promise, as it is a-making,   120
You must not take for fire. From this time
Be something scanter of your maiden presence.
Set your entreatments° at a higher rate
Than a command to parle.° For Lord Hamlet,
Believe so much in him° that he is young,   125
And with a larger tether may he walk
Than may be given you. In few,° Ophelia,
Do not believe his vows, for they are brokers,°
Not of that dye° which their investments° show,
But mere implorators° of unholy suits,   130
Breathing° like sanctified and pious bawds,
The better to beguile. This is for all:
I would not, in plain terms, from this time forth
Have you so slander° any moment leisure
As to give words or talk with the Lord Hamlet.   135
Look to 't, I charge you. Come your ways.
OPHELIA: I shall obey, my lord.   (*Exeunt.*)

[*Scene IV*]°

(*Enter Hamlet, Horatio, and Marcellus.*)

HAMLET: The air bites shrewdly; it is very cold.
HORATIO: It is a nipping and an eager air.
HAMLET: What hour now?
HORATIO: I think it lacks of twelve.
MARCELLUS: No, it is struck.
HORATIO: Indeed? I heard it not.
It then draws near the season   5
Wherein the spirit held his wont to walk.

(*A flourish of trumpets, and two pieces° go off* [*within*].)

123. entreatments: Negotiations for surrender (a military term).   124. parle:
Discuss terms with the enemy. (Polonius urges his daughter, in the metaphor of
military language, not to meet with Hamlet and consider giving in to him merely
because he requests an interview.)   125. so . . . him: This much concerning him.
127. In few: Briefly.   128. brokers: Go-betweens, procurers.   129. dye: Color
or sort.   investments: Clothes (i.e., they are not what they seem).   130. mere
implorators: Out-and-out solicitors.   131. Breathing: Speaking.   134. slander: Bring disgrace or reproach upon.   I, IV. Location: The guard platform.
[s.d.] *pieces:* I.e., of ordnance, cannon.

What does this mean, my lord?
HAMLET: The King doth wake° tonight and takes his rouse,°
Keeps wassail,° and the swagg'ring up-spring° reels;
And as he drains his draughts of Rhenish° down,   10
The kettle-drum and trumpet thus bray out
The triumph of his pledge.°
HORATIO: Is it a custom?
HAMLET: Ay, marry, is 't,
But to my mind, though I am native here
And to the manner° born, it is a custom   15
More honor'd in the breach than the observance.°
This heavy-headed revel east and west°
Makes us traduc'd and tax'd of° other nations.
They clepe° us drunkards, and with swinish phrase°
Soil our addition;° and indeed it takes   20
From our achievements, though perform'd at height,°
The pith and marrow of our attribute.
So, oft it chances in particular men,
That for some vicious mole of nature° in them,
As in their birth—wherein they are not guilty,   25
Since nature cannot choose his° origin—
By the o'ergrowth of some complexion,°
Oft breaking down the pales° and forts of reason,
Or by some habit that too much o'er-leavens°
The form of plausive° manners, that these men,   30
Carrying, I say, the stamp of one defect,
Being nature's livery,° or fortune's star,°
Their virtues else, be they as pure as grace,
As infinite as man may undergo,
Shall in the general censure take corruption   35

---

8. **wake:** Stay awake and hold revel.   **rouse:** Carouse, drinking bout.   9. **wassail:** Carousal.   **up-spring:** Wild German dance.   10. **Rhenish:** Rhine wine.
12. **triumph . . . pledge:** His feat in draining the wine in a single draft.
15. **manner:** Custom (of drinking).   16. **More . . . observance:** Better neglected than followed.   17. **east and west:** I.e., everywhere.   18. **tax'd of:** Censured by.
19. **clepe:** Call.   **with swinish phrase:** By calling us swine.   20. **addition:** Reputation.   21. **at height:** Outstandingly.   24. **mole of nature:** Natural blemish in one's constitution.   26. **his:** Its.   27. **complexion:** Humor (i.e., one of the four humors or fluids thought to determine temperament).   28. **pales:** Palings, fences (as of a fortification).   29. **o'er-leavens:** Induces a change throughout (as yeast works in dough).   30. **plausive:** Pleasing.   32. **nature's livery:** Endowment from nature. . . .   **fortune's star:** Mark placed by fortune.

From that particular fault. The dram of eale°
Doth all the noble substance of a doubt°
To his own scandal.°

(*Enter Ghost.*)

HORATIO: Look, my lord, it comes!
HAMLET: Angels and ministers of grace defend us!
Be thou a spirit of health° or goblin damn'd,   40
Bring with thee airs from heaven or blasts from hell,
Be thy intents wicked or charitable,
Thou com'st in such a questionable° shape
That I will speak to thee. I'll call thee Hamlet,
King, father, royal Dane. O, answer me!   45
Let me not burst in ignorance, but tell
Why thy canoniz'd° bones, hearsed° in death,
Have burst their cerements;° why the sepulcher
Wherein we saw thee quietly interr'd
Hath op'd his ponderous and marble jaws   50
To cast thee up again. What may this mean,
That thou, dead corse, again in complete steel
Revisits thus the glimpses of the moon,°
Making night hideous, and we fools of nature°
So horridly to shake our disposition   55
With thoughts beyond the reaches of our souls?
Say, why is this? Wherefore? What should we do?

([*Ghost*] *beckons* [*Hamlet*].)

HORATIO: It beckons you to go away with it,
As if it some impartment° did desire
To you alone.
MARCELLUS: Look with what courteous action   60
It waves you to a more removed ground.
But do not go with it.
HORATIO: No, by no means.

---

36. dram of eale: Small amount of evil (?).   37. of a doubt: A famous crux, sometimes emended to *oft about* or *often dout*, i.e., often erase or do out, or to *antidote*, counteract.   38. To . . . scandal: To the disgrace of the whole enterprise.   40. of health: Of spiritual good.   43. questionable: Inviting question or conversation.   47. canoniz'd: Buried according to the canons of the church. . . . hearsed: Coffined.   48. cerements: Grave-clothes.   53. glimpses of the moon: Earth by night.   54. fools of nature: Mere men, limited to natural knowledge.   59. impartment: Communication.

HAMLET: It will not speak. Then I will follow it.
HORATIO: Do not, my lord.
HAMLET: Why, what should be the fear?
  I do not set my life at a pin's fee,°   65
  And for my soul, what can it do to that,
  Being a thing immortal as itself?
  It waves me forth again. I'll follow it.
HORATIO: What if it tempt you toward the flood, my lord
  Or to the dreadful summit of the cliff   70
  That beetles o'er° his° base into the sea,
  And there assume some other horrible form
  Which might deprive your sovereignty of reason,°
  And draw you into madness? Think of it.
  The very place puts toys of desperation,°   75
  Without more motive, into every brain
  That looks so many fathoms to the sea
  And hears it roar beneath.
HAMLET: It waves me still.
  Go on, I'll follow thee.
MARCELLUS: You shall not go, my lord.

                                       [*They try to stop him.*]

HAMLET: Hold off your hands!   80
HORATIO: Be rul'd, you shall not go.
HAMLET: My fate cries out,
  And makes each petty artery° in this body
  As hardy as the Nemean lion's° nerve.°
  Still am I call'd. Unhand me, gentlemen.
  By heaven, I'll make a ghost of him that lets° me!   85
  I say, away! Go on. I'll follow thee.

                          (*Exeunt Ghost and Hamlet.*)

HORATIO: He waxes desperate with imagination.
MARCELLUS: Let's follow. 'Tis not fit thus to obey him.
HORATIO: Have after. To what issue° will this come?
MARCELLUS: Something is rotten in the state of Denmark.   90

---

65. fee: Value.   **71. beetles o'er:** Overhangs threateningly.   **his:** Its.   **73. deprive . . . reason:** Take away the rule of reason over your mind.   **75. toys of desperation:** Fancies of desperate acts, i.e., suicide.   **82. artery:** Sinew.   **83. Nemean lion:** One of the monsters slain by Hercules in his twelve labors.   **nerve:** Sinew.   **85. lets:** Hinders.   **89. issue:** Outcome.

HORATIO: Heaven will direct it.°
MARCELLUS: Nay, let's follow him.   (*Exeunt.*)

{*Scene v*}°

(*Enter Ghost and Hamlet.*)

HAMLET: Whither wilt thou lead me? Speak. I'll go no further.
GHOST: Mark me.
HAMLET: I will.
GHOST: My hour is almost come,
   When I to sulph'rous and tormenting flames
   Must render up myself.
HAMLET: Alas, poor ghost!
GHOST: Pity me not, but lend thy serious hearing   5
   To what I shall unfold.
HAMLET: Speak. I am bound to hear.
GHOST: So art thou to revenge, when thou shalt hear.
HAMLET: What?
GHOST: I am thy father's spirit,   10
   Doom'd for a certain term to walk the night,
   And for the day confin'd to fast° in fires,
   Till the foul crimes° done in my days of nature
   Are burnt and purg'd away. But that° I am forbid
   To tell the secrets of my prison-house,   15
   I could a tale unfold whose lightest word
   Would harrow up thy soul, freeze thy young blood,
   Make thy two eyes, like stars, start from their spheres,°
   Thy knotted and combined locks° to part,
   And each particular hair to stand an end,°   20
   Like quills upon the fearful porpentine.°
   But this eternal blazon° must not be
   To ears of flesh and blood. List, list, O, list!
   If thou didst ever thy dear father love—
HAMLET: O God!   25

---

91. **it:** The outcome. **I, v. Location:** The battlements of the castle. **12. fast:** Do penance. **13. crimes:** Sins. **14. But that:** Were it not that. **18. spheres:** Eye sockets, here compared to the orbits or transparent revolving spheres in which, according to Ptolemaic astronomy, the heavenly bodies were fixed. **19. knotted . . . locks:** Hair neatly arranged and confined. **20. an end:** On end. **21. fearful porpentine:** Frightened porcupine. **22. eternal blazon:** Revelation of the secrets of eternity.

GHOST: Revenge his foul and most unnatural murder.
HAMLET: Murder?
GHOST: Murder most foul, as in the best it is,
  But this most foul, strange, and unnatural.
HAMLET: Haste me to know 't, that I, with wings as swift   30
  As meditation or the thoughts of love,
  May sweep to my revenge.
GHOST: I find thee apt;
  And duller shouldst thou be than the fat weed
  That roots itself in ease on Lethe° wharf,°
  Wouldst thou not stir in this. Now, Hamlet, hear.   35
  'Tis given out that, sleeping in my orchard,
  A serpent stung me. So the whole ear of Denmark
  Is by a forged process° of my death
  Rankly abus'd.° But know, thou noble youth,
  The serpent that did sting thy father's life   40
  Now wears his crown.
HAMLET: O my prophetic soul!
  My uncle!
GHOST: Ay, that incestuous, that adulterate° beast,
  With witchcraft of his wits, with traitorous gifts—
  O wicked wit and gifts, that have the power   45
  So to seduce!—won to his shameful lust
  The will of my most seeming-virtuous queen.
  O Hamlet, what a falling-off was there!
  From me, whose love was of that dignity
  That it went hand in hand even with the vow   50
  I made to her in marriage, and to decline
  Upon a wretch whose natural gifts were poor
  To those of mine!
  But virtue, as it never will be moved,
  Though lewdness court it in a shape of heaven,°   55
  So lust, though to a radiant angel link'd,
  Will sate itself in a celestial bed,
  And prey on garbage.
  But, soft, methinks I scent the morning air.
  Brief let me be. Sleeping within my orchard,   60
  My custom always of the afternoon,
  Upon my secure° hour thy uncle stole,

---

34. Lethe: The river of forgetfulness in Hades. **wharf:** Bank. **38. forged process:** Falsified account. **39. abus'd:** Deceived. **43. adulterate:** Adulterous.
55. shape of heaven: Heavenly form. **62. secure:** Confident, unsuspicious.

With juice of cursed hebona° in a vial,
And in the porches of my ears did pour
The leprous° distillment, whose effect   65
Holds such an enmity with blood of man
That swift as quicksilver it courses through
The natural gates and alleys of the body,
And with a sudden vigor it doth posset°
And curd, like eager° droppings into milk,   70
The thin and wholesome blood. So did it mine,
And a most instant tetter° bark'd° about,
Most lazar-like,° with vile and loathsome crust,
All my smooth body.
Thus was I, sleeping, by a brother's hand   75
Of life, of crown, of queen, at once dispatch'd,°
Cut off even in the blossoms of my sin,
Unhous'led,° disappointed,° unanel'd,°
No reck'ning made, but sent to my account
With all my imperfections on my head.   80
O, horrible! O, horrible, most horrible!
If thou hast nature° in thee, bear it not.
Let not the royal bed of Denmark be
A couch for luxury° and damned incest.
But, howsomever thou pursues this act,   85
Taint not thy mind, nor let thy soul contrive
Against thy mother aught. Leave her to heaven
And to those thorns that in her bosom lodge,
To prick and sting her. Fare thee well at once.
The glow-worm shows the matin° to be near,   90
And 'gins to pale his uneffectual fire.°
Adieu, adieu, adieu! Remember me.   [*Exit.*]
HAMLET: O all you host of heaven! O earth! What else?
And shall I couple° hell? O fie! Hold, hold, my heart,

---

63. hebona: Poison. (The word seems to be a form of *ebony,* though it is thought
perhaps to be related to *henbane,* a poison, or to *ebenus,* yew.) **65. leprous:**
Causing leprosy-like disfigurement. **69. posset:** Coagulate, curdle. **70. eager:**
Sour, acid. **72. tetter:** Eruption of scabs. **bark'd:** Covered with a rough cover-
ing, like bark on a tree. **73. lazar-like:** Leper-like. **76. dispatch'd:** Suddenly
deprived. **78. Unhous'led:** Without having received the sacrament [of Holy
Communion]. **disappointed:** Unready (spiritually) for the last journey.
unanel'd: Without having received extreme unction. **82. nature:** The promptings of a son. **84. luxury:** Lechery. **90. matin:** Morning. **91. uneffectual
fire:** Cold light. **94. couple:** Add.

And you, my sinews, grow not instant old,   95
But bear me stiffly up. Remember thee!
Ay, thou poor ghost, whiles memory holds a seat
In this distracted globe.° Remember thee!
Yea, from the table° of my memory
I'll wipe away all trivial fond° records,   100
All saws° of books, all forms,° all pressures° past
That youth and observation copied there,
And thy commandment all alone shall live
Within the book and volume of my brain,
Unmix'd with baser matter. Yes, by heaven!   105
O most pernicious woman!
O villain, villain, smiling, damned villain!
My tables—meet it is I set it down,
That one may smile, and smile, and be a villain.
At least I am sure it may be so in Denmark.   110
                                              [*Writing.*]

So, uncle, there you are. Now to my word;
It is "Adieu, adieu! Remember me."
I have sworn 't.

(*Enter Horatio and Marcellus.*)

HORATIO: My lord, my lord!
MARCELLUS: Lord Hamlet!
HORATIO: Heavens secure him!
HAMLET: So be it!   115
MARCELLUS: Illo, ho, ho, my lord!
HAMLET: Hillo, ho, ho,° boy! Come, bird, come.
MARCELLUS: How is 't, my noble lord?
HORATIO: What news, my lord?
HAMLET: O, wonderful!
HORATIO: Good my lord, tell it.
HAMLET: No, you will reveal it.   120
HORATIO: Not I, my lord, by heaven.
MARCELLUS: Nor I, my lord.
HAMLET: How say you, then, would heart of man once think it?
    But you'll be secret?
HORATIO, MARCELLUS: Ay, by heaven, my lord.

---

98. **globe:** Head.   99. **table:** Writing tablet.   100. **fond:** Foolish.   101. **saws:** Wise sayings.   **forms:** Images.   **pressures:** Impressions stamped.   117. **Hillo, ho, ho:** A falconer's call to a hawk in air. Hamlet is playing upon Marcellus's *Illo*, i.e., *halloo*.

HAMLET: There's never a villain dwelling in all Denmark
  But he's an arrant° knave.   125
HORATIO: There needs no ghost, my lord, come from the grave
  To tell us this.
HAMLET: Why, right, you are in the right.
  And so, without more circumstance° at all,
  I hold it fit that we shake hands and part,
  You, as your business and desire shall point you—   130
  For every man hath business and desire,
  Such as it is—and for my own poor part,
  Look you, I'll go pray.
HORATIO: These are but wild and whirling words, my lord.
HAMLET: I am sorry they offend you, heartily;   135
  Yes, faith, heartily.
HORATIO: There's no offense, my lord.
HAMLET: Yes, by Saint Patrick,° but there is, Horatio,
  And much offense too. Touching this vision here,
  It is an honest° ghost, that let me tell you.
  For your desire to know what is between us,   140
  O'ermaster 't as you may. And now, good friends
  As you are friends, scholars, and soldiers,
  Give me one poor request.
HORATIO: What is 't, my lord? We will.
HAMLET: Never make known what you have seen tonight.   145
HORATIO, MARCELLUS: My lord, we will not.
HAMLET: Nay, but swear 't.
HORATIO: In faith,
  My lord, not I.
MARCELLUS: Nor I, my lord, in faith.
HAMLET: Upon my sword.°   [*Holds out his sword.*]
MARCELLUS: We have sworn, my lord, already.
HAMLET: Indeed, upon my sword, indeed.

                    (*Ghost cries under the stage.*)

GHOST: Swear.   150
HAMLET: Ha, ha, boy, say'st thou so? Art thou there, truepenny?°
  Come on, you hear this fellow in the cellarage.
  Consent to swear.

---

125. arrant: Thoroughgoing. **128. circumstance:** Ceremony. **137. Saint Patrick:** The keeper of purgatory and patron saint of all blunders and confusion. **139. honest:** I.e., a real ghost and not an evil spirit. **148. sword:** The hilt in the form of a cross. **151. truepenny:** Honest old fellow.

HORATIO: Propose the oath, my lord.
HAMLET: Never to speak of this that you have seen,
    Swear by my sword.   155
GHOST [*beneath*]: Swear.
HAMLET: Hic et ubique?° Then we'll shift our ground.

                              [*He moves to another spot.*]

    Come hither, gentlemen,
    And lay your hands again upon my sword.
    Swear by my sword   160
    Never to speak of this that you have heard.
GHOST [*beneath*]: Swear by his sword.
HAMLET: Well said, old mole! Canst work i' th' earth so fast?
    A worthy pioner!° Once more remove, good friends.

                                        [*Moves again.*]

HORATIO: O day and night, but this is wondrous strange!   165
HAMLET: And therefore as a stranger give it welcome.
    There are more things in heaven and earth, Horatio,
    Than are dreamt of in your philosophy.°
    But come;
    Here, as before, never, so help you mercy,   170
    How strange or odd soe'er I bear myself—
    As I perchance hereafter shall think meet
    To put an antic° disposition on—
    That you, at such times seeing me, never shall,
    With arms encumb'red° thus, or this headshake,   175
    Or by pronouncing of some doubtful phrase,
    As "Well, well, we know," or "We could, an if° we would,"
    Or "If we list° to speak," or "There be, an if they might,"
    Or such ambiguous giving out,° to note°
    That you know aught of me—this do swear,   180
    So grace and mercy at your most need help you.
GHOST [*beneath*]: Swear.   [*They swear.*]
HAMLET: Rest, rest, perturbed spirit! So, gentlemen,
    With all my love I do commend me to you;
    And what so poor a man as Hamlet is   185

---

157. Hic et ubique: Here and everywhere (Latin).   **164. pioner:** Pioneer, digger, miner.   **168. your philosophy:** This subject called "natural philosophy" or "science" that people talk about.   **173. antic:** Fantastic.   **175. encumb'red:** Folded or entwined.   **177. an if:** If.   **178. list:** Were inclined.   **179. giving out:** Profession of knowledge.   **note:** Give a sign, indicate.

May do, t' express his love and friending to you,
God willing, shall not lack. Let us go in together,
And still° your fingers on your lips, I pray.
The time is out of joint. O cursed spite,
That ever I was born to set it right!   190

                              [*They wait for him to leave first.*]

Nay, come, let's go together.   (*Exeunt.*)

                         {ACT II   *Scene 1*}°

(*Enter old Polonius, with his man* [*Reynaldo*].)

POLONIUS: Give him this money and these notes, Reynaldo.
REYNALDO: I will, my lord.
POLONIUS: You shall do marvel's° wisely, good Reynaldo,
    Before you visit him, to make inquire
    Of his behavior.
REYNALDO: My lord, I did intend it.   5
POLONIUS: Marry, well said, very well said. Look you, sir,
    Inquire me first what Danskers° are in Paris,
    And how, and who, what means,° and where they keep,°
    What company, at what expense; and finding
    By this encompassment° and drift° of question   10
    That they do know my son, come you more nearer
    Than your particular demands will touch it.°
    Take° you, as 'twere, some distant knowledge of him,
    As thus, "I know his father and his friends,
    And in part him." Do you mark this, Reynaldo?   15
REYNALDO: Ay, very well, my lord.
POLONIUS: "And in part him, but," you may say, "not well.
    But, if 't be he I mean, he's very wild,
    Addicted so and so," and there put on° him
    What forgeries° you please—marry, none so rank   20

---

188. still: Always.   **II, i. Location:** Polonius's chambers.   **3. marvel's:** Marvelous(ly).   **7. Danskers:** Danes.   **8. what means:** What wealth (they have).   **keep:** Dwell.   **10. encompassment:** Roundabout talking.   **drift:** Gradual approach or course.   **11–12. come . . . it:** You will find out more this way than by asking pointed questions (particular demands).   **13. Take:** Assume, pretend.   **19. put on:** Impute to.   **20. forgeries:** Invented tales.

As may dishonor him, take heed of that,
But, sir, such wanton,° wild, and usual slips,
As are companions noted and most known
To youth and liberty.
REYNALDO: As gaming, my lord.
POLONIUS: Ay, or drinking, fencing, swearing,   25
    Quarreling, drabbing°—you may go so far.
REYNALDO: My lord, that would dishonor him.
POLONIUS: Faith, no, as you may season° it in the charge.
    You must not put another scandal on him
    That he is open to incontinency;°   30
    That's not my meaning. But breathe his faults so quaintly°
    That they may seem the taints of liberty,°
    The flash and outbreak of a fiery mind,
    A savageness in unreclaimed° blood,
    Of general assault.°
REYNALDO: But, my good lord—   35
POLONIUS: Wherefore should you do this?
REYNALDO: Ay, my lord,
    I would know that.
POLONIUS: Marry, sir, here's my drift,
    And, I believe, it is a fetch of wit.°
    You laying these slight sullies on my son,
    As 'twere a thing a little soil'd i' th' working,°   40
    Mark you,
    Your party in converse,° him you would sound,°
    Having ever° seen in the prenominate crimes°
    The youth you breathe° of guilty, be assur'd
    He closes with you in this consequence:°   45
    "Good sir," or so, or "friend," or "gentleman,"
    According to the phrase or the addition°
    Of man and country.
REYNALDO: Very good, my lord.

22. wanton: Sportive, unrestrained. 26. drabbing: Whoring. 28. season:
Temper, soften. 30. incontinency: Habitual loose behavior. 31. quaintly:
Delicately, ingeniously. 32. taints of liberty: Faults resulting from freedom.
34. unreclaimed: Untamed. 35. general assault: Tendency that assails all unrestrained youth. 38. fetch of wit: Clever trick. 40. soil'd i' th' working: Shop-
worn. 42. converse: Conversation. sound: Sound out. 43. Having ever: If
he has ever. prenominate crimes: Before-mentioned offenses. 44. breathe:
Speak. 45. closes . . . consequence: Follows your lead in some fashion as follows. 47. addition: Title.

POLONIUS: And then, sir, does 'a this—'a does—what was I about to
   say?
   By the mass, I was about to say something.   50
   Where did I leave?
REYNALDO: At "closes in the consequence."
POLONIUS: At "closes in the consequence," ay, marry.
   He closes thus: "I know the gentleman;
   I saw him yesterday, or th' other day,
   Or then, or then, with such, or such, and, as you say,   55
   There was 'a gaming, there o'ertook in 's rouse,°
   There falling out° at tennis," or perchance,
   "I saw him enter such a house of sale,"
   Videlicet,° a brothel, or so forth. See you now,
   Your bait of falsehood takes this carp° of truth;   60
   And thus do we of wisdom and of reach,°
   With windlasses° and with assays of bias,°
   By indirections find directions° out.
   So by my former lecture and advice
   Shall you my son. You have me, have you not?   65
REYNALDO: My lord, I have.
POLONIUS: God buy ye; fare ye well.
REYNALDO: Good my lord.
POLONIUS: Observe his inclination in yourself.°
REYNALDO: I shall, my lord.
POLONIUS: And let him ply° his music.
REYNALDO: Well, my lord.   70
POLONIUS: Farewell.   (*Exit Reynaldo.*)

(*Enter Ophelia.*)

         How now, Ophelia, what's the matter?
OPHELIA: O, my lord, my lord, I have been so affrighted!
POLONIUS: With what, i' th' name of God?
OPHELIA: My lord, as I was sewing in my closet,°
   Lord Hamlet, with his doublet° all unbrac'd,°   75

---

56. o'ertook in 's rouse: Overcome by drink.   57. falling out: Quarreling.
59. Videlicet: Namely.   60. carp: A fish.   61. reach: Capacity, ability.   62. wind-
lasses: Circuitous paths (literally, circuits made to head off the game in hunting).
assays of bias: Attempts through indirection (like the curving path of the bowling
ball, which is biased or weighted to one side).   63. directions: The way things
really are.   68. in yourself: In your own person (as well as by asking questions).
70. let him ply: See that he continues to study.   74. closet: Private chamber.
75. doublet: Close-fitting jacket.   unbrac'd: Unfastened.

No hat upon his head, his stockings fouled,
Ungart'red, and down-gyved to his ankle,°
Pale as his shirt, his knees knocking each other,
And with a look so piteous in purport
As if he had been loosed out of hell   80
To speak of horrors — he comes before me.
POLONIUS: Mad for thy love?
OPHELIA: My lord, I do not know,
But truly I do fear it.
POLONIUS: What said he?
OPHELIA: He took me by the wrist and held me hard.
Then goes he to the length of all his arm,   85
And, with his other hand thus o'er his brow
He falls to such perusal of my face
As 'a would draw it. Long stay'd he so.
At last, a little shaking of mine arm
And thrice his head thus waving up and down,   90
He rais'd a sigh so piteous and profound
As it did seem to shatter all his bulk°
And end his being. That done, he lets me go,
And, with his head over his shoulder turn'd,
He seem'd to find his way without his eyes,   95
For out o' doors he went without their helps,
And, to the last, bended their light on me.
POLONIUS: Come, go with me. I will go seek the King.
This is the very ecstasy° of love
Whose violent property° fordoes° itself   100
And leads the will to desperate undertakings
As oft as any passion under heaven
That does afflict our natures. I am sorry.
What, have you given him any hard words of late?
OPHELIA: No, my good lord, but, as you did command,   105
I did repel his letters and denied
His access to me.
POLONIUS: That hath made him mad.
I am sorry that with better heed and judgment
I had not quoted° him. I fear'd he did but trifle
And meant to wrack thee; but, beshrew my jealousy!°   110

---

77. **down-gyved to his ankle:** Fallen to the ankles (like gyves or fetters).
92. **bulk:** Body. 99. **ecstasy:** Madness. 100. **property:** Nature. **fordoes:**
Destroys. 109. **quoted:** Observed. 110. **beshrew my jealousy:** A plague upon
my suspicious nature.

122

By heaven, it is as proper to our age°
To cast beyond° ourselves in our opinions
As it is common for the younger sort
To lack discretion. Come, go we to the King.
This must be known, which, being kept close,° might move   115
More grief to hide than hate to utter love.°
Come.   ˙   (*Exeunt.*)

[*Scene II*]°

(*Flourish. Enter King and Queen, Rosencrantz, and Guildenstern* [*with others*].)

KING: Welcome, dear Rosencrantz and Guildenstern.
   Moreover that° we much did long to see you,
   The need we have to use you did provoke
   Our hasty sending. Something have you heard
   Of Hamlet's transformation—so call it,   5
   Sith° nor th' exterior nor° the inward man
   Resembles that° it was. What it should be,
   More than his father's death, that thus hath put him
   So much from th' understanding of himself,
   I cannot dream of. I entreat you both   10
   That, being of so young days° brought up with him,
   And sith so neighbor'd to his youth and havior,
   That you vouchsafe your rest° here in our court
   Some little time, so by your companies
   To draw him on to pleasures, and to gather   15
   So much as from occasion you may glean,
   Whether aught to us unknown afflicts him thus,
   That, open'd,° lies within our remedy.
QUEEN: Good gentlemen, he hath much talk'd of you
   And sure I am two men there is not living   20
   To whom he more adheres. If it will please you
   To show us so much gentry° and good will

111. proper...age: Characteristic of us (old) men.   112. cast beyond:
Overshoot, miscalculate.   115. close: Secret.   115–16. might...love: Might
cause more grief (to others) by hiding the knowledge of Hamlet's strange behavior
to Ophelia than hatred by telling it.   II, II. Location: The castle.   2. Moreover
that: Besides the fact that.   6. Sith: Since.   nor...nor: Neither...nor.
7. that: What.   11. of...days: From such early youth.   13. vouchsafe your
rest: Please to stay.   18. open'd: Revealed.   22. gentry: Courtesy.

As to expend your time with us awhile
For the supply and profit° of our hope,
Your visitation shall receive such thanks   25
As fits a king's remembrance.
ROSENCRANTZ: Both your Majesties
Might, by the sovereign power you have of us,
Put your dread pleasures more into command
Than to entreaty.
GUILDENSTERN: But we both obey,
And here give up ourselves in the full bent°   30
To lay our service freely at your feet,
To be commanded.
KING: Thanks, Rosencrantz and gentle Guildenstern.
QUEEN: Thanks, Guildenstern and gentle Rosencrantz.
And I beseech you instantly to visit   35
My too much changed son. Go, some of you,
And bring these gentlemen where Hamlet is.
GUILDENSTERN: Heavens make our presence and our practices
Pleasant and helpful to him!
QUEEN: Ay, amen!

(*Exeunt Rosencrantz and Guildenstern [with some Attendants].*)

(*Enter Polonius.*)

POLONIUS: Th' ambassadors from Norway, my good lord,   40
Are joyfully return'd.
KING: Thou still° hast been the father of good news.
POLONIUS: Have I, my lord? I assure my good liege
I hold my duty, as I hold my soul,
Both to my God and to my gracious king;   45
And I do think, or else this brain of mine
Hunts not the trail of policy so sure
As it hath us'd to do, that I have found
The very cause of Hamlet's lunacy.
KING: O, speak of that! That do I long to hear.   50
POLONIUS: Give first admittance to th' ambassadors.
My news shall be the fruit° to that great feast.
KING: Thyself do grace to them, and bring them in.

(*Exit Polonius.*)

24. **supply and profit:** Aid and successful outcome.   30. **in . . . bent:** To the utmost degree of our capacity.   42. **still:** Always.   52. **fruit:** Dessert.

He tells me, my dear Gertrude, he hath found
The head and source of all your son's distemper.   55
QUEEN: I doubt° it is no other but the main,°
His father's death, and our o'erhasty marriage.

(*Enter Ambassadors [Voltimand and Cornelius, with Polonius].*)

KING: Well, we shall sift him.—Welcome, my good friends!
Say, Voltimand, what from our brother Norway?
VOLTIMAND: Most fair return of greetings and desires.   60
Upon our first,° he sent out to suppress
His nephew's levies, which to him appear'd
To be a preparation 'gainst the Polack,
But, better look'd into, he truly found
It was against your Highness. Whereat griev'd   65
That so his sickness, age, and impotence
Was falsely borne in hand,° sends out arrests
On Fortinbras, which he, in brief, obeys,
Receives rebuke from Norway, and in fine°
Makes vow before his uncle never more   70
To give th' assay° of arms against your Majesty.
Whereon old Norway, overcome with joy,
Gives him three score thousand crowns in annual fee,
And his commission to employ those soldiers,
So levied as before, against the Polack,   75
With an entreaty, herein further shown,

[*Giving a paper.*]

That it might please you to give quiet pass
Through your dominions for this enterprise,
On such regards of safety and allowance°
As therein are set down.
KING: It likes° us well;   80
And at our more consider'd° time we'll read,
Answer, and think upon this business.
Meantime we thank you for your well-took labor.
Go to your rest; at night we'll feast together.
Most welcome home!   (*Exeunt Ambassadors.*)

56. **doubt:** Fear, suspect. **main:** Chief point, principal concern. 61. **Upon our first:** At our first words on the business. 67. **borne in hand:** Deluded, taken advantage of. 69. **in fine:** In the end. 71. **assay:** Trial. 79. **On...allowance:** With such pledges of safety and provisos. 80. **likes:** Pleases. 81. **consider'd:** Suitable for deliberation.

POLONIUS: This business is well ended.   85
  My liege, and madam, to expostulate°
  What majesty should be, what duty is,
  Why day is day, night night, and time is time,
  Were nothing but to waste night, day, and time.
  Therefore, since brevity is the soul of wit,°   90
  And tediousness the limbs and outward flourishes,
  I will be brief. Your noble son is mad.
  Mad call I it, for, to define true madness,
  What is 't but to be nothing else but mad?
  But let that go.
QUEEN: More matter, with less art.   95
POLONIUS: Madam, I swear I use no art at all.
  That he is mad, 'tis true; 'tis true 'tis pity,
  And pity 'tis 'tis true—a foolish figure,°
  But farewell it, for I will use no art.
  Mad let us grant him, then, and now remains   100
  That we find out the cause of this effect,
  Or rather say, the cause of this defect,
  For this effect defective comes by cause.°
  Thus it remains, and the remainder thus.
  Perpend.°   105
  I have a daughter—have while she is mine—
  Who, in her duty and obedience, mark,
  Hath given me this. Now gather, and surmise.
  [Reads the letter.] "To the celestial and my soul's idol,
  the most beautified Ophelia"—   110
  That's an ill phrase, a vile phrase; "beautified" is a vile
  phrase. But you shall hear. Thus: [Reads.]
  "In her excellent white bosom, these, etc."
QUEEN: Came this from Hamlet to her?
POLONIUS: Good madam, stay awhile; I will be faithful.   [Reads.] 115
  "Doubt° thou the stars are fire,
      Doubt that the sun doth move,
  Doubt truth to be a liar,
      But never doubt I love.
  O dear Ophelia, I am ill at these numbers.° I have   120

---

86. expostulate: Expound.   90. wit: Sound sense or judgment.   98. figure:
Figure of speech.   103. For . . . cause: I.e., for this defective behavior, this madness has a cause.   105. Perpend: Consider.   116. Doubt: Suspect, question.
120. ill . . . numbers: Unskilled at writing verses.

not art to reckon° my groans. But that I love thee
best, O most best, believe it. Adieu.
    Thine evermore, most dear lady, whilst this
           machine° is to him, Hamlet."
This in obedience hath my daughter shown me,   125
And, more above,° hath his solicitings,
As they fell out° by time, by means, and place,
All given to mine ear.
KING: But how hath she
Receiv'd his love?
POLONIUS: What do you think of me?
KING: As of a man faithful and honorable.   130
POLONIUS: I would fain prove so. But what might you think,
When I had seen this hot love on the wing—
As I perceiv'd it, I must tell you that,
Before my daughter told me—what might you,
Or my dear Majesty your Queen here, think,   135
If I had play'd the desk or table-book,°
Or given my heart a winking,° mute and dumb,
Or look'd upon this love with idle sight?°
What might you think? No, I went round° to work,
And my young mistress thus I did bespeak:°   140
"Lord Hamlet is a prince, out of thy star;°
This must not be." And then I prescripts gave her,
That she should lock herself from his resort,
Admit no messengers, receive no tokens.
Which done, she took the fruits of my advice;   145
And he, repelled—a short tale to make—
Fell into a sadness, then into a fast,
Thence to a watch,° thence into a weakness,
Thence to a lightness,° and, by this declension,°
Into the madness wherein now he raves,   150
And all we mourn for.
KING: Do you think this?
QUEEN: It may be, very like.

121. reckon: (1) Count, (2) number metrically, scan.   124. machine: Body.
126. more above: Moreover.   127. fell out: Occurred.   136. play'd . . . table-book: Remained shut up, concealing the information.   137. winking: Closing of the eyes.   138. with idle sight: Complacently or uncomprehendingly.   139. round: Roundly, plainly.   140. bespeak: Address.   141. out of thy star: Above your sphere, position.   148. watch: State of sleeplessness.   149. lightness: Light-headedness.   declension: Decline, deterioration.

POLONIUS: Hath there been such a time—I would fain know that—
  That I have positively said "'Tis so,"
  When it prov'd otherwise?
KING: Not that I know.   155
POLONIUS [*pointing to his head and shoulder*]: Take this from this, if this
  be otherwise.
  If circumstances lead me, I will find
  Where truth is hid, though it were hid indeed
  Within the center.°
KING: How may we try it further?
POLONIUS: You know, sometimes he walks four hours together   160
  Here in the lobby.
QUEEN: So he does indeed.
POLONIUS: At such a time I'll loose my daughter to him.
  Be you and I behind an arras° then.
  Mark the encounter. If he love her not
  And be not from his reason fall'n thereon,°   165
  Let me be no assistant for a state,
  But keep a farm and carters.
KING: We will try it.

(*Enter Hamlet [reading on a book].*)

QUEEN: But look where sadly the poor wretch comes reading.
POLONIUS: Away, I do beseech you both, away.
  I'll board° him presently.

                    (*Exeunt King and Queen [with Attendants].*)

                    O, give me leave.   170
  How does my good Lord Hamlet?
HAMLET: Well, God-a-mercy.°
POLONIUS: Do you know me, my lord?
HAMLET: Excellent well. You are a fishmonger.°
POLONIUS: Not I, my lord.   175
HAMLET: Then I would you were so honest a man.
POLONIUS: Honest, my lord?
HAMLET: Ay, sir. To be honest, as this world goes, is to be one man pick'd
  out of ten thousand.
POLONIUS: That's very true, my lord.   180

---

159. center: Middle point of the earth (which is also the center of the Ptolemaic
universe).   **163. arras:** Hanging, tapestry.   **165. thereon:** On that account.
170. board: Accost.   **172. God-a-mercy:** Thank you.   **174. fishmonger:** Fish
merchant (with connotation of *bawd, procurer*[?]).

HAMLET: For if the sun breed maggots in a dead dog, being a good kissing carrion° — Have you a daughter?

POLONIUS: I have, my lord.

HAMLET: Let her not walk i' th' sun.° Conception° is a blessing, but as
your daughter may conceive, friend, look to 't.   185

POLONIUS [aside]: How say you by that? Still harping on my daughter. Yet
he knew me not at first; 'a said I was a fishmonger. 'A is far gone. And
truly in my youth I suff'red much extremity for love, very near this. I'll
speak to him again. — What do you read, my lord?

HAMLET: Words, words, words.   190

POLONIUS: What is the matter,° my lord?

HAMLET: Between who?

POLONIUS: I mean, the matter that you read, my lord.

HAMLET: Slanders, sir, for the satirical rogue says here that old men have
gray beards, that their faces are wrinkled, their eyes purging° thick   195
amber and plum-tree gum, and that they have a plentiful lack of wit,
together with most weak hams. All which, sir, though I most power-
fully and potently believe, yet I hold it not honesty° to have it thus set
down, for you yourself, sir, shall grow old as I am, if like a crab you
could go backward.   200

POLONIUS [aside]: Though this be madness, yet there is method in 't. —
Will you walk out of the air, my lord?

HAMLET: Into my grave.

POLONIUS: Indeed, that's out of the air. [Aside.] How pregnant° sometimes his replies are! A happiness° that often madness hits on, which   205
reason and sanity could not so prosperously° be deliver'd of. I will
leave him, [and suddenly contrive the means of meeting between him]
and my daughter. — My honorable lord, I will most humbly take my
leave of you.

HAMLET: You cannot, sir, take from me any thing that I will more will-   210
ingly part withal — except my life, except my life, except my life.

(Enter Guildenstern and Rosencrantz.)

POLONIUS: Fare you well, my lord.

HAMLET: These tedious old fools!°

181–82. good kissing carrion: A good piece of flesh for kissing, or for the sun to
kiss.   184. i' th' sun: With additional implication of the sunshine of princely
favors.   Conception: (1) Understanding, (2) pregnancy.   191. matter: Substance
(but Hamlet plays on the sense of *basis for a dispute*).   195. purging: Dis-
charging.   198. honesty: Decency.   204. pregnant: Full of meaning.   205. happiness: Felicity of expression.   206. prosperously: Successfully.   213. old
fools: I.e., old men like Polonius.

POLONIUS: You go to seek the Lord Hamlet; there he is.
ROSENCRANTZ [*to Polonius*]: God save you, sir!   215

[*Exit Polonius.*]

GUILDENSTERN: My honor'd lord!
ROSENCRANTZ: My most dear lord!
HAMLET: My excellent good friends! How dost thou, Guildenstern? Ah,
Rosencrantz! Good lads, how do you both?
ROSENCRANTZ: As the indifferent° children of the earth.   220
GUILDENSTERN: Happy in that we are not over-happy. On Fortune's cap
we are not the very button.
HAMLET: Nor the soles of her shoe?
ROSENCRANTZ: Neither, my lord.
HAMLET: Then you live about her waist, or in the middle of her favors?   225
GUILDENSTERN: Faith, her privates° we.
HAMLET: In the secret parts of Fortune? O, most true; she is a strumpet.°
What news?
ROSENCRANTZ: None, my lord, but the world's grown honest.
HAMLET: Then is doomsday near. But your news is not true. [Let me   230
question more in particular. What have you, my good friends, deserv'd
at the hands of Fortune that she sends you to prison hither?
GUILDENSTERN: Prison, my lord?
HAMLET: Denmark's a prison.
ROSENCRANTZ: Then is the world one.   235
HAMLET: A goodly one, in which there are many confines,° wards,° and
dungeons, Denmark being one o' th' worst.
ROSENCRANTZ: We think not so, my lord.
HAMLET: Why then 'tis none to you, for there is nothing either good or
bad but thinking makes it so. To me it is a prison.   240
ROSENCRANTZ: Why then, your ambition makes it one. 'Tis too narrow
for your mind.
HAMLET: O God, I could be bounded in a nutshell and count myself a
king of infinite space, were it not that I have bad dreams.
GUILDENSTERN: Which dreams indeed are ambition, for the very sub-   245
stance of the ambitious° is merely the shadow of a dream.
HAMLET: A dream itself is but a shadow.

---

220. **indifferent:** Ordinary.   226. **privates:** Close acquaintances (with sexual
pun on *private parts*).   227. **strumpet:** Prostitute (a common epithet for in-
discriminate Fortune.   236. **confines:** Places of confinement.   **wards:** Cells.
245–46. **the very . . . ambitious:** That seemingly very substantial thing which the
ambitious pursue.

ROSENCRANTZ: Truly, and I hold ambition of so airy and light a quality
that it is but a shadow's shadow.

HAMLET: Then are our beggars bodies,° and our monarchs and out-   250
stretch'd° heroes the beggars' shadows. Shall we to th' court? For, by
my fay,° I cannot reason.

ROSENCRANTZ, GUILDENSTERN: We'll wait upon° you.

HAMLET: No such matter. I will not sort° you with the rest of my servants, for, to speak to you like an honest man, I am most dreadfully   255
attended.°] But, in the beaten way° of friendship, what make° you at
Elsinore?

ROSENCRANTZ: To visit you, my lord, no other occasion.

HAMLET: Beggar that I am, I am even poor in thanks; but I thank you,
and sure, dear friends, my thanks are too dear a halfpenny.° Were you   260
not sent for? Is it your own inclining? Is it a free visitation? Come,
come, deal justly with me. Come, come; nay, speak.

GUILDENSTERN: What should we say, my lord?

HAMLET: Why, anything, but to th' purpose. You were sent for; and there
is a kind of confession in your looks which your modesties have not   265
craft enough to color. I know the good King and Queen have sent
for you.

ROSENCRANTZ: To what end, my lord?

HAMLET: That you must teach me. But let me conjure° you, by the rights
of our fellowship, by the consonancy of our youth,° by the obligation   270
of our ever-preserv'd love, and by what more dear a better proposer°
could charge° you withal, be even° and direct with me, whether you
were sent for, or no?

ROSENCRANTZ [aside to Guildenstern]: What say you?

HAMLET [aside]: Nay then, I have an eye of° you.—If you love me, hold   275
not off.

GUILDENSTERN: My lord, we were sent for.

HAMLET: I will tell you why; so shall my anticipation prevent your discovery,° and your secrecy to the King and Queen molt no feather.° I

---

250. **bodies:** Solid substances rather than shadows (since beggars are not ambitious).   250–51. **outstretch'd:** (1) Far-reaching in their ambition, (2) elongated
as shadows.   252. **fay:** Faith.   253. **wait upon:** Accompany, attend.   254. **sort:**
Class, associate.   255–56. **dreadfully attended:** Waited upon in slovenly fashion.   256. **beaten way:** Familiar path.   **make:** Do.   260. **dear a halfpenny:**
Expensive at the price of a halfpenny, i.e., of little worth.   269. **conjure:** Adjure,
entreat.   270. **consonancy of our youth:** The fact that we are of the same age.
271. **better proposer:** More skillful propounder.   272. **charge:** Urge.   **even:**
Straight, honest.   275. **of:** On.   278–79. **prevent your discovery:** Forestall your
disclosure.   279. **molt no feather:** Not diminish in the least.

have of late—but wherefore I know not—lost all my mirth, forgone 280
all custom of exercises; and indeed it goes so heavily with my disposition that this goodly frame, the earth, seems to me a sterile promon-
tory; this most excellent canopy, the air, look you, this brave°
o'erhanging firmament, this majestical roof fretted° with golden fire,
why, it appeareth nothing to me but a foul and pestilent congregation 285
of vapors. What a piece of work is a man! How noble in reason, how
infinite in faculties, in form and moving how express° and admirable,
in action how like an angel, in apprehension how like a god! The
beauty of the world, the paragon of animals! And yet, to me, what is
this quintessence° of dust? Man delights not me—no, nor woman nei- 290
ther, though by your smiling you seem to say so.
ROSENCRANTZ: My lord, there was no such stuff in my thoughts.
HAMLET: Why did you laugh then, when I said "man delights not me"?
ROSENCRANTZ: To think, my lord, if you delight not in man, what lenten
entertainment° the players shall receive from you. We coted° them on 295
the way, and hither are they coming, to offer you service.
HAMLET: He that plays the king shall be welcome; his Majesty shall have
tribute of me. The adventurous knight shall use his foil and target,°
the lover shall not sigh gratis, the humorous man° shall end his part in
peace, [the clown shall make those laugh whose lungs are tickle o' th' 300
sere°], and the lady shall say her mind freely, or the blank verse shall
halt° for 't. What players are they?
ROSENCRANTZ: Even those you were wont to take such delight in, the
tragedians of the city.
HAMLET: How chances it they travel? Their residence,° both in reputa- 305
tion and profit, was better both ways.
ROSENCRANTZ: I think their inhibition° comes by the means of the
innovation.°

283. **brave:** Splendid.   284. **fretted:** Adorned (with fret-work, as in a vaulted
ceiling).   287. **express:** Well-framed (?), exact (?).   290. **quintessence:** The
fifth essence of ancient philosophy, beyond earth, water, air, and fire, supposed to
be the substance of the heavenly bodies and to be latent in all things.
294–95. **lenten entertainment:** Meager reception (appropriate to Lent).
295. **coted:** Overtook and passed beyond.   298. **foil and target:** Sword and
shield.   299. **humorous man:** Eccentric character, dominated by one trait or
"humor."   300–01. **tickle o' th' sere:** Easy on the trigger, ready to laugh easily.
(*Sere* is part of a gunlock.)   302. **halt:** Limp.   305. **residence:** Remaining in
one place, i.e., in the city.   307. **inhibition:** Formal prohibition (from acting
plays in the city).   308. **innovation:** I.e., the new fashion in satirical plays performed by boy actors in the "private" theaters; or possibly a political uprising; or
the strict limitations set on the theater in London in 1600.

HAMLET: Do they hold the same estimation they did when I was in the
city? Are they so follow'd?   310
ROSENCRANTZ: No, indeed, are they not.
[HAMLET: How comes it? Do they grow rusty?
ROSENCRANTZ: Nay, their endeavor keeps in the wonted° pace. But there
is, sir, an aery° of children, little eyases,° that cry out on the top of
question,° and are most tyrannically° clapp'd for 't. These are now the 315
fashion, and so berattle° the common stages°—so they call them—
that many wearing rapiers° are afraid of goose-quills° and dare scarce
come thither.
HAMLET: What, are they children? Who maintains 'em? How are they
escoted?° Will they pursue the quality° no longer than they can sing?° 320
Will they not say afterwards, if they should grow themselves to
common° players—as it is most like, if their means are no better—
their writers do them wrong, to make them exclaim against their own
succession?°
ROSENCRANTZ: Faith, there has been much to do° on both sides, and the 325
nation holds it no sin to tarre° them to controversy. There was, for a
while, no money bid for argument° unless the poet and the player
went to cuffs in the question.°
HAMLET: Is 't possible?
GUILDENSTERN: O, there has been much throwing about of brains.   330
HAMLET: Do the boys carry it away?°
ROSENCRANTZ: Ay, that they do, my lord—Hercules and his load° too.°]
HAMLET: It is not very strange, for my uncle is King of Denmark, and
those that would make mouths° at him while my father liv'd, give

---

313. **wonted:** Usual.   314. **aery:** Nest.   **eyases:** Young hawks.   314–15. **cry . . .
question:** Speak shrilly, dominating the controversy (in decrying the public theaters).   315. **tyrannically:** Outrageously.   316. **berattle:** Berate.   **common stages:**
Public theaters.   317. **many wearing rapiers:** Many men of fashion, who were
afraid to patronize the common players for fear of being satirized by the poets
who wrote for the children.   **goose-quills:** Pens of satirists.   320. **escoted:**
Maintained.   **quality:** (Acting) profession.   **no longer . . . sing:** Only until their
voices change.   322. **common:** Regular, adult.   324. **succession:** Future careers.
325. **to do:** Ado.   326. **tarre:** Set on (as dogs).   327. **argument:** Plot for a play.
328. **went . . . question:** Came to blows in the play itself.   331. **carry it away:**
Win the day.   332. **Hercules . . . load:** Thought to be an allusion to the sign of
the Globe Theatre, which was Hercules bearing the world on his shoulder.
312–32. **How . . . load too:** The passage, omitted from the early quartos, alludes
to the so-called War of the Theatres, 1599–1602, the rivalry between the children's
companies and the adult actors.   334. **mouths:** Faces.

twenty, forty, fifty, a hundred ducats° apiece for his picture in little.°   335
'Sblood,° there is something in this more than natural, if philosophy
could find it out.
(*A flourish* [*of trumpets within*].)
GUILDENSTERN: There are the players.
HAMLET: Gentlemen, you are welcome to Elsinore. Your hands, come
then. Th' appurtenance of welcome is fashion and ceremony. Let me   340
comply° with you in this garb,° lest my extent° to the players, which, I
tell you, must show fairly outwards,° should more appear like enter-
tainment° than yours. You are welcome. But my uncle-father and
aunt-mother are deceiv'd.
GUILDENSTERN: In what, my dear lord?   345
HAMLET: I am but mad north-north-west.° When the wind is southerly I
know a hawk from a handsaw.°

(*Enter Polonius.*)

POLONIUS: Well be with you, gentlemen!
HAMLET: Hark you, Guildenstern, and you too; at each ear a hearer. That
great baby you see there is not yet out of his swaddling-clouts.°   350
ROSENCRANTZ: Happily° he is the second time come to them; for they say
an old man is twice a child.
HAMLET: I will prophesy he comes to tell me of the players; mark it.—
You say right, sir, o' Monday morning, 'twas then indeed.
POLONIUS: My lord, I have news to tell you.   355
HAMLET: My lord, I have news to tell you. When Roscius° was an actor in
Rome—
POLONIUS: The actors are come hither, my lord.
HAMLET: Buzz,° buzz!
POLONIUS: Upon my honor—   360
HAMLET: Then came each actor on his ass—
POLONIUS: The best actors in the world, either for tragedy, comedy,
history, pastoral, pastoral-comical, historical-pastoral, tragical-

---

335. **ducats:** Gold coins.   **in little:** In miniature.   336. **'Sblood:** By His (God's,
Christ's) blood.   341. **comply:** Observe the formalities of courtesy.   **garb:** Manner.   **my extent:** The extent of my showing courtesy.   342. **show fairly outwards:** Look cordial to outward appearances.   342–43. **entertainment:** A (warm)
reception.   346. **north-north-west:** Only partly, at times.   347. **hawk, handsaw:** Mattock (or *hack*) and a carpenter's cutting tool respectively; also birds,
with a play on *hernshaw* or heron.   350. **swaddling-clouts:** Cloths in which
to wrap a newborn baby.   351. **Happily:** Haply, perhaps.   356. **Roscius:** A
famous Roman actor who died in 62 B.C.E.   359. **Buzz:** An interjection used to
denote stale news.

historical, tragical-comical-historical-pastoral, scene individable,° or
poem unlimited.° Seneca° cannot be too heavy, nor Plautus° too light. 365
For the law of writ and the liberty,° these are the only men.
HAMLET: O Jephthah, judge of Israel,° what a treasure hadst thou!
POLONIUS: What a treasure had he, my lord?
HAMLET: Why,
  "One fair daughter, and no more,   370
  The which he loved passing° well."
POLONIUS [*aside*]: Still on my daughter.
HAMLET: Am I not i' th' right, old Jephthah?
POLONIUS: If you call me Jephthah, my lord, I have a daughter that I love
  passing well.   375
HAMLET: Nay, that follows not.
POLONIUS: What follows, then, my lord?
HAMLET: Why,
  "As by lot, God wot,"°
  and then, you know,   380
  "It came to pass, as most like° it was."
The first row° of the pious chanson° will show you more, for look
  where my abridgement° comes.

(*Enter the Players.*)

You are welcome, masters; welcome, all. I am glad to see thee well.
Welcome, good friends. O, old friend! Why, thy face is valanc'd° since I 385
saw thee last. Com'st thou to beard° me in Denmark? What, my young
lady° and mistress? By 'r lady, your ladyship is nearer to heaven than
when I saw you last, by the altitude of a chopine.° Pray God your
voice, like a piece of uncurrent° gold, be not crack'd within the ring.°

---

364. scene individable: A play observing the unity of place.   **365. poem unlimited:** A play disregarding the unities of time and place.   **Seneca:** Writer of Latin
tragedies.   **Plautus:** Writer of Latin comedy.   **366. law . . . liberty:** Dramatic
composition both according to rules and without rules, i.e., "classical" and
"romantic" dramas.   **367. Jephthah . . . Israel:** Jephthah had to sacrifice his
daughter; see Judges 11. Hamlet goes on to quote from a ballad on the theme.
371. passing: Surpassingly.   **379. wot:** Knows.   **381. like:** Likely, probable.
382. row: Stanza.   **chanson:** Ballad, song.   **383. my abridgement:** Something
that cuts short my conversation; also, a diversion.   **385. valanc'd:** Fringed (with a
beard).   **386. beard:** Confront (with obvious pun).   **386–87. young lady:** Boy
playing women's parts.   **388. chopine:** Thick-soled shoe of Italian fashion.
389. uncurrent: Not passable as lawful coinage.   **crack'd . . . ring:** Changed
from adolescent to male voice, no longer suitable for women's roles. (Coins fea-
tured rings enclosing the sovereign's head; if the coin was cracked within this ring,
it was unfit for currency.)

Masters, you are all welcome. We'll e'en to 't like French falconers, fly 390
at anything we see. We'll have a speech straight.° Come, give us a taste
of your quality; come, a passionate speech.
FIRST PLAYER: What speech, my good lord?
HAMLET: I heard thee speak me a speech once, but it was never acted, or,
if it was, not above once, for the play, I remember, pleas'd not the mil- 395
lion; 'twas caviary to the general.° But it was—as I receiv'd it, and others, whose judgments in such matters cried in the top of° mine—an
excellent play, well digested in the scenes, set down with as much
modesty as cunning.° I remember one said there were no sallets° in
the lines to make the matter savory, nor no matter in the phrase that 400
might indict° the author of affectation, but call'd it an honest method,
as wholesome as sweet, and by very much more handsome than fine.°
One speech in 't I chiefly lov'd: 'twas Aeneas' tale to Dido, and there-
about of it especially when he speaks of Priam's slaughter.° If it live in
your memory, begin at this line: let me see, let me see— 405
"The rugged Pyrrhus,° like th' Hyrcanian beast"°—
'Tis not so. It begins with Pyrrhus:
"The rugged Pyrrhus, he whose sable° arms,
Black as his purpose, did the night resemble
When he lay couched in the ominous horse,° 410
Hath now this dread and black complexion smear'd
With heraldry more dismal.° Head to foot
Now is he total gules,° horridly trick'd°
With blood of fathers, mothers, daughters, sons,
Bak'd and impasted° with the parching streets,° 415
That lend a tyrannous and a damned light
To their lord's° murder. Roasted in wrath and fire,

391. **straight:** At once.   **396. caviary to the general:** Caviar to the multitude, i.e.,
a choice dish too elegant for coarse tastes.   **397. cried in the top of:** Spoke with
greater authority than.   **399. cunning:** Skill.   **sallets:** Salad, i.e., spicy impro-
prieties.   **401. indict:** Convict.   **402. fine:** Elaborately ornamented, showy.
404. Priam's slaughter: The slaying of the ruler of Troy, when the Greeks finally
took the city.   **406. Pyrrhus:** A Greek hero in the Trojan War, also known as
Neoptolemus, son of Achilles.   **Hyrcanian beast:** I.e., the tiger. (See Virgil,
Aeneid, IV, 266; compare the whole speech with Marlowe's *Dido Queen of
Carthage,* II, i, 214 ff.)   **408. sable:** Black (for reasons of camouflage during the
episode of the Trojan horse).   **410. ominous horse:** Trojan horse, by which the
Greeks gained access to Troy.   **412. dismal:** Ill-omened.   **413. gules:** Red (a
heraldic term).   **trick'd:** Adorned, decorated.   **415. impasted:** Crusted, like a
thick paste.   **with . . . streets:** By the parching heat of the streets (because of the
fires everywhere).   **417. their lord's:** Priam's.

And thus o'er-sized° with coagulate gore,
With eyes like carbuncles, the hellish Pyrrhus
Old grandsire Priam seeks."   420
So proceed you.
POLONIUS: 'Fore God, my lord, well spoken, with good accent and good
discretion.
FIRST PLAYER: "Anon he finds him
Striking too short at Greeks. His antique sword,   425
Rebellious to his arm, lies where it falls,
Repugnant° to command. Unequal match'd,
Pyrrhus at Priam drives, in rage strikes wide,
But with the whiff and wind of his fell° sword
Th' unnerved father falls. [Then senseless Ilium,°]   430
Seeming to feel this blow, with flaming top
Stoops to his° base, and with a hideous crash
Takes prisoner Pyrrhus' ear. For, lo! His sword,
Which was declining on the milky head
Of reverend Priam, seem'd i' th' air to stick.   435
So as a painted° tyrant Pyrrhus stood,
And, like a neutral to his will and matter,°
Did nothing.
But, as we often see, against° some storm,
A silence in the heavens, the rack° stand still,   440
The bold winds speechless, and the orb below
As hush as death, anon the dreadful thunder
Doth rend the region,° so, after Pyrrhus' pause,
Aroused vengeance sets him new a-work,
And never did the Cyclops'° hammers fall   445
On Mars's armor forg'd for proof eterne°
With less remorse than Pyrrhus' bleeding sword
Now falls on Priam.
Out, out, thou strumpet Fortune! All you gods,
In general synod,° take away her power!   450
Break all the spokes and fellies° from her wheel,

---

418. o'er-sized: Covered as with size or glue.   427. Repugnant: Disobedient,
resistant.   429. fell: Cruel.   430. senseless Ilium: Insensate Troy.   432. his:
Its.   436. painted: Painted in a picture.   437. like . . . matter: As though poised
indecisively between his intention and its fulfillment.   439. against: Just before.
440. rack: Mass of clouds.   443. region: Sky.   445. Cyclops: Giant armor
makers in the smithy of Vulcan.   446. proof eterne: Eternal resistance to
assault.   450. synod: Assembly.   451. fellies: Pieces of wood forming the rim
of a wheel.

And bowl the round nave° down the hill of heaven,
As low as to the fiends!"
POLONIUS: This is too long.
HAMLET: It shall to the barber's with your beard.—Prithee say on. He's   455
for a jig° or a tale of bawdry, or he sleeps. Say on, come to Hecuba.°
FIRST PLAYER: "But who, ah woe! had seen the mobled° queen"—
HAMLET: "The mobled queen?"
POLONIUS: That's good. "Mobled queen" is good.
FIRST PLAYER: "Run barefoot up and down, threat'ning the flames   460
With bisson rheum,° a clout° upon that head
Where late the diadem stood, and for a robe,
About her lank and all o'er-teemed° loins,
A blanket, in the alarm of fear caught up—
Who this had seen, with tongue in venom steep'd,   465
'Gainst Fortune's state° would treason have pronounc'd.°
But if the gods themselves did see her then
When she saw Pyrrhus make malicious sport
In mincing with his sword her husband's limbs,
The instant burst of clamor that she made,   470
Unless things mortal move them not at all,
Would have made milch° the burning eyes of heaven,
And passion in the gods."
POLONIUS: Look whe'er° he has not turn'd his color and has tears in 's
eyes. Prithee, no more.   475
HAMLET: 'Tis well; I'll have thee speak out the rest of this soon. Good my
lord, will you see the players well bestow'd?° Do you hear, let them be
well us'd, for they are the abstract° and brief chronicles of the time.
After your death you were better have a bad epitaph than their ill
report while you live.   480
POLONIUS: My lord, I will use them according to their desert.
HAMLET: God's bodkin,° man, much better! Use every man after his
desert, and who shall scape whipping? Use them after your own honor
and dignity. The less they deserve, the more merit is in your bounty.
Take them in.   485

---

452. nave: Hub.   456. jig: Comic song and dance often given at the end of a
play. Hecuba: Wife of Priam   457. mobled: Muffled.   461. bisson rheum:
Blinding tears. clout: Cloth.   463. o'er-teemed: Worn out with bearing children.   466. state: Rule, managing. pronounc'd: Proclaimed.   472. milch:
Milky, moist with tears.   474. whe'er: Whether.   477. bestow'd: Lodged.
478. abstract: Summary account.   482. God's bodkin: By God's (Christ's) little
body, *bodykin* (not to be confused with *bodkin*, dagger).

POLONIUS: Come, sirs.

HAMLET: Follow him, friends. We'll hear a play tomorrow. [*As they start to leave, Hamlet detains the First Player.*] Dost thou hear me, old friend? Can you play the Murder of Gonzago?

FIRST PLAYER: Ay, my lord.   490

HAMLET: We'll ha 't tomorrow night. You could, for need, study a speech of some dozen or sixteen lines, which I would set down and insert in 't, could you not?

FIRST PLAYER: Ay, my lord.

HAMLET: Very well. Follow that lord, and look you mock him not. — My   495
good friends, I'll leave you till night. You are welcome to Elsinore.

(*Exeunt Polonius and Players.*)

ROSENCRANTZ: Good my lord!

(*Exeunt [Rosencrantz and Guildenstern].*)

HAMLET: Ay, so, God buy you. — Now I am alone.
    O, what a rogue and peasant slave am I!
    Is it not monstrous that this player here,   500
    But in a fiction, in a dream of passion,
    Could force his soul so to his own conceit°
    That from her working all his visage wann'd,°
    Tears in his eyes, distraction in his aspect,
    A broken voice, and his whole function suiting   505
    With forms to his conceit?° And all for nothing!
    For Hecuba!
    What's Hecuba to him, or he to Hecuba,
    That he should weep for her? What would he do,
    Had he the motive and the cue for passion   510
    That I have? He would drown the stage with tears
    And cleave the general ear with horrid speech,
    Make mad the guilty and appall the free,°
    Confound the ignorant, and amaze indeed
    The very faculties of eyes and ears. Yet I,   515
    A dull and muddy-mettled° rascal, peak,°
    Like John-a-dreams,° unpregnant of° my cause,
    And can say nothing — no, not for a king

---

502. **conceit:** Conception.   503. **wann'd:** Grew pale.   505–06. **his whole . . . conceit:** His whole being responded with actions to suit his thought.   513. **free:** Innocent.   516. **muddy-mettled:** Dull-spirited.   **peak:** Mope, pine.   517. **John-a-dreams:** Sleepy, dreaming idler.   **unpregnant of:** Not quickened by.

Upon whose property° and most dear life
A damn'd defeat was made. Am I a coward?   520
Who calls me villain? Breaks my pate across?
Plucks off my beard, and blows it in my face?
Tweaks me by the nose? Gives me the lie° i' th' throat,
As deep as to the lungs? Who does me this?
Ha, 'swounds, I should take it; for it cannot be   525
But I am pigeon-liver'd,° and lack gall
To make oppression bitter, or ere this
I should have fatted all the region kites°
With this slave's offal. Bloody, bawdy villain!
Remorseless, treacherous, lecherous, kindless° villain!   530
[O, vengeance!]
Why, what an ass am I! This is most brave,
That I, the son of a dear father murder'd,
Prompted to my revenge by heaven and hell,
Must, like a whore, unpack my heart with words,   535
And fall a-cursing, like a very drab,°
A stallion!° Fie upon 't, foh! About,° my brains!
Hum, I have heard
That guilty creatures sitting at a play
Have by the very cunning of the scene   540
Been struck so to the soul that presently°
They have proclaim'd their malefactions;
For murder, though it have no tongue, will speak
With most miraculous organ. I'll have these players
Play something like the murder of my father   545
Before mine uncle. I'll observe his looks;
I'll tent° him to the quick. If 'a do blench,°
I know my course. The spirit that I have seen
May be the devil, and the devil hath power
T' assume a pleasing shape; yea, and perhaps   550
Out of my weakness and my melancholy,
As he is very potent with such spirits,°

---

519. **property:** The crown; perhaps also character, quality.   523. **Gives me the
lie:** Calls me a liar.   526. **pigeon-liver'd:** The pigeon or dove was popularly supposed to be mild because it secreted no gall.   528. **region kites:** Kites (birds of
prey) of the air, from the vicinity.   530. **kindless:** Unnatural.   536. **drab:**
Prostitute.   537. **stallion:** Prostitute (male or female). (Many editors follow the
Folio reading of *scullion*.)   **About:** About it, to work.   541. **presently:** At once.
547. **tent:** Probe.   **blench:** Quail, flinch.   552. **spirits:** Humors (of melancholy).

Abuses° me to damn me. I'll have grounds
More relative° than this. The play's the thing
Wherein I'll catch the conscience of the King.   555

(Exit.)

[ACT III   *Scene I*]°

(Enter King, Queen, Polonius, Ophelia, Rosencrantz, Guildenstern, Lords.)

KING: And can you, by no drift of conference,°
Get from him why he puts on this confusion,
Grating so harshly all his days of quiet
With turbulent and dangerous lunacy?
ROSENCRANTZ: He does confess he feels himself distracted,   5
But from what cause 'a will by no means speak.
GUILDENSTERN: Nor do we find him forward° to be sounded,°
But with a crafty madness keeps aloof
When we would bring him on to some confession
Of his true state.
QUEEN: Did he receive you well?   10
ROSENCRANTZ: Most like a gentleman.
GUILDENSTERN: But with much forcing of his disposition.°
ROSENCRANTZ: Niggard of question,° but of our demands
Most free in his reply.
QUEEN: Did you assay° him
To any pastime?   15
ROSENCRANTZ: Madam, it so fell out that certain players
We o'er-raught° on the way. Of these we told him,
And there did seem in him a kind of joy
To hear of it. They are here about the court,
And, as I think, they have already order   20
This night to play before him.
POLONIUS: 'Tis most true,
And he beseech'd me to entreat your Majesties
To hear and see the matter.

553. **Abuses:** Deludes.   554. **relative:** Closely related, pertinent.   III, I.
Location: The castle.   1. **drift of conference:** Direction of conversation.
7. **forward:** Willing.   **sounded:** Tested deeply.   12. **disposition:** Inclination.
13. **question:** Conversation.   14. **assay:** Try to win.   17. **o'er-raught:** Overtook
and passed.

KING: With all my heart, and it doth much content me
    To hear him so inclin'd.   25
    Good gentlemen, give him a further edge,°
    And drive his purpose into these delights.
ROSENCRANTZ: We shall, my lord.

                     (*Exeunt Rosencrantz and Guildenstern.*)

KING: Sweet Gertrude, leave us too,
    For we have closely° sent for Hamlet hither,
    That he, as 'twere by accident, may here   30
    Affront° Ophelia.
    Her father and myself, [lawful espials,°]
    Will so bestow ourselves that seeing, unseen,
    We may of their encounter frankly judge,
    And gather by him, as he is behav'd,   35
    If 't be th' affliction of his love or no
    That thus he suffers for.
QUEEN: I shall obey you.
    And for your part, Ophelia, I do wish
    That your good beauties be the happy cause
    Of Hamlet's wildness. So shall I hope your virtues   40
    Will bring him to his wonted way again,
    To both your honors.
OPHELIA: Madam, I wish it may.

                            [*Exit Queen.*]

POLONIUS: Ophelia, walk you here. — Gracious,° so please you,
    We will bestow ourselves. [*To Ophelia.*] Read on this book,
                        [*Gives her a book.*]
    That show of such an exercise° may color°   45
    Your loneliness. We are oft to blame in this —
    'Tis too much prov'd° — that with devotion's visage
    And pious action we do sugar o'er
    The devil himself.
KING [*aside*]: O, 'tis too true!   50
    How smart a lash that speech doth give my conscience!
    The harlot's cheek, beautied with plast'ring art,

---

26. **edge:** Incitement.   29. **closely:** Privately.   31. **Affront:** Confront, meet.
32. **espials:** Spies.   43. **Gracious:** Your Grace (i.e., the King).   45. **exercise:** Act of
devotion. (The book she reads is one of devotion.)   **color:** Give a plausible appearance to.   47. **too much prov'd:** Too often shown to be true, too often practiced.

Is not more ugly to° the thing° that helps it
Than is my deed to my most painted word.
O heavy burden!   55
POLONIUS: I hear him coming. Let's withdraw, my lord.
                              [*King and Polonius withdraw.*°]

(*Enter Hamlet.* [*Ophelia pretends to read a book.*])

HAMLET: To be, or not to be, that is the question:
  Whether 'tis nobler in the mind to suffer
  The slings and arrows of outrageous fortune,
  Or to take arms against a sea of troubles,   60
  And by opposing end them. To die, to sleep—
  No more—and by a sleep to say we end
  The heart-ache and the thousand natural shocks
  That flesh is heir to. 'Tis a consummation
  Devoutly to be wish'd. To die, to sleep;   65
  To sleep, perchance to dream. Ay, there's the rub,°
  For in that sleep of death what dreams may come
  When we have shuffled° off this mortal coil,°
  Must give us pause. There's the respect°
  That makes calamity of so long life.°   70
  For who would bear the whips and scorns of time,
  Th' oppressor's wrong, the proud man's contumely,°
  The pangs of despis'd° love, the law's delay,
  The insolence of office,° and the spurns°
  That patient merit of th' unworthy takes,   75
  When he himself might his quietus° make
  With a bare bodkin?° Who would fardels° bear,
  To grunt and sweat under a weary life,
  But that the dread of something after death,
  The undiscover'd country from whose bourn°   80
  No traveler returns, puzzles the will,
  And makes us rather bear those ills we have
  Than fly to others that we know not of?

---

53. to: Compared to. **thing:** I.e., the cosmetic. **[S.D.]** *withdraw:* The King and Polonius may retire behind an arras. The stage directions specify that they "enter" again near the end of the scene. **66. rub:** Literally, an obstacle in the game of bowls. **68. shuffled:** Sloughed, cast. **coil:** Turmoil. **69. respect:** Consideration. **70. of . . . life:** So long-lived. **72. contumely:** Insolent abuse. **73. despis'd:** Rejected. **74. office:** Officialdom. **spurns:** Insults. **76. quietus:** Acquittance; here, death. **77. bodkin:** Dagger. **fardels:** Burdens. **80. bourn:** Boundary.

Thus conscience does make cowards of us all
And thus the native hue° of resolution   85
Is sicklied o'er with the pale cast° of thought,
And enterprises of great pitch° and moment°
With this regard° their currents° turn awry,
And lose the name of action. — Soft you now,
The fair Ophelia. Nymph, in thy orisons°   60
Be all my sins rememb'red.
OPHELIA: Good my lord,
How does your honor for this many a day?
HAMLET: I humbly thank you; well, well, well.
OPHELIA: My lord, I have remembrances of yours,
That I have longed long to re-deliver.   95
I pray you, now receive them.   [*Offers tokens.*]
HAMLET: No, not I, I never gave you aught.
OPHELIA: My honor'd lord, you know right well you did,
And with them words of so sweet breath compos'd
As made these things more rich. Their perfume lost,   100
Take these again, for to the noble mind
Rich gifts wax poor when givers prove unkind.
There, my lord.   [*Gives tokens.*]
HAMLET: Ha, ha! Are you honest?°
OPHELIA: My lord?   105
HAMLET: Are you fair?°
OPHELIA: What means your lordship?
HAMLET: That if you be honest and fair, your honesty° should admit no
discourse° to your beauty.
OPHELIA: Could beauty, my lord, have better commerce° than with   110
honesty?
HAMLET: Ay, truly, for the power of beauty will sooner transform honesty
from what it is to a bawd than the force of honesty can translate
beauty into his likeness. This was sometime° a paradox,° but now the
time° gives it proof. I did love you once.   115
OPHELIA: Indeed, my lord, you made me believe so.

---

85. native hue: Natural color, complexion.   86. cast: Shade of color.   87. pitch:
Height (as of a falcon's flight).   moment: Importance.   88. regard: Respect, consideration.   currents: Courses.   90. orisons: Prayers.   104. honest: (1) Truth-
ful; (2) chaste.   106. fair: (1) Beautiful; (2) just, honorable.   108. your honesty:
Your chastity.   109. discourse: Familiar dealings.   110. commerce: Dealings.
114. sometime: Formerly.   paradox: A view opposite to commonly held opinion.
114–15. the time: The present age.

HAMLET: You should not have believ'd me, for virtue cannot so inocu-
late° our old stock but we shall relish of it.° I lov'd you not.

OPHELIA: I was the more deceiv'd.

HAMLET: Get thee to a nunn'ry.° Why wouldst thou be a breeder of sin- 120
ners? I am myself indifferent honest;° but yet I could accuse me of
such things that it were better my mother had not borne me: I am very
proud, revengeful, ambitious, with more offenses at my beck° than I
have thoughts to put them in, imagination to give them shape, or time
to act them in. What should such fellows as I do crawling between 125
earth and heaven? We are arrant knaves, all; believe none of us. Go thy
ways to a nunn'ry. Where's your father?

OPHELIA: At home, my lord.

HAMLET: Let the doors be shut upon him, that he may play the fool
nowhere but in 's own house. 130
Farewell.

OPHELIA: O, help him, you sweet heavens!

HAMLET: If thou dost marry, I'll give thee this plague for thy dowry: be
thou as chaste as ice, as pure as snow, thou shalt not escape calumny.
Get thee to a nunn'ry, farewell. Or, if thou wilt needs marry, marry a 135
fool, for wise men know well enough what monsters° you° make of
them. To a nunn'ry, go, and quickly too. Farewell.

OPHELIA: Heavenly powers, restore him!

HAMLET: I have heard of your paintings too, well enough. God hath
given you one face, and you make yourselves another. You jig,° and 140
amble, and you lisp, you nickname God's creatures, and make your
wantonness your ignorance.° Go to, I'll no more on 't; it hath made me
mad. I say, we will have no moe marriage. Those that are married
already—all but one—shall live. The rest shall keep as they are. To a
nunn'ry, go.   (*Exit.*) 145

OPHELIA: O, what a noble mind is here o'erthrown!
The courtier's, soldier's, scholar's, eye, tongue, sword,
Th' expectancy and rose of the fair state,°

117–18. **inoculate:** Graft, be engrafted to.   118. **but . . . it:** That we do not still
have about us a taste of the old stock; i.e., retain our sinfulness.   120. **nunn'ry:**
(1) Convent, (2) brothel.   121. **indifferent honest:** Reasonably virtuous.
123. **beck:** Command.   136. **monsters:** An allusion to the horns of a cuckold.
you: You women.   140. **jig:** Dance and sing affectedly and wantonly.
141–42. **make . . . ignorance:** Excuse your affection on the grounds of your ignorance.   148. **Th' expectancy . . . state:** The hope and ornament of the kingdom
made fair (by him).

The glass of fashion and the mold of form,°
Th' observ'd of all observers,° quite, quite down!   150
And I, of ladies most deject and wretched,
That suck'd the honey of his music vows,
Now see that noble and most sovereign reason,
Like sweet bells jangled, out of time and harsh,
That unmatch'd form and feature of blown° youth   155
Blasted with ecstasy.° O, woe is me,
T' have seen what I have seen, see what I see!

(*Enter King and Polonius.*)

KING: Love? His affections do not that way tend;
    Nor what he spake, though it lack'd form a little,
    Was not like madness. There's something in his soul,   160
    O'er which his melancholy sits on brood,
    And I do doubt° the hatch and the disclose°
    Will be some danger; which for to prevent,
    I have in quick determination
    Thus set it down: he shall with speed to England,   165
    For the demand of° our neglected tribute.
    Haply the seas and countries different
    With variable° objects shall expel
    This something-settled° matter in his heart,
    Whereon his brains still beating puts him thus   170
    From fashion of himself.° What think you on 't?
POLONIUS: It shall do well. But yet do I believe
    The origin and commencement of his grief
    Sprung from neglected love.—How now, Ophelia?
    You need not tell us what Lord Hamlet said;   175
    We heard it all.—My lord, do as you please,
    But, if you hold it fit, after the play
    Let his queen mother all alone entreat him
    To show his grief. Let her be round° with him;
    And I'll be plac'd, so please you, in the ear   180
    Of all their conference. If she find him not,

---

149. **The glass . . . form:** The mirror of fashion and the pattern of courtly behavior. 150. **observ'd . . . observers:** The center of attention and honor in the
court. 155. **blown:** Blooming. 156. **ecstasy:** Madness. 162. **doubt:** Fear.
disclose: Disclosure. 166. **For . . . of:** To demand. 168. **variable:** Various.
169. **something-settled:** Somewhat settled. 171. **From . . . himself:** Out of his
natural manner. 179. **round:** Blunt.

To England send him, or confine him where
Your wisdom best shall think.
KING: It shall be so.
Madness in great ones must not unwatch'd go.

(Exeunt.)

{*Scene II*}°

(Enter Hamlet and three of the Players.)

HAMLET: Speak the speech, I pray you, as I pronounc'd it to you, trip-
pingly on the tongue. But if you mouth it, as many of our players° do, I
had as lief the town-crier spoke my lines. Nor do not saw the air too
much with your hand, thus, but use all gently; for in the very torrent,
tempest, and, as I may say, whirlwind of your passion, you must   5
acquire and beget a temperance that may give it smoothness. O, it
offends me to the soul to hear a robustious° periwig-pated° fellow tear
a passion to tatters, to very rags, to split the ears of the groundlings,°
who for the most part are capable of° nothing but inexplicable dumb-
shows and noise. I would have such a fellow whipp'd for o'er-doing   10
Termagant.° It out-herods Herod.° Pray you, avoid it.
FIRST PLAYER: I warrant your honor.
HAMLET: Be not too tame neither, but let your own discretion be your
tutor. Suit the action to the word, the word to the action, with this special observance, that you o'erstep not the modesty of nature. For any-   15
thing so o'erdone is from° the purpose of playing, whose end, both at
the first and now, was and is, to hold, as 't were, the mirror up to
nature, to show virtue her feature, scorn her own image, and the very
age and body of the time his° form and pressure.° Now this overdone,
or come tardy off,° though it makes the unskillful laugh, cannot but   20
make the judicious grieve, the censure of which one° must in your

III, II. **Location:** The castle. **2. our players:** Indefinite use; i.e., *players now-
adays.* **7. robustious:** Violent, boisterous. **periwig-pated:** Wearing a wig.
8. groundlings: Spectators who paid least and stood in the yard of the theater.
9. capable of: Susceptible of being influenced by. **11. Termagant:** A god of the
Saracens; a character in the St. Nicholas play, where one of his worshipers, leaving him in charge of goods, returns to find them stolen; whereupon he beats the
god or idol, which howls vociferously. **Herod:** Herod of Jewry. (A character in
The Slaughter of the Innocents and other cycle plays. The part was played with
great noise and fury.) **16. from:** Contrary to. **19. his:** Its. **pressure:** Stamp,
impressed character. **20. come tardy off:** Inadequately done. **21. the censure . . . one:** The judgment of even one of whom.

allowance o'erweigh a whole theater of others. O, there be players that
I have seen play, and heard others praise, and that highly, not to speak
it profanely, that, neither having th' accent of Christians nor the gait of
Christian, pagan, nor man, have so strutted and bellow'd that I have 25
thought some of nature's journeymen° had made men and not made
them well, they imitated humanity so abominably.
FIRST PLAYER: I hope we have reform'd that indifferently° with us, sir.
HAMLET: O, reform it altogether. And let those that play your clowns
speak no more than is set down for them; for there be of them° that 30
will themselves laugh, to set on some quantity of barren° spectators to
laugh too, though in the mean time some necessary question of the
play be then to be consider'd. That's villainous, and shows a most pitiful ambition in the fool that uses it. Go, make you ready.

[*Exeunt Players.*]

(*Enter Polonius, Guildenstern, and Rosencrantz.*)

How now, my lord? Will the King hear this piece of work? 35
POLONIUS: And the Queen too, and that presently.°
HAMLET: Bid the players make haste.

[*Exit Polonius.*]

Will you two help to hasten them?
ROSENCRANTZ: Ay, my lord.   (*Exeunt they two.*)
HAMLET: What ho, Horatio!

(*Enter Horatio.*)

HORATIO: Here, sweet lord, at your service. 40
HAMLET: Horatio, thou art e'en as just a man
As e'er my conversation cop'd withal.°
HORATIO: O, my dear lord—
HAMLET: Nay, do not think I flatter;
For what advancement may I hope from thee
That no revenue hast but thy good spirits, 45
To feed and clothe thee? Why should the poor be flatter'd?
No, let the candied° tongue lick absurd pomp,
And crook the pregnant° hinges of the knee

26. **journeymen:** Laborers not yet masters in their trade. 28. **indifferently:**
Tolerably. 30. **of them:** Some among them. 31. **barren:** I.e., of wit.
36. **presently:** At once. 42. **my . . . withal:** My contact with people provided
opportunity for encounter with. 47. **candied:** Sugared, flattering. 48. **pregnant:** Compliant.

Where thrift° may follow fawning. Dost thou hear?
Since my dear soul was mistress of her choice   50
And could of men distinguish her election,
Sh' hath seal'd thee for herself, for thou hast been
As one, in suff'ring all, that suffers nothing,
A man that Fortune's buffets and rewards
Hast ta'en with equal thanks; and blest are those   55
Whose blood° and judgment are so well commeddled°
That they are not a pipe for Fortune's finger
To sound what stop° she please. Give me that man
That is not passion's slave, and I will wear him
In my heart's core, ay, in my heart of heart,   60
As I do thee.—Something too much of this.—
There is a play tonight before the King.
One scene of it comes near the circumstance
Which I have told thee of my father's death.
I prithee, when thou seest that act afoot,   65
Even with the very comment of thy soul°
Observe my uncle. If his occulted° guilt
Do not itself unkennel in one speech,
It is a damned° ghost that we have seen,
And my imaginations are as foul   70
As Vulcan's stithy.° Give him heedful note,
For I mine eyes will rivet to his face,
And after we will both our judgments join
In censure of his seeming.°
HORATIO: Well, my lord.
If 'a steal aught the whilst this play is playing,   75
And scape detecting, I will pay the theft.

(*[Flourish.]* Enter trumpets and kettledrums, King, Queen, Polonius, Ophelia, *[Rosencrantz, Guildenstern, and other Lords, with Guards carrying torches]*.)

HAMLET: They are coming to the play. I must be idle. Get you a place.

[*The King, Queen, and courtiers sit.*]

---

49. **thrift:** Profit.   56. **blood:** Passion.   **commeddled:** Commingled.   58. **stop:** Hole in a wind instrument for controlling the sound.   66. **very . . . soul:** Inward and sagacious criticism.   67. **occulted:** Hidden.   69. **damned:** In league with Satan.   71. **stithy:** Smithy, place of stiths (anvils).   74. **censure of his seeming:** Judgment of his appearance or behavior.

KING: How fares our cousin Hamlet?
HAMLET: Excellent, i' faith, of the chameleon's dish:° I eat the air, promise-
cramm'd. You cannot feed capons so.   80
KING: I have nothing with° this answer, Hamlet. These words are not
mine.°
HAMLET: No, nor mine now. [*To Polonius.*] My lord, you played once i' th'
university, you say?
POLONIUS: That did I, my lord; and was accounted a good actor.   85
HAMLET: What did you enact?
POLONIUS: I did enact Julius Caesar. I was killed i' th' Capitol; Brutus
kill'd me.
HAMLET: It was a brute part of him to kill so capital a calf there. Be the
players ready?   90
ROSENCRANTZ: Ay, my lord; they stay upon your patience.
QUEEN: Come hither, my dear Hamlet, sit by me.
HAMLET: No, good mother, here's metal more attractive.
POLONIUS [*to the King*]: O, ho, do you mark that?
HAMLET: Lady, shall I lie in your lap?   95

[*Lying down at Ophelia's feet.*]

OPHELIA: No, my lord.
[HAMLET: I mean, my head upon your lap?
OPHELIA: Ay, my lord.]
HAMLET: Do you think I meant country° matters?
OPHELIA: I think nothing, my lord.   100
HAMLET: That's a fair thought to lie between maids' legs.
OPHELIA: What is, my lord?
HAMLET: Nothing.
OPHELIA: You are merry, my lord.
HAMLET: Who, I?   105
OPHELIA: Ay, my lord.
HAMLET: O God, your only jig-maker.° What should a man do but be
merry? For look you how cheerfully my mother looks, and my father
died within 's° two hours.
OPHELIA: Nay, 'tis twice two months, my lord.   110

---

79. chameleon's dish: Chameleons were supposed to feed on air. Hamlet deliber-
ately misinterprets the King's *fares* as *feeds*. By his phrase *eat the air* he also plays
on the idea of feeding himself with the promise of succession, of being the *heir*.
81. have . . . with: Make nothing of.   **81–82. are not mine:** Do not respond to
what I asked.   **99. country:** With a bawdy pun.   **107. only jig-maker:** Very best
composer of jigs (song and dance).   **109. within 's:** Within this.

HAMLET: So long? Nay then, let the devil wear black for I'll have a suit of sables.° O heavens! Die two months ago, and not forgotten yet? Then there's hope a great man's memory may outlive his life half a year. But, by 'r lady, 'a must build churches, then, or else shall 'a suffer not think- ing on,° with the hobby-horse, whose epitaph is "For, O, for, O, the hobby-horse is forgot."°   115

(The trumpets sound. Dumb show follows.)

(Enter a King and a Queen [very lovingly]; the Queen embracing him, and he her. [She kneels and makes show of protestation unto him.] He takes her up, and declines his head upon her neck. He lies him down upon a bank of flowers. She, seeing him asleep, leaves him. Anon comes in another man, takes off his crown, kisses it, pours poison in the sleeper's ears, and leaves him. The Queen returns; finds the King dead, makes passionate action. The Poisoner, with some three or four, come in again, seem to condole with her. The dead body is carried away. The Poisoner woos the Queen with gifts; she seems harsh awhile but in the end accepts love.)

                                                                    [Exeunt.]

OPHELIA: What means this, my lord?
HAMLET: Marry, this' miching mallecho;° it means mischief.
OPHELIA: Belike° this show imports the argument° of the play.

(Enter Prologue.)

HAMLET: We shall know by this fellow. The players cannot keep counsel;°   120
they'll tell all.
OPHELIA: Will 'a tell us what this show meant?
HAMLET: Ay, or any show that you will show him. Be not you° asham'd to show, he'll not shame to tell you what it means.
OPHELIA: You are naught, you are naught.° I'll mark the play.   125
PROLOGUE: For us, and for our tragedy,
    Here stooping° to your clemency,
    We beg your hearing patiently.   *[Exit.]*

111–12. **suit of sables:** Garments trimmed with the fur of the sable and hence suited for a wealthy person, not a mourner (with a pun on *sable* black). 114–15. **suffer . . . on:** Undergo oblivion.   115–16. **"For . . . forgot":** Verse of a song occurring also in *Love's Labor's Lost*, III, I, 30. The hobby-horse was a char- acter made up to resemble a horse, appearing in the Morris dance and such May- game sports. This song laments the disappearance of such customs under pressure from the Puritans.   118. **this' miching mallecho:** This is sneaking mis- chief.   119. **Belike:** Probably.   **argument:** Plot.   120. **counsel:** Secret.   123. **Be not you:** If you are not.   125. **naught:** Indecent.   127. **stooping:** Bowing.

HAMLET: Is this a prologue, or the posy of a ring?°
OPHELIA: 'Tis brief, my lord.   130
HAMLET: As woman's love.

(*Enter [two Players as] King and Queen.*)

PLAYER KING: Full thirty times hath Phoebus' cart° gone round
  Neptune's salt wash° and Tellus'° orbed ground,
  And thirty dozen moons with borrowed° sheen
  About the world have times twelve thirties been,   135
  Since love our hearts and Hymen° did our hands
  Unite commutual° in most sacred bands.
PLAYER QUEEN: So many journeys may the sun and moon
  Make us again count o'er ere love be done!
  But, woe is me, you are so sick of late,   140
  So far from cheer and from your former state,
  That I distrust you. Yet, though I distrust,°
  Discomfort you, my lord, it nothing° must.
  For women's fear and love hold quantity;°
  In neither aught, or in extremity.   145
  Now, what my love is, proof° hath made you know,
  And as my love is siz'd, my fear is so.
  Where love is great, the littlest doubts are fear;
  Where little fears grow great, great love grows there.
PLAYER KING: Faith, I must leave thee, love, and shortly too;   150
  My operant° powers their functions leave to do.°
  And thou shalt live in this fair world behind,
  Honor'd, belov'd; and haply one as kind
  For husband shalt thou—
PLAYER QUEEN: O, confound the rest!
  Such love must needs be treason in my breast.   155
  In second husband let me be accurst!
  None wed the second but who kill'd the first.
HAMLET: Wormwood, wormwood.

---

129. **posy . . . ring:** Brief motto in verse inscribed in a ring.   132. **Phoebus'
cart:** The sun god's chariot.   133. **salt wash:** The sea.   **Tellus:** Goddess of the
earth, of the *orbed ground.*   134. **borrowed:** Reflected.   136. **Hymen:** God of
matrimony.   137. **commutual:** Mutually.   142. **distrust:** Am anxious about.
143. **nothing:** Not at all.   144. **hold quantity:** Keep proportion with one another.   146. **proof:** Experience.   151. **operant:** Active.   **leave to do:** Cease to
perform.

PLAYER QUEEN: The instances° that second marriage move°
  Are base respects of thrift,° but none of love.   160
  A second time I kill my husband dead,
  When second husband kisses me in bed.
PLAYER KING: I do believe you think what now you speak,
  But what we do determine oft we break.
  Purpose is but the slave to memory,°   165
  Of violent birth, but poor validity,°
  Which now, like fruit unripe, sticks on the tree,
  But fall unshaken when they mellow be.
  Most necessary 'tis that we forget
  To pay ourselves what to ourselves is debt.°   170
  What to ourselves in passion we propose,
  The passion ending, doth the purpose lose.
  The violence of either grief or joy
  Their own enactures° with themselves destroy.
  Where joy most revels, grief doth most lament;   175
  Grief joys, joy grieves, on slender accident.
  This world is not for aye,° nor 'tis not strange
  That even our loves should with our fortunes change;
  For 'tis a question left us yet to prove,
  Whether love lead fortune, or else fortune love.   180
  The great man down, you mark his favorite flies;
  The poor advanc'd makes friends of enemies.
  And hitherto doth love on fortune tend;
  For who not needs° shall never lack a friend,
  And who in want° a hollow friend doth try,°   185
  Directly seasons him° his enemy.
  But, orderly to end where I begun,
  Our wills and fates do so contrary run
  That our devices still° are overthrown;
  Our thoughts are ours, their ends° none of our own.   190
  So think thou wilt no second husband wed,

159. instances: Motives. move: Motivate. 160. base . . . thrift: Ignoble considerations of material prosperity. 165. Purpose . . . memory: Our good intentions are subject to forgetfulness. 166. validity: Strength, durability. 169–70. Most . . . debt: It's inevitable that in time we forget the obligations we have imposed on ourselves. 174. enactures: Fulfillments. 177. aye: Ever. 184. who not needs: He who is not in need (of wealth). 185. who in want: He who is in need. try: Test (his generosity). 186. seasons him: Ripens him into. 189. devices still: Intentions continually. 190. ends: Results.

But die thy thoughts when thy first lord is dead.
PLAYER QUEEN: Nor earth to me give food, nor heaven light,
  Sport and repose lock from me day and night,
  To desperation turn my trust and hope,   195
  An anchor's cheer° in prison be my scope!°
  Each opposite° that blanks° the face of joy
  Meet what I would have well and it destroy!
  Both here and hence° pursue me lasting strife,
  If, once a widow, ever I be wife!   200
HAMLET: If she should break it now!
PLAYER KING: 'Tis deeply sworn. Sweet, leave me here awhile;
  My spirits grow dull, and fain I would beguile
  The tedious day with sleep.   [*Sleeps.*]
PLAYER QUEEN: Sleep rock thy brain,
  And never come mischance between us twain!   205

                                                              [*Exit.*]

HAMLET: Madam, how like you this play?
QUEEN: The lady doth protest too much, methinks.
HAMLET: O, but she'll keep her word.
KING: Have you heard the argument?° Is there no offense in 't?
HAMLET: No, no, they do but jest, poison in jest; no offense i' th' world.   210
KING: What do you call the play?
HAMLET: "The Mouse-trap." Marry, how? Tropically.° This play is the
  image of a murder done in Vienna. Gonzago is the Duke's name; his
  wife, Baptista. You shall see anon. 'Tis a knavish piece of work, but
  what of that? Your Majesty, and we that have free° souls, it touches us   215
  not. Let the gall'd jade° winch,° our withers° are unwrung.°

(*Enter Lucianus.*)

  This is one Lucianus, nephew to the King.
OPHELIA: You are as good as a chorus,° my lord.

---

196. anchor's cheer: Anchorite's or hermit's fare. **my scope:** The extent of my
happiness. **197. opposite:** Adverse thing. **blanks:** Causes to blanch or grow
pale. **199. hence:** In the life hereafter. **209. argument:** Plot. **212. Tropically:**
Figuratively. (The first quarto reading, *trapically,* suggests a pun on *trap* in *Mouse-*
trap.) **215. free:** Guiltless. **216. gall'd jade:** Horse whose hide is rubbed by sad-
dle or harness. **winch:** Wince. **withers:** The part between the horse's shoulder
blades. **unwrung:** Not rubbed sore. **218. chorus:** In many Elizabethan plays
the forthcoming action was explained by an actor known as the "chorus"; at a pup-
pet show the actor who spoke the dialogue was known as an "interpreter," as indicated by the lines following.

HAMLET: I could interpret between you and your love, if I could see the
   puppets dallying.°   220
OPHELIA: You are keen, my lord, you are keen.
HAMLET: It would cost you a groaning to take off mine edge.
OPHELIA: Still better, and worse.°
HAMLET: So° you mistake° your husbands. Begin, murderer, leave thy
   damnable faces, and begin. Come, the croaking raven doth bellow for 225
   revenge.
LUCIANUS: Thoughts black, hands apt, drugs fit, and time agreeing,
   Confederate season,° else no creature seeing,
   Thou mixture rank, of midnight weeds collected,
   With Hecate's ban° thrice blasted, thrice infected,   230
   Thy natural magic and dire property
   On wholesome life usurp immediately.

                            [Pours the poison into the sleeper's ears.]

HAMLET: 'A poisons him i' th' garden for his estate. His name's Gonzago.
   The story is extant, and written in very choice Italian. You shall see
   anon how the murderer gets the love of Gonzago's wife.   235

                                    [Claudius rises.]

OPHELIA: The King rises.
[HAMLET: What, frighted with false fire?°]
QUEEN: How fares my lord?
POLONIUS: Give o'er the play.
KING: Give me some light. Away!   240
POLONIUS: Lights, lights, lights!

                     (Exeunt all but Hamlet and Horatio.)

HAMLET: "Why, let the strucken deer go weep,
   The hart ungalled° play.
For some must watch,° while some must sleep;
   Thus runs the world away."°   245

---

220. **dallying:** With sexual suggestion, continued in *keen*, i.e., sexually aroused,
groaning, i.e., moaning in pregnancy, and *edge*, i.e., sexual desire or impetuosity.
223. **Still . . . worse:** More keen-witted and less decorous.   224. **So:** Even thus (in
marriage).   **mistake:** Mistake, take erringly, falseheartedly.   228. **Confederate
season:** The time and occasion conspiring (to assist the murderer).   230. **Hecate's
ban:** The curse of Hecate, the goddess of witchcraft.   237. **false fire:** The blank
discharge of a gun loaded with powder but not shot.   243. **ungalled:** Unafflicted.
244. **watch:** Remain awake.   242–45. **Why . . . away:** Probably from an old ballad, with allusion to the popular belief that a wounded deer retires to weep and
die; cf. *As You Like It,* II, i, 66.

Would not this,° sir, and a forest of feathers°—if the rest of my for-
tunes turn Turk with° me—with two Provincial roses° on my raz'd°
shoes, get me a fellowship in a cry of players?°
HORATIO: Half a share.
HAMLET: A whole one, I.   250
  "For thou dost know, O Damon dear,
    This realm dismantled° was
  Of Jove himself, and now reigns here
    A very, very—pajock."°
HORATIO: You might have rhym'd.   255
HAMLET: O good Horatio, I'll take the ghost's word for a thousand
  pound. Didst perceive?
HORATIO: Very well, my lord.
HAMLET: Upon the talk of pois'ning?
HORATIO: I did very well note him.   260
HAMLET: Ah, ha! Come, some music! Come, the recorders!°
  "For if the King like not the comedy,
  Why then, belike, he likes it not, perdy"°
  Come, some music!

(*Enter Rosencrantz and Guildenstern.*)

GUILDENSTERN: Good my lord, vouchsafe me a word with you.   265
HAMLET: Sir, a whole history.
GUILDENSTERN: The King, sir—
HAMLET: Ay, sir, what of him?
GUILDENSTERN: Is in his retirement marvelous distemp'red.
HAMLET: With drink, sir?   270
GUILDENSTERN: No, my lord, with choler.°
HAMLET: Your wisdom should show itself more richer to signify this to
  the doctor, for for me to put him to his purgation would perhaps
  plunge him into more choler.
GUILDENSTERN: Good my lord, put your discourse into some frame° and   275
  start not so wildly from my affair.

---

246. this: The play. **feathers:** Allusion to the plumes that Elizabethan actors
were fond of wearing. **247. turn Turk with:** Turn renegade against, go back on.
Provincial roses: Rosettes of ribbon like the roses of a part of France. **raz'd:**
With ornamental slashing. **248. fellowship ... players:** Partnership in a theatrical company. **252. dismantled:** Stripped, divested. **254. pajock:** Peacock,
a bird with a bad reputation (here substituted for the obvious rhyme-word *ass*).
261. recorders: Wind instruments like the flute. **263. perdy:** A corruption of
the French *par dieu*, by God. **271. choler:** Anger. (But Hamlet takes the word in
its more basic humors sense of *bilious disorder*.) **275. frame:** Order.

HAMLET: I am tame, sir. Pronounce.

GUILDENSTERN: The Queen, your mother, in most great affliction of spirit, hath sent me to you.

HAMLET: You are welcome. 280

GUILDENSTERN: Nay, good my lord, this courtesy is not of the right breed. If it shall please you to make me a wholesome answer, I will do your mother's commandment; if not, your pardon° and my return shall be the end of my business.

HAMLET: Sir, I cannot. 285

ROSENCRANTZ: What, my lord?

HAMLET: Make you a wholesome answer; my wit's diseas'd. But, sir, such answer as I can make, you shall command, or rather, as you say, my mother. Therefore no more, but to the matter. My mother, you say—

ROSENCRANTZ: Then thus she says: your behavior hath struck her into 290 amazement and admiration.°

HAMLET: O wonderful son, that can so stonish a mother! But is there no sequel at the heels of this mother's admiration? Impart.

ROSENCRANTZ: She desires to speak with you in her closet,° ere you go to bed. 295

HAMLET: We shall obey, were she ten times our mother. Have you any further trade with us?

ROSENCRANTZ: My lord, you once did love me.

HAMLET: And do still, by these pickers and stealers.°

ROSENCRANTZ: Good my lord, what is your cause of distemper? You do 300 surely bar the door upon your own liberty, if you deny your griefs to your friend.

HAMLET: Sir, I lack advancement.

ROSENCRANTZ: How can that be, when you have the voice of the King himself for your succession in Denmark? 305

HAMLET: Ay, sir, but "While the grass grows"°—the proverb is some-thing° musty.

(*Enter the Players with recorders.*)

O, the recorders! Let me see one. [*He takes a recorder.*] To withdraw° with you: why do you go about to recover the wind° of me, as if you would drive me into a toil?° 310

---

283. pardon: Permission to depart.   **291. admiration:** Wonder.   **294. closet:** Private chamber.   **299. pickers and stealers:** Hands (so called from the cate-chism, "to keep my hands from picking and stealing").   **306. While . . . grows:** The rest of the proverb is "the silly horse starves"; Hamlet may not live long enough to succeed to the kingdom.   **306–07. something:** Somewhat.   **308. withdraw:** Speak privately.   **309. recover the wind:** Get the windward side.   **310. toil:** Snare.

GUILDENSTERN: O, my lord, if my duty be too bold, my love is too unmannerly.°
HAMLET: I do not well understand that. Will you play upon this pipe?
GUILDENSTERN: My lord, I cannot.
HAMLET: I pray you.   315
GUILDENSTERN: Believe me, I cannot.
HAMLET: I do beseech you.
GUILDENSTERN: I know no touch of it, my lord.
HAMLET: It is as easy as lying. Govern these ventages° with your fingers and thumb, give it breath with your mouth, and it will discourse most   320
eloquent music. Look you, these are the stops.
GUILDENSTERN: But these cannot I command to any utt'rance of harmony; I have not the skill.
HAMLET: Why, look you now, how unworthy a thing you make of me! You would play upon me, you would seem to know my stops, you would   325
pluck out the heart of my mystery, you would sound me from my lowest note to the top of my compass,° and there is much music, excellent voice, in this little organ,° yet cannot you make it speak. 'Sblood, do you think I am easier to be play'd on than a pipe? Call me what instrument you will, though you can fret° me, you cannot play upon me.   330

(*Enter Polonius.*)

God bless you, sir!
POLONIUS: My lord, the Queen would speak with you, and presently.°
HAMLET: Do you see yonder cloud that's almost in shape of a camel?
POLONIUS: By th' mass, and 'tis like a camel, indeed.
HAMLET: Methinks it is like a weasel.   335
POLONIUS: It is back'd like a weasel.
HAMLET: Or like a whale?
POLONIUS: Very like a whale.
HAMLET: Then I will come to my mother by and by.° [*Aside.*] They fool me° to the top of my bent.°—I will come by and by.   340
POLONIUS: I will say so.   [*Exit.*]
HAMLET: "By and by" is easily said. Leave me, friends.

[*Exeunt all but Hamlet.*]

311–12. if . . . unmannerly: If I am using an unmannerly boldness, it is my love that occasions it.   319. ventages: Stops of the recorder.   327. compass: Range (of voice).   328. organ: Musical instrument.   330. fret: Irritate (with a quibble on *fret* meaning the piece of wood, gut, or metal that regulates the fingering on an instrument).   332. presently: At once.   339. by and by: Immediately. 339–40. fool me: Make me play the fool.   340. top of my bent: Limit of my ability or endurance (literally, the extent to which a bow may be bent).

'Tis now the very witching time° of night,
When churchyards yawn and hell itself breathes out
Contagion to this world. Now could I drink hot blood,   345
And do such bitter business as the day
Would quake to look on. Soft, now to my mother.
O heart, lose not thy nature! Let not ever
The soul of Nero° enter this firm bosom.
Let me be cruel, not unnatural;   350
I will speak daggers to her, but use none.
My tongue and soul in this be hypocrites:
How in my words somever° she be shent,°
To give them seals° never, my soul, consent!

                                                              (*Exit.*)

                            {*Scene III*}°

(*Enter King, Rosencrantz, and Guildenstern.*)

KING: I like him not, nor stands it safe with us
   To let his madness range. Therefore prepare you.
   I your commission will forthwith dispatch,°
   And he to England shall along with you.
   The terms° of our estate° may not endure   5
   Hazard so near 's as doth hourly grow
   Out of his brows.°
GUILDENSTERN: We will ourselves provide.
   Most holy and religious fear it is
   To keep those many many bodies safe
   That live and feed upon your Majesty.   10
ROSENCRANTZ: The single and peculiar° life is bound
   With all the strength and armor of the mind
   To keep itself from noyance,° but much more
   That spirit upon whose weal depends and rests
   The lives of many. The cess° of majesty   15

---

343. witching time: Time when spells are cast and evil is abroad.   **349. Nero:**
Murderer of his mother, Agrippina.   **353. How . . . somever:** However much by
my words.   **shent:** Rebuked.   **354. give them seals:** Confirm them with deeds.
III, III. Location: The castle.   **3. dispatch:** Prepare, cause to be drawn up.
5. terms: Condition, circumstances.   **our estate:** My royal position.   **7. brows:**
Effronteries, threatening frowns (?), brain (?).   **11. single and peculiar:**
Individual and private.   **13. noyance:** Harm.   **15. cess:** Decease.

Dies not alone, but like a gulf° doth draw
What's near it with it; or it is a messy wheel
Fix'd on the summit of the highest mount,
To whose huge spokes ten thousand lesser things
Are mortis'd and adjoin'd, which, when it falls,   20
Each small annexment, petty consequence,
Attends° the boist'rous ruin. Never alone
Did the King sigh, but with a general groan.
KING: Arm° you, I pray you, to this speedy voyage,
For we will fetters put about this fear,   25
Which now goes too free-footed.
ROSENCRANTZ: We will haste us.

(Exeunt Gentlemen [Rosencrantz and Guildenstern].)

(Enter Polonius.)

POLONIUS: My lord, he's going to his mother's closet.
Behind the arras° I'll convey myself
To hear the process.° I'll warrant she'll tax him home,°
And, as you said, and wisely was it said,   30
'Tis meet that some more audience than a mother,
Since nature makes them partial, should o'erhear
The speech, of vantage.° Fare you well, my liege.
I'll call upon you ere you go to bed,
And tell you what I know.
KING: Thanks, dear my lord.   35

(Exit [Polonius].)

O, my offense is rank, it smells to heaven;
It hath the primal eldest curse° upon 't,
A brother's murder. Pray can I not,
Though inclination be as sharp as will.°
My stronger guilt defeats my strong intent,   40
And, like a man to double business bound,
I stand in pause where I shall first begin,

---

16. gulf: Whirlpool.   22. Attends: Participates in.   24. Arm: Prepare.   28. arras:
Screen of tapestry placed around the walls of household apartments. (On the
Elizabethan stage, the arras was presumably over a door or discovery space in the
tiring-house façade.)   29. process: Proceedings.   tax him home: Reprove him
severely.   33. of vantage: From an advantageous place.   37. primal eldest
curse: The curse of Cain, the first murderer; he killed his brother Abel.
39. Though . . . will: Though my desire is as strong as my determination.

And both neglect. What if this cursed hand
Were thicker than itself with brother's blood,
Is there not rain enough in the sweet heavens   45
To wash it white as snow? Whereto serves mercy
But to confront the visage of offense?°
And what's in prayer but this twofold force,
To be forestalled° ere we come to fall,
Or pardon'd being down? Then I'll look up;   50
My fault is past. But, O, what form of prayer
Can serve my turn? "Forgive me my foul murder"?
That cannot be, since I am still possess'd
Of those effects for which I did the murder,
My crown, mine own ambition, and my queen.   55
May one be pardon'd and retain th' offense?
In the corrupted currents° of this world
Offense's gilded hand° may shove by justice,
And oft 'tis seen the wicked prize° itself
Buys out the law. But 'tis not so above.   60
There is no shuffling,° there the action lies°
In his° true nature, and we ourselves compell'd,
Even to the teeth and forehead° of our faults,
To give in evidence. What then? What rests?°
Try what repentance can. What can it not?   65
Yet what can it, when one cannot repent?
O wretched state! O bosom black as death!
O limed° soul, that, struggling to be free,
Art more engag'd!° Help, angels! Make assay.°
Bow, stubborn knees, and heart with strings of steel,   70
Be soft as sinews of the new-born babe!
All may be well.

                                             [*He kneels.*]

46–47. Whereto . . . offense: For what function does mercy serve other than to undo the effects of sin?   **49. forestalled:** Prevented (from sinning).   **57. currents:** Courses.   **58. gilded hand:** Hand offering gold as a bribe.   **59. wicked prize:** Prize won by wickedness.   **61. shuffling:** Escape by trickery.   **the action lies:** The accusation is made manifest, comes up for consideration (a legal metaphor).   **62. his:** Its.   **63. teeth and forehead:** Face to face, concealing nothing.   **64. rests:** Remains.   **68. limed:** Caught as with birdlime, a sticky substance used to ensnare birds.   **69. engag'd:** Embedded.   **assay:** Trial.

161

(Enter Hamlet [with sword drawn].)

HAMLET: Now might I do it pat,° now 'a is a-praying;
And now I'll do 't. And so 'a goes to heaven;
And so am I reveng'd. That would be scann'd:°   75
A villain kills my father, and for that,
I, his sole son, do this same villain send
To heaven.
Why, this is hire and salary, not revenge.
'A took my father grossly,° full of bread,°   80
With all his crimes broad blown,° as flush° as May;
And how his audit° stands who knows save heaven?
But in our circumstance and course° of thought,
'Tis heavy with him. And am I then reveng'd,
To take him in the purging of his soul,   85
When he is fit and season'd for his passage?
No!
Up, sword, and know thou a more horrid hent.°

                                        [*Puts up his sword.*]

When he is drunk asleep, or in his rage,
Or in th' incestuous pleasure of his bed,   90
At game a-swearing, or about some act
That has no relish of salvation in 't—
Then trip him, that his heels may kick at heaven,
And that his soul may be as damn'd and black
As hell, whereto it goes. My mother stays.   95
This physic° but prolongs thy sickly days.   (*Exit.*)
KING: My words fly up, my thoughts remain below.
Words without thoughts never to heaven go.

                                                     (*Exit.*)

73. pat: Opportunely.   **75. would be scann'd:** Needs to be looked into.
80. grossly: Not spiritually prepared.   **full of bread:** Enjoying his worldly pleasures. (See Ezek. 16:49.)   **81. crimes broad blown:** Sins in full bloom.   **flush:** Lusty.   **82. audit:** Account.   **83. in . . . course:** As we see it in our mortal situation.   **88. know . . . hent:** Await to be grasped by me on a more horrid occasion.
96. physic: Purging (by prayer).

[*Scene IV*]°

(*Enter [Queen] Gertrude and Polonius.*)

POLONIUS: 'A will come straight. Look you lay° home to him.
  Tell him his pranks have been too broad° to bear with,
  And that your Grace hath screen'd and stood between
  Much heat° and him. I'll sconce° me even here.
  Pray you, be round° [with him.   5
HAMLET (*within*): Mother, mother, mother!]
QUEEN: I'll warrant you, fear me not.
  Withdraw, I hear him coming.

                                        [*Polonius hides behind the arras.*]

(*Enter Hamlet.*)

HAMLET: Now, mother, what's the matter?
QUEEN: Hamlet, thou hast thy father° much offended.   10
HAMLET: Mother, you have my father much offended.
QUEEN: Come, come, you answer with an idle° tongue.
HAMLET: Go, go, you question with a wicked tongue.
QUEEN: Why, how now, Hamlet?
HAMLET: What's the matter now?
QUEEN: Have you forgot me?
HAMLET: No, by the rood,° not so: 15
  You are the Queen, your husband's brother's wife
  And—would it were not so!—you are my mother.
QUEEN: Nay, then, I'll set those to you that can speak.
HAMLET: Come, come, and sit you down; you shall not budge.
  You go not till I set you up a glass   20
  Where you may see the inmost part of you.
QUEEN: What wilt thou do? Thou wilt not murder me?
  Help, ho!
POLONIUS [*behind*]: What, ho! Help!
HAMLET [*drawing*]: How now? A rat? Dead, for a ducat, dead!   25

                                        [*Makes a pass through the arras.*]

POLONIUS [*behind*]: O, I am slain! [*Falls and dies.*]
QUEEN: O me, what hast thou done?

III, IV. Location: The queen's private chamber.   **1. lay:** Thrust (i.e., reprove him
soundly).   **2. broad:** Unrestrained.   **4. Much heat:** The king's anger.   **sconce:**
Ensconce, hide.   **5. round:** Blunt.   **10. thy father:** Your stepfather, Claudius.
12. idle: Foolish.   **15. rood:** Cross.

HAMLET: Nay, I know not. Is it the King?
QUEEN: O, what a rash and bloody deed is this!
HAMLET: A bloody deed—almost as bad, good mother,
  As kill a king, and marry with his brother.   30
QUEEN: As kill a king!
HAMLET: Ay, lady, it was my word.

                       [Parts the arras and discovers Polonius.]

  Thou wretched, rash, intruding fool, farewell!
  I took thee for thy better. Take thy fortune.
  Thou find'st to be too busy is some danger.—
  Leave wringing of your hands. Peace, sit you down,   35
  And let me wring your heart, for so I shall,
  If it be made of penetrable stuff,
  If damned custom° have not braz'd° it so
  That it be proof° and bulwark against sense.°
QUEEN: What have I done, that thou dar'st wag thy tongue   40
  In noise so rude against me?
HAMLET: Such an art
  That blurs the grace and blush of modesty,
  Calls virtue hypocrite, takes off the rose
  From the fair forehead of an innocent love
  And sets a blister° there, makes marriage-vows   45
  As false as dicers' oaths. O, such a deed
  As from the body of contraction° plucks
  The very soul, and sweet religion° makes
  A rhapsody° of words. Heaven's face does glow
  O'er this solidity and compound mass   50
  With heated visage, as against the doom,
  Is thought-sick at the act.°
QUEEN: Ay me, what act,
  That roars so loud and thunders in the index?°
HAMLET: Look here, upon this picture, and on this,
  The counterfeit presentment° of two brothers.   55

---

38. damned custom: Habitual wickedness. **braz'd:** Brazened, hardened.
39. proof: Armor. **sense:** Feeling. **45. sets a blister:** Brands as a harlot.
47. contraction: The marriage contract. **48. religion:** Religious vows.
49. rhapsody: Senseless string. **49–52. Heaven's . . . act:** Heaven's face flushes
with anger to look down upon this solid world, this compound mass, with
hot face as though the day of doom were near, and is thought-sick at the deed
(i.e., Gertrude's marriage). **53. index:** Table of contents, prelude, or preface.
55. counterfeit presentment: Portrayed representation.

[Shows her two likenesses.]

See, what a grace was seated on this brow:
Hyperion's° curls, the front° of Jove himself,
An eye like Mars, to threaten and command,
A station° like the herald Mercury
New-lighted on a heaven-kissing hill—   60
A combination and a form indeed,
Where every god did seem to set his seal,
To give the world assurance of a man.
This was your husband. Look you now, what follows:
Here is your husband, like a mildew'd ear,°   65
Blasting his wholesome brother. Have you eyes?
Could you on this fair mountain leave to feed,
And batten° on this moor?° Ha, have you eyes?
You cannot call it love, for at your age
The heyday° in the blood is tame, it's humble,   70
And waits upon the judgment, and what judgment
Would step from this to this? Sense,° sure, you have,
Else could you not have motion, but sure that sense
Is apoplex'd,° for madness would not err,
Nor sense to ecstasy was ne'er so thrall'd   75
But it reserv'd some quantity of choice
To serve in such a difference. What devil was 't
That thus hath cozen'd° you at hoodman-blind?°
Eyes without feeling, feeling without sight,
Ears without hands or eyes, smelling sans° all,   80
Or but a sickly part of one true sense
Could not so mope.°
O shame, where is thy blush? Rebellious hell,
If thou canst mutine° in a matron's bones,
To flaming youth let virtue be as wax,   85

---

57. **Hyperion:** The sun god.   **front:** Brow.   59. **station:** Manner of standing.
65. **ear:** I.e., of grain.   68. **batten:** Gorge.   **moor:** Barren upland.   70. **heyday:** State of excitement.   72. **Sense:** Perception through the five senses (the functions of the middle or sensible soul).   74. **apoplex'd:** Paralyzed. (Hamlet goes on to explain that without such a paralysis of will, mere madness would not so err, nor would the five senses so enthrall themselves to *ecstasy* or lunacy; even such deranged states of mind would be able to make the obvious choice between Hamlet Senior and Claudius.)   78. **cozen'd:** Cheated.   **hoodman-blind:** Blindman's bluff.   80. **sans:** Without.   82. **mope:** Be dazed, act aimlessly.
84. **mutine:** Mutiny.

And melt in her own fire. Proclaim no shame
When the compulsive ardor gives the charge,
Since frost itself as actively doth burn,
And reason panders will.°
QUEEN: O Hamlet, speak no more!   90
Thou turn'st mine eyes into my very soul,
And there I see such black and grainèd° spots
As will not leave their tinct.°
HAMLET: Nay, but to live
In the rank sweat of an enseamèd° bed,
Stew'd in corruption, honeying and making love   95
Over the nasty sty—
QUEEN: O, speak to me no more.
These words, like daggers, enter in my ears.
No more, sweet Hamlet!
HAMLET: A murderer and a villain,
A slave that is not twentieth part the tithe°   100
Of your precedent° lord, a vice° of kings,
A cutpurse of the empire and the rule,
That from a shelf the precious diadem stole,
And put it in his pocket!
QUEEN: No more!   105

(*Enter Ghost* [*in his nightgown*].)

HAMLET: A king of shreds and patches°—
Save me, and hover o'er me with your wings,
You heavenly guards! What would your gracious figure?
QUEEN: Alas, he's mad!
HAMLET: Do you not come your tardy son to chide,   110
That, laps'd in time and passion,° lets go by
Th' important° acting of your dread command?
O, say!

86–89. **Proclaim . . . will:** Call it no shameful business when the compelling ardor of youth delivers the attack, i.e., commits lechery, since the frost of advanced age burns with as active a fire of lust and reason perverts itself by fomenting lust rather than restraining it.   **92. grainèd:** Dyed in grain, indelible.   **93. tinct:** Color.   **94. enseamèd:** Laden with grease.   **100. tithe:** Tenth part.   **101. precedent:** Former (i.e., the elder Hamlet).   **vice:** Buffoon (a reference to the vice of the morality plays).   **106. shreds and patches:** Motley, the traditional costume of the clown or fool.   **111. laps'd . . . passion:** Having allowed time to lapse and passion to cool.   **112. important:** Importunate, urgent.

GHOST: Do not forget. This visitation
  Is but to whet thy almost blunted purpose.   115
  But, look, amazement° on thy mother sits.
  O, step between her and her fighting soul!
  Conceit° in weakest bodies strongest works.
  Speak to her, Hamlet.
HAMLET: How is it with you, lady?
QUEEN: Alas, how is 't with you,   120
  That you do bend your eye on vacancy,
  And with th' incorporal° air do hold discourse?
  Forth at your eyes your spirits wildly peep,
  And, as the sleeping soldiers in th' alarm,
  Your bedded° hair, like life in excrements,°   125
  Start up and stand an° end. O gentle son,
  Upon the heat and flame of thy distemper
  Sprinkle cool patience. Whereon do you look?
HAMLET: On him, on him! Look you how pale he glares!
  His form and cause conjoin'd,° preaching to stones,   130
  Would make them capable.°—Do not look upon me,
  Lest with this piteous action you convert
  My stern effects.° Then what I have to do
  Will want true color°—tears perchance for blood.
QUEEN: To whom do you speak this?   135
HAMLET: Do you see nothing there?
QUEEN: Nothing at all, yet all that is I see.
HAMLET: Nor did you nothing hear?
QUEEN: No, nothing but ourselves.
HAMLET: Why, look you there, look how it steals away!   140
  My father, in his habit° as he lived!
  Look, where he goes, even now, out at the portal!

                                            (*Exit Ghost.*)

QUEEN: This is the very coinage of your brain.
  This bodiless creation ecstasy°
  Is very cunning in.   145

---

116. **amazement:** Distraction.   118. **Conceit:** Imagination.   122. **incorporal:**
Immaterial.   125. **bedded:** Laid in smooth layers.   **excrements:** Outgrowths.
126. **an:** On.   130. **His . . . conjoin'd:** His appearance joined to his cause for
speaking.   131. **capable:** Receptive.   132–33. **convert . . . effects:** Divert me
from my stern duty.   134. **want true color:** Lack plausibility so that (with a play
on the normal sense of *color*) I shall shed tears instead of blood.   141. **habit:**
Dress.   144. **ecstasy:** Madness.

HAMLET: Ecstasy?
My pulse, as yours, doth temperately keep time,
And makes as healthful music. It is not madness
That I have utter'd. Bring me to the test,
And I the matter will reword, which madness   150
Would gambol° from. Mother, for love of grace,
Lay not that flattering unction° to your soul
That not your trespass but my madness speaks.
It will but skin and film the ulcerous place,
Whiles rank corruption, mining° all within,   155
Infects unseen. Confess yourself to heaven,
Repent what's past, avoid what is to come,
And do not spread the compost° on the weeds
To make them ranker. Forgive me this my virtue;°
For in the fatness° of these pursy° times   160
Virtue itself of vice must pardon beg,
Yea, curb° and woo for leave° to do him good.
QUEEN: O Hamlet, thou hast cleft my heart in twain.
HAMLET: O, throw away the worser part of it,
And live the purer with the other half.   165
Good night. But go not to my uncle's bed;
Assume a virtue, if you have it not.
That monster, custom, who all sense doth eat,°
Of habits devil,° is angel yet in this,
That to the use of actions fair and good   170
He likewise gives a frock or livery°
That aptly is put on. Refrain tonight,
And that shall lend a kind of easiness
To the next abstinence; the next more easy;
For use° almost can change the stamp of nature,   175
And either° . . . the devil, or throw him out
With wondrous potency. Once more, good night;

---

151. gambol: Skip away.   **152. unction:** Ointment.   **155. mining:** Working under the surface.   **158. compost:** Manure.   **159. this my virtue:** My virtuous talk in reproving you.   **160. fatness:** Grossness.   **pursy:** Short-winded, corpulent.   **162. curb:** Bow, bend the knee.   **leave:** Permission.   **168. who . . . eat:** Who consumes all proper or natural feeling.   **169. Of habits devil:** Devil-like in prompting evil habits.   **171. livery:** An outer appearance, a customary garb (and hence a predisposition easily assumed in time of stress).   **175. use:** Habit.   **176. And either:** A defective line usually emended by inserting the word *master* after *either,* following the fourth quarto and early editors.

And when you are desirous to be bless'd,°
I'll blessing beg of you. For this same lord,

                                          [Pointing to Polonius.]

I do repent; but heaven hath pleas'd it so   180
To punish me with this, and this with me,
That I must be their scourge and minister.°
I will bestow° him, and will answer well
The death I gave him. So, again, good night.
I must be cruel only to be kind.   185
Thus bad begins and worse remains behind.°
One word more, good lady.
QUEEN: What shall I do?
HAMLET: Not this, by no means, that I bid you do:
Let the bloat° king tempt you again to bed,
Pinch wanton on your cheek, call you his mouse,   190
And let him, for a pair of reechy° kisses,
Or paddling in your neck with his damn'd fingers,
Make you to ravel all this matter out,
That I essentially am not in madness,
But mad in craft. 'Twere good° you let him know,   195
For who that's but a queen, fair, sober, wise,
Would from a paddock,° from a bat, a gib,°
Such dear concernings° hide? Who would do so?
No, in despite of sense and secrecy,
Unpeg the basket° on the house's top,   200
Let the birds fly, and, like the famous ape,°
To try conclusions,° in the basket creep
And break your own neck down.
QUEEN: Be thou assur'd, if words be made of breath,
And breath of life, I have no life to breathe   205
What thou hast said to me.

---

178. be bless'd: Become blessed, i.e., repentant. **182. their scourge and minister:** Agent of heavenly retribution. (By *scourge,* Hamlet also suggests that he himself will eventually suffer punishment in the process of fulfilling heaven's will.)
183. bestow: Stow, dispose of. **186. behind:** To come. **189. bloat:** Bloated.
191. reechy: Dirty, filthy. **195. good:** Said ironically; also the following eight
lines. **197. paddock:** Toad. **gib:** Tomcat. **198. dear concernings:** Important affairs. **200. Unpeg the basket:** Open the cage, i.e., let out the secret.
201. famous ape: In a story now lost. **202. conclusions:** Experiments (in
which the ape apparently enters a cage from which birds have been released and
then tries to fly out of the cage as they have done, falling to his death).

HAMLET: I must to England; you know that?
QUEEN: Alack,
  I had forgot. 'Tis so concluded on.
HAMLET: There's letters seal'd, and my two school-fellows,
  Whom I will trust as I will adders fang'd,   210
  They bear the mandate; they must sweep my way,°
  And marshal me to knavery. Let it work.
  For 'tis the sport to have the enginer°
  Hoist with° his own petar,° and 't shall go hard
  But I will delve one yard below their mines,°   215
  And blow them at the moon. O, 'tis most sweet,
  When in one line two crafts° directly meet.
  This man shall set me packing.°
  I'll lug the guts into the neighbor room.
  Mother, good night indeed. This counselor   220
  Is now most still, most secret, and most grave,
  Who was in life a foolish prating knave.
  Come, sir, to draw toward an end° with you.
  Good night, mother.

                    (*Exeunt* [*severally, Hamlet dragging in Polonius*].)

                    {ACT IV   *Scene 1*}°

(*Enter King and Queen, with Rosencrantz and Guildenstern.*)

KING: There's matter in these sighs, these profound heaves
  You must translate; 'tis fit we understand them.
  Where is your son?
QUEEN: Bestow this place on us a little while.

                    [*Exeunt Rosencrantz and Guildenstern.*]

  Ah, mine own lord, what have I seen tonight!   5

211. sweep my way: Go before me.   **213. enginer:** Constructor of military con-
trivances.   **214. Hoist with:** Blown up by.   **petar:** Petard, an explosive used to
blow in a door or make a breach.   **215. mines:** Tunnels used in warfare to
undermine the enemy's emplacements; Hamlet will countermine by going under
their mines.   **217. crafts:** Acts of guile, plots.   **218. set me packing:** Set me to
making schemes, and set me to lugging (him) and, also, send me off in a hurry.
223. draw . . . end: Finish up (with a pun on *draw*, pull).   **IV, I. Location:** The
castle.

KING: What, Gertrude? How does Hamlet?
QUEEN: Mad as the sea and wind when both contend
  Which is the mightier. In his lawless fit,
  Behind the arras hearing something stir,
  Whips out his rapier, cries, "A rat, a rat!"   10
  And, in this brainish apprehension,° kills
  The unseen good old man.
KING: O heavy deed!
  It had been so with us, had we been there.
  His liberty is full of threats to all—
  To you yourself, to us, to everyone.   15
  Alas, how shall this bloody deed be answer'd?
  It will be laid to us, whose providence°
  Should have kept short,° restrain'd, and out of haunt°
  This mad young man. But so much was our love
  We would not understand what was most fit,   20
  But, like the owner of a foul disease,
  To keep it from divulging,° let it feed
  Even on the pith of life. Where is he gone?
QUEEN: To draw apart the body he hath kill'd,
  O'er whom his very madness, like some ore°   25
  Among a mineral° of metals base,
  Shows itself pure: 'a weeps for what is done.
KING: O Gertrude, come away!
  The sun no sooner shall the mountains touch
  But we will ship him hence, and this vile deed   30
  We must, with all our majesty and skill,
  Both countenance and excuse. Ho, Guildenstern!

(*Enter Rosencrantz and Guildenstern.*)

  Friends both, go join you with some further aid.
  Hamlet in madness hath Polonius slain,
  And from his mother's closet hath he dragg'd him.   35
  Go seek him out; speak fair, and bring the body
  Into the chapel. I pray you, haste in this.

                [*Exeunt Rosencrantz and Guildenstern.*]

  Come, Gertrude, we'll call up our wisest friends
  And let them know both what we mean to do

---

11. brainish apprehension: Headstrong conception. **17. providence:** Foresight. **18. short:** On a short tether. **out of haunt:** Secluded. **22. divulging:** Becoming evident. **25. ore:** Vein of gold. **26. mineral:** Mine.

And what's untimely done°   40
Whose whisper o'er the world's diameter,°
As level° as the cannon to his blank,°
Transports his pois'ned shot, may miss our name,
And hit the woundless° air. O, come away!
My soul is full of discord and dismay.   (*Exeunt.*) 45

[*Scene II*]°

(*Enter Hamlet.*)

HAMLET: Safely stow'd.
[ROSENCRANTZ, GUILDENSTERN (*within*): Hamlet! Lord Hamlet!]
HAMLET: But soft, what noise? Who calls on Hamlet? O, here they come.

(*Enter Rosencrantz and Guildenstern.*)

ROSENCRANTZ: What have you done, my lord, with the dead body?
HAMLET: Compounded it with dust, whereto 'tis kin.   5
ROSENCRANTZ: Tell us where 'tis, that we may take it thence
   And bear it to the chapel.
HAMLET: Do not believe it.
ROSENCRANTZ: Believe what?
HAMLET: That I can keep your counsel and not mine own. Besides, to be 10
   demanded of° a sponge, what replication° should be made by the son
   of a king?
ROSENCRANTZ: Take you me for a sponge, my lord?
HAMLET: Ay, sir, that soaks up the King's countenance,° his rewards, his
   authorities. But such officers do the King best service in the end. He 15
   keeps them, like an ape an apple, in the corner of his jaw, first
   mouth'd, to be last swallow'd. When he needs what you have glean'd, it
   is but squeezing you, and, sponge, you shall be dry again.
ROSENCRANTZ: I understand you not, my lord.
HAMLET: I am glad of it. A knavish speech sleeps in° a foolish ear.   20
ROSENCRANTZ: My lord, you must tell us where the body is, and go with
   us to the King.

40. And . . . done: A defective line; conjectures as to the missing words include
so, haply, slander (Capell and others); *for, haply, slander* (Theobald and others).
41. diameter: Extent from side to side.   42. As level: With as direct aim.
blank: White spot in the center of a target.   44. woundless: Invulnerable.   IV,
II. Location: The castle.   11. demanded of: Questioned by.   replication:
Reply.   14. countenance: Favor.   20. sleeps in: Has no meaning to.

HAMLET: The body is with the King, but the King is not with the body.°
    The King is a thing—
GUILDENSTERN: A thing, my lord?   25
HAMLET: Of nothing.° Bring me to him. [Hide fox, and all after.°]

                                                            (*Exeunt.*)

                              {*Scene III*}°

(*Enter King, and two or three.*)

KING: I have sent to seek him, and to find the body.
    How dangerous is it that this man goes loose!
    Yet must not we put the strong law on him.
    He's lov'd of the distracted° multitude,
    Who like not in their judgment, but their eyes,   5
    And where 'tis so, th' offender's scourge° is weigh'd,°
    But never the offense. To bear° all smooth and even,
    This sudden sending him away must seem
    Deliberate pause.° Diseases desperate grown
    By desperate appliance are reliev'd,   10
    Or not at all.

(*Enter Rosencrantz, [Guildenstern,] and all the rest.*)

                    How now? What hath befall'n?
ROSENCRANTZ: Where the dead body is bestow'd, my lord,
    We cannot get from him.
KING: But where is he?
ROSENCRANTZ: Without, my lord; guarded, to know your pleasure.
KING: Bring him before us.
ROSENCRANTZ: Ho! Bring in the lord.   15

(*They enter [with Hamlet].*)

KING: Now, Hamlet, where's Polonius?
HAMLET: At supper.

23. The . . . body: Perhaps alludes to the legal commonplace of "the king's two
bodies," which drew a distinction between the sacred office of kingship and the
particular mortal who possessed it at any given time.   26. Of nothing: Of no
account.   Hide . . . after: An old signal cry in the game of hide-and-seek, suggesting that Hamlet now runs away from them.   IV, III. Location: The castle.
4. distracted: Fickle, unstable.   6. scourge: Punishment.   weigh'd: Taken into
consideration.   7. bear: Manage.   9. Deliberate pause: Carefully considered
action.

                                  173

KING: At supper? Where?

HAMLET: Not where he eats, but where 'a is eaten. A certain convocation
of politic worms° are e'en at him. Your worm is your only emperor for 20
diet.° We fat all creatures else to fat us, and we fat ourselves for maggots. Your fat king and your lean beggar is but variable service,° two
dishes, but to one table—that's the end.

KING: Alas, alas!

HAMLET: A man may fish with the worm that hath eat° of a king, and eat 25
of the fish that hath fed of that worm.

KING: What dost thou mean by this?

HAMLET: Nothing but to show you how a king may go a progress°
through the guts of a beggar.

KING: Where is Polonius?   30

HAMLET: In heaven. Send thither to see. If your messenger find him not
there, seek him i' th' other place yourself. But if indeed you find him
not within this month, you shall nose him as you go up the stairs into
the lobby.

KING [to some Attendants]: Go seek him there.   35

HAMLET: 'A will stay till you come.

[Exit Attendants.]

KING: Hamlet, this deed, for thine especial safety.—
Which we do tender,° as we dearly° grieve
For that which thou hast done—must send thee hence
[With fiery quickness.] Therefore prepare thyself.   40
The bark° is ready, and the wind at help,
Th' associates tend,° and everything is bent°
For England.

HAMLET: For England!

KING: Ay, Hamlet.   45

HAMLET: Good.

KING: So is it, if thou knew'st our purposes.

HAMLET: I see a cherub° that sees them. But, come, for England! Farewell,
dear mother.

KING: Thy loving father, Hamlet.   50

20. politic worms: Crafty worms (suited to a master spy like Polonius).
21. diet: Food, eating (with perhaps a punning reference to the Diet of Worms, a
famous convocation held in 1521).   22. variable service: Different courses of a
single meal.   25. eat: Eaten (pronounced et).   28. progress: Royal journey of
state.   38. tender: Regard, hold dear.   dearly: Intensely.   41. bark: Sailing
vessel.   42. tend: Wait.   bent: In readiness.   48. cherub: Cherubim are angels
of knowledge.

HAMLET: My mother. Father and mother is man and wife, man and wife
   is one flesh, and so, my mother. Come, for England!   (*Exit.*)
KING: Follow him at foot;° tempt him with speed aboard.
   Delay it not; I'll have him hence tonight.
   Away! For everything is seal'd and done   55
   That else leans on° th' affair. Pray you, make haste.

                              [*Exeunt all but the King.*]

   And, England,° if my love thou hold'st at aught—
   As my great power thereof may give thee sense,
   Since yet thy cicatrice° looks raw and·red
   After the Danish sword, and thy free awe°   60
   Pays homage to us—thou mayst not coldly set°
   Our sovereign process,° which imports at full,
   By letters congruing° to that effect,
   The present° death of Hamlet. Do it, England,
   For like the hectic° in my blood he rages,   65
   And thou must cure me. Till I know 'tis done,
   Howe'er my haps,° my joys were ne'er begun.

                                    (*Exit.*)

[*Scene IV*]°

(*Enter Fortinbras with his Army over the stage.*)

FORTINBRAS: Go, captain, from me greet the Danish king.
   Tell him that, by his license,° Fortinbras
   Craves the conveyance° of a promis'd march
   Over his kingdom. You know the rendezvous.
   If that his Majesty would aught with us,   5
   We shall express our duty in his eye;°
   And let him know so.
CAPTAIN: I will do 't, my lord.
FORTINBRAS: Go softly° on.   [*Exeunt all but the Captain.*]

(*Enter Hamlet, Rosencrantz, [Guildenstern,] etc.*)

---

53. at foot: Close behind, at heel. **56. leans on:** Bears upon, is related to.
57. England: King of England. **59. cicatrice:** Scar. **60. free awe:** Voluntary
show of respect. **61. set:** Esteem. **62. process:** Command. **63. congruing:**
Agreeing. **64. present:** Immediate. **65. hectic:** Persistent fever. **67. haps:**
Fortunes. **IV, IV. Location:** The coast of Denmark. **2. license:** Permission.
3. conveyance: Escort, convoy. **6. eye:** Presence. **8. softly:** Slowly.

HAMLET: Good sir, whose powers° are these?
CAPTAIN: They are of Norway, sir.   10
HAMLET: How purposed, sir, I pray you?
CAPTAIN: Against some part of Poland.
HAMLET: Who commands them, sir?
CAPTAIN: The nephew to old Norway, Fortinbras.
HAMLET: Goes it against the main° of Poland, sir,   15
   Or for some frontier?
CAPTAIN: Truly to speak, and with no addition,°
   We go to gain a little patch of ground
   That hath in it no profit but the name.
   To pay° five ducats, five, I would not farm it;°   20
   Nor will it yield to Norway or the Pole
   A ranker° rate, should it be sold in fee.°
HAMLET: Why, then the Polack never will defend it.
CAPTAIN: Yes, it is already garrison'd.
HAMLET: Two thousand souls and twenty thousand ducats   25
   Will not debate the question of this straw.°
   This is th' imposthume° of much wealth and peace,
   That inward breaks, and shows no cause without
   Why the man dies. I humbly thank you, sir.
CAPTAIN: God buy you, sir.   [Exit.]
ROSENCRANTZ: Will 't please you go, my lord?   30
HAMLET: I'll be with you straight. Go a little before.

                                          [Exit all except Hamlet.]

   How all occasions do inform against° me,
   And spur my dull revenge! What is a man,
   If his chief good and market of° his time
   Be but to sleep and feed? A beast, no more.   35
   Sure he that made us with such large discourse,°
   Looking before and after, gave us not
   That capability and god-like reason
   To fust° in us unus'd. Now, whether it be
   Bestial oblivion,° or some craven scruple   40

---

9. powers: Forces.   15. main: Main part.   17. addition: Exaggeration.
20. To pay: I.e., for a yearly rental of.   farm it: Take a lease of it.   22. ranker:
Higher.   in fee: Fee simple, outright.   26. debate . . . straw: Settle this trifling
matter.   27. imposthume: Abscess.   32. inform against: Denounce, betray;
take shape against.   34. market of: Profit of, compensation for.   36. discourse:
Power of reasoning.   39. fust: Grow moldy.   40. oblivion: Forgetfulness.

Of thinking too precisely on th' event° —
A thought which, quarter'd, hath but one part wisdom
And ever three parts coward — I do not know
Why yet I live to say "This thing's to do,"
Sith° I have cause and will and strength and means   45
To do 't. Examples gross° as earth exhort me:
Witness this army of such mass and charge°
Led by a delicate and tender prince,
Whose spirit, with divine ambition puff'd
Makes mouths° at the invisible event,   50
Exposing what is mortal and unsure
To all that fortune, death, and danger dare,
Even for an egg-shell. Rightly to be great
Is not to stir without great argument,
But greatly to find quarrel in a straw   55
When honor's at the stake. How stand I then,
That have a father kill'd, a mother stain'd,
Excitements of° my reason and my blood,
And let all sleep, while, to my shame, I see
The imminent death of twenty thousand men,   60
That, for a fantasy° and trick° of fame,
Go to their graves like beds, fight for a plot°
Whereon the numbers cannot try the cause,°
Which is not tomb enough and continent°
To hide the slain? O, from this time forth,   65
My thoughts be bloody, or be nothing worth!

                                                  (*Exit.*)

                        {*Scene v*}°

(*Enter Horatio, [Queen] Gertrude, and a Gentleman.*)

QUEEN: I will not speak with her.
GENTLEMAN: She is importunate, indeed distract.
   Her mood will needs be pitied.

41. **event:** Outcome.   45. **Sith:** Since.   46. **gross:** Obvious.   47. **charge:** Expense.   50. **Makes mouths:** Makes scornful faces.   58. **Excitements of:** Promptings by.   61. **fantasy:** Fanciful caprice.   **trick:** Trifle.   62. **plot:** I.e., of ground.   63. **Whereon . . . cause:** On which there is insufficient room for the soldiers needed to engage in a military contest.   64. **continent:** Receptacle, container.   **IV, v. Location:** The castle.

QUEEN: What would she have?
GENTLEMAN: She speaks much of her father, says she hears
  There's tricks° i' th' world, and hems, and beats her heart,°   5
  Spurns enviously at straws,° speaks things in doubt°
  That carry but half sense. Her speech is nothing,
  Yet the unshaped use° of it doth move
  The hearers to collection;° they yawn° at it,
  And botch° the words up fit to their own thoughts,   10
  Which, as her winks and nods and gestures yield° them,
  Indeed would make one think there might be thought,°
  Though nothing sure, yet much unhappily.
HORATIO: 'twere good she were spoken with, for she may strew
  Dangerous conjectures in ill-breeding° minds.   15
QUEEN: Let her come in.   [*Exit Gentlemen.*]
  [*Aside.*] To my sick soul, as sin's true nature is,
  Each toy° seems prologue to some great amiss.°
  So full of artless jealousy is guilt,
  It spills itself in fearing to be spilt.°   20

(*Enter Ophelia [distracted].*)

OPHELIA: Where is the beauteous majesty of Denmark?
QUEEN: How now, Ophelia?
OPHELIA (*she sings*): "How should I your true love know
    From another one?
  By his cockle hat° and staff,   25
    And his sandal shoon."°
QUEEN: Alas, sweet lady, what imports this song?
OPHELIA: Say you? Nay, pray you, mark.
  "He is dead and gone, lady,   (*Song.*)
    He is dead and gone;   30
  At his head a grass-green turf,
    At his heels a stone."
  O, ho!

---

5. **tricks:** Deceptions. **heart:** Breast. 6. **Spurns . . . straws:** Kicks spitefully, takes offense at trifles. **in doubt:** Obscurely. 8. **unshaped use:** Distracted manner. 9. **collection:** Inference, a guess at some sort of meaning. **yawn:** Wonder, grasp. 10. **botch:** Patch. 11. **yield:** Delivery, bring forth (her words). 12. **thought:** Conjectured. 15. **ill-breeding:** Prone to suspect the worst. 18. **toy:** Trifle. **amiss:** Calamity. 19–20. **So . . . spilt:** Guilt is so full of suspicion that it unskillfully betrays itself in fearing betrayal. 25. **cockle hat:** Hat with cockleshell stuck in it as a sign that the wearer had been a pilgrim to the shrine of St. James of Compostella in Spain. 26. **shoon:** Shoes.

QUEEN: Nay, but Ophelia—
OPHELIA: Pray you mark.   35
   [*Sings.*] "White his shroud as the mountain snow"—

(*Enter King.*)

QUEEN: Alas, look here, my lord.
OPHELIA: "Larded° all with flowers   (*Song.*)
   Which bewept to the ground did not go
     With true-love showers."   40
KING: How do you, pretty lady?
OPHELIA: Well, God 'ild° you! They say the owl° was a baker's daughter.
   Lord, we know what we are, but know not what we may be. God be at
   your table!
KING: Conceit° upon her father.   45
OPHELIA: Pray let's have no words of this; but when they ask you what it
   means, say you this:
   "Tomorrow is Saint Valentine's° day.   (*Song.*)
     All in the morning betime,
   And I a maid at your window,   50
     To be your Valentine.
   Then up he rose, and donn'd his clo'es,
     And dupp'd° the chamber-door,
   Let in the maid, that out a maid
     Never departed more."   55
KING: Pretty Ophelia!
OPHELIA: Indeed, la, without an oath, I'll make an end on 't:
   [*Sings.*] "By Gis° and by Saint Charity,
     Alack, and fie for shame!
   Young men will do 't, if they come to 't;   60
     By Cock,° they are to blame.
   Quoth she, 'Before you tumbled me,
     You promised me to wed.'"
   He answers:
   "'So would I ha' done, by yonder sun,   65
     An thou hadst not come to my bed.'"
KING: How long hath she been thus?

---

38. Larded: Decorated.   **42. God 'ild:** God yield or reward.   **owl:** Refers to a
legend about a baker's daughter who was turned into an owl for refusing Jesus
bread.   **45. Conceit:** Brooding.   **48. Valentine's:** This song alludes to the belief
that the first girl seen by a man on the morning of this day was his valentine or
true love.   **53. dupp'd:** Opened.   **58. Gis:** Jesus.   **61. Cock:** A perversion of
God in oaths.

OPHELIA: I hope all will be well. We must be patient, but I cannot choose
but weep, to think they would lay him i' th' cold ground. My brother
shall know of it; and so I thank you for your good counsel. Come, my   70
coach! Good night, ladies; good night, sweet ladies; good night, good
night.

                                                                  [Exit.]

KING: Follow her close; give her good watch, I pray you.

                                                          [Exit Horatio.]

O, this is the poison of deep grief; it springs
All from her father's death—and now behold!   75
O Gertrude, Gertrude,
When sorrows come, they come not single spies,°
But in battalions. First, her father slain;
Next, your son gone, and he most violent author
Of his own just remove; the people muddied,°   80
Thick and unwholesome in their thoughts and whispers,
For good Polonius' death; and we have done but greenly,°
In hugger-mugger° to inter him; poor Ophelia
Divided from herself and her fair judgment,
Without the which we are pictures, or mere beasts;   85
Last, and as much containing as all these,
Her brother is in secret come from France,
Feeds on his wonder, keeps himself in clouds,°
And wants° not buzzers° to infect his ear
With pestilent speeches of his father's death,   90
Wherein necessity, of matter beggar'd,°
Will nothing stick our person to arraign
In ear and ear.° O my dear Gertrude, this,
Like to a murd'ring-piece,° in many places
Gives me superfluous death.   (A noise within.)   95
[QUEEN: Alack, what noise is this?]
KING: Attend!
Where are my Switzers?° Let them guard the door.

---

77. **spies:** Scouts sent in advance of the main force.   80. **muddied:** Stirred up,
confused.   82. **greenly:** Imprudently, foolishly.   83. **hugger-mugger:** Secret
haste.   88. **in clouds:** I.e., of suspicion and rumor.   89. **wants:** Lacks.
buzzers: Gossipers, informers.   91. **of matter beggar'd:** Unprovided with facts.
92–93. **Will . . . and ear:** Will not hesitate to accuse my (royal) person in everybody's ears.   94. **murd'ring-piece:** Cannon loaded so as to scatter its shot.
98. **Switzers:** Swiss guards, mercenaries.

(*Enter a Messenger.*)

What is the matter?
MESSENGER: Save yourself, my lord!
  The ocean, overpeering of his list,°   100
  Eats not the flats° with more impiteous° haste
  Than young Laertes, in a riotous head,°
  O'erbears your officers. The rabble call him lord,
  And, as° the world were now but to begin,
  Antiquity forgot, custom not known,   105
  The ratifiers and props° of every word,°
  They cry, "Choose we! Laertes shall be king!"
  Caps, hands, and tongues applaud it to the clouds,
  "Laertes shall be king, Laertes king!"

(*A noise within.*)

QUEEN: How cheerfully on the false trail they cry!   110
  O, this is counter,° you false Danish dogs!

(*Enter Laertes with others.*)

KING: The doors are broke.
LAERTES: Where is this King? Sirs, stand you all without.
ALL: No, let's come in.
LAERTES: I pray you, give me leave.
ALL: We will, we will.   115

[*They retire without the door.*]

LAERTES: I thank you. Keep the door. O thou vile king,
  Give me my father!
QUEEN: Calmly, good Laertes.

[*She tries to hold him back.*]

LAERTES: That drop of blood that's calm proclaims me bastard,
  Cries cuckold to my father, brands the harlot
  Even here, between the chaste unsmirched brow   120
  Of my true mother.

---

100. overpeering of his list: Overflowing its shore. **101. flats:** Flatlands near shore. **impiteous:** Pitiless. **102. head:** Armed force. **104. as:** As if. **106. ratifiers and props:** Refer to *antiquity* and *custom*. **word:** Promise. **111. counter:** A hunting term meaning to follow the trail in a direction opposite to that which the game has taken.

KING: What is the cause, Laertes,
  That thy rebellion looks so giant-like?
  Let him go, Gertrude. Do not fear our° person.
  There's such divinity doth hedge a king
  That treason can but peep to what it would,°   125
  Acts little of his will.° Tell me, Laertes,
  Why thou art thus incens'd. Let him go, Gertrude.
  Speak, man.
LAERTES: Where is my father?
KING: Dead.
QUEEN: But not by him.
KING: Let him demand his fill.
LAERTES: How came he dead? I'll not be juggled with.   130
  To hell, allegiance! Vows, to the blackest devil!
  Conscience and grace, to the profoundest pit!
  I dare damnation. To this point I stand,
  That both the worlds I give to negligence,°
  Let come what comes, only I'll be reveng'd   135
  Most throughly° for my father.
KING: Who shall stay you?
LAERTES: My will, not all the world's.°
  And for my means, I'll husband them so well,
  They shall go far with little.
KING: Good Laertes,
  If you desire to know the certainty   140
  Of your dear father, is 't writ in your revenge
  That, swoopstake,° you will draw both friend and foe,
  Winner and loser?
LAERTES: None but his enemies.
KING: Will you know them then?
LAERTES: To his good friends thus wide I'll ope my arms,   145
  And, like the kind life-rend'ring pelican,°
  Repast° them with my blood.

123. fear our: Fear for my.   125. can . . . would: Can only glance; as from far off
or through a barrier, at what it would intend.   126. Acts . . . will: (But) performs
little of what it intends.   134. both . . . negligence: Both this world and the next
are of no consequence to me.   136. throughly: Thoroughly.   137. My will . . .
world's: I'll stop (stay) when my will is accomplished, not for anyone else's.
142. swoopstake: Literally, taking all stakes on the gambling table at once, i.e.,
indiscriminately; draw is also a gambling term.   146. pelican: Refers to the
belief that the female pelican fed its young with its own blood.   147. Repast:
Feed.

KING: Why, now you speak
Like a good child and a true gentleman.
That I am guiltless of your father's death,
And am most sensibly° in grief for it,   150
It shall as level° to your judgment 'pear
As day does to your eye.
                          (*A noise within:*) "Let her come in."
LAERTES: How now? What noise is that?

(*Enter Ophelia.*)

O heat, dry up my brains! Tears seven times salt
Burn out the sense and virtue° of mine eye!   155
By heaven, thy madness shall be paid with weight°
Till our scale turn the beam.° O rose of May!
Dear maid, kind sister, sweet Ophelia!
O heavens, is 't possible a young maid's wits
Should be as mortal as an old man's life?   160
[Nature is fine in° love, and where 'tis fine,
It sends some precious instance° of itself
After the thing it loves.°]
OPHELIA: "They bore him barefac'd on the bier;

                                              (*Song.*)

[Hey non nonny, nonny, hey nonny,]   165
And in his grave rain'd many a tear"—
Fare you well, my dove!
LAERTES: Hadst thou thy wits, and didst persuade° revenge,
It could not move thus.
OPHELIA: You must sing "A-down a-down,   170
And you call him a-down-a."
O, how the wheel° becomes it! It is the false steward° that stole his
master's daughter.
LAERTES: This nothing's more than matter.°

150. **sensibly:** Feelingly.   151. **level:** Plain.   155. **virtue:** Faculty, power.
156. **paid with weight:** Repaid, avenged equally or more.   157. **beam:** Crossbar
of a balance.   161. **fine in:** Refined by.   162. **instance:** Token.   163. **After . . .**
loves: Into the grave, along with Polonius.   168. **persuade:** Argue cogently for.
172. **wheel:** Spinning wheel as accompaniment to the song, or refrain.   **false**
steward: The story is unknown.   174. **This . . . matter:** This seeming nonsense
is more meaningful than sane utterance.

OPHELIA: There's rosemary,° that's for remembrance; pray you, love, 175
   remember. And there is pansies,° that's for thoughts.
LAERTES: A document° in madness, thoughts and remembrance fitted.
OPHELIA: There's fennel° for you, and columbines.° There's rue° for you,
   and here's some for me; we may call it herb of grace o' Sundays. You
   may wear your rue with a difference.° There's a daisy.° I would give 180
   you some violets,° but they wither'd all when my father died. They say
   'a made a good end—
   [Sings.] "For bonny sweet Robin is all my joy."
LAERTES: Thought° and affliction, passion, hell itself,
   She turns to favor° and to prettiness.   185
OPHELIA: "And will 'a not come again? (Song.)
   And will 'a not come again?
      No, no, he is dead,
      Go to thy death-bed,
   He never will come again.   190

   "His beard was as white as snow,
   All flaxen was his poll.°
      He is gone, he is gone,
      And we cast away moan.
   God 'a' mercy on his soul!"   195
   And of all Christians' souls, I pray God. God buy you.

                                                                [Exit.]

LAERTES: Do you see this, O God?
KING: Laertes, I must commune with your grief,
   Or you deny me right. Go but apart,
   Make choice of whom your wisest friends you will,   200
   And they shall hear and judge 'twixt you and me.
   If by direct or by collateral° hand
   They find us touch'd,° we will our kingdom give,

175. **rosemary:** Used as a symbol of remembrance both at weddings and at
funerals.   176. **pansies:** Emblems of love and courtship; perhaps from French
pensées, thoughts.   177. **document:** Instruction, lesson.   178. **fennel:** Emblem
of flattery.   **columbines:** Emblems of unchastity (?) or ingratitude (?).   **rue:**
Emblem of repentance; when mingled with holy water, it was known as *herb of
grace*.   180. **with a difference:** Suggests that Ophelia and the queen have different causes of sorrow and repentance; perhaps with a play on *rue* in the sense
of ruth, pity.   **daisy:** Emblem of dissembling, faithlessness.   181. **violets:** Emblems of faithfulness.   184. **Thought:** Melancholy.   185. **favor:** Grace.
192. **poll:** Head.   202. **collateral:** Indirect.   203. **us touch'd:** Me implicated.

Our crown, our life, and all that we call ours,
To you in satisfaction; but if not,   205
Be you content to lend your patience to us,
And we shall jointly labor with your soul
To give it due content.
LAERTES: Let this be so.
His means of death, his obscure funeral—
No trophy,° sword, nor hatchment° o'er his bones,   210
No noble rite nor formal ostentation°—
Cry to be heard, as 'twere from heaven to earth,
That I must call 't in question.
KING: So you shall;
And where th' offense is, let the great ax fall.
I pray you go with me.   (*Exeunt.*) 215

[*Scene VI*]°

(*Enter Horatio and others.*)

HORATIO: What are they that would speak with me?
GENTLEMAN: Seafaring men, sir. They say they have letters for you.
HORATIO: Let them come in.   [*Exit Gentleman.*]
   I do not know from what part of the world
   I should be greeted, if not from lord Hamlet.   5

(*Enter Sailors.*)

FIRST SAILOR: God bless you sir.
HORATIO: Let him bless thee too.
FIRST SAILOR: 'A shall, sir, an 't please him. There's a letter for you, sir—
it came from th' ambassador that was bound for England—if your
name be Horatio, as I am let to know it is.   [*Gives letter.*] 10
HORATIO [*reads*]: "Horatio, when thou shalt have over-look'd this, give
these fellows some means° to the King; they have letters for him. Ere
we were two days old at sea, a pirate of very warlike appointment°
gave us chase. Finding ourselves too slow of sail, we put on a compell'd valor, and in the grapple I boarded them. On the instant they got 15
clear of our ship, so I alone became their prisoner. They have dealt
with me like thieves of mercy,° but they knew what they did: I am to do

---

210. **trophy:** Memorial.   **hatchment:** Tablet displaying the armorial bearings of
a deceased person.   211. **ostentation:** Ceremony.   **IV, VI. Location:** The castle.
12. **means:** Means of access.   13. **appointment:** Equipage.   17. **thieves of
mercy:** Merciful thieves.

a good turn for them. Let the King have the letters I have sent, and
repair thou to me with as much speed as thou wouldest fly death. I
have words to speak in thine ear will make thee dumb; yet are they   20
much too light for the bore° of the matter. These good fellows will
bring thee where I am. Rosencrantz and Guildenstern hold their
course for England. Of them I have much to tell thee. Farewell.

                              He that thou knowest thine, Hamlet."
Come, I will give you way for these your letters,   25
And do 't the speedier that you may direct me
To him from whom you brought them.   (*Exeunt.*)

                          {*Scene VII*}°

(*Enter King and Laertes.*)

KING: Now must your conscience my acquittance seal,°
    And you must put me in your heart for friend,
    Sith you have heard, and with a knowing ear,
    That he which hath your noble father slain
    Pursued my life.
LAERTES: It well appears. But tell me   5
    Why you proceeded not against these feats°
    So criminal and so capital° in nature,
    As by your safety, greatness, wisdom, all things else,
    You mainly° were stirr'd up.
KING: O, for two special reasons,
    Which may to you, perhaps, seem much unsinew'd,°   10
    But yet to me th' are strong. The Queen his mother
    Lives almost by his looks, and for myself—
    My virtue or my plague, be it either which—
    She's so conjunctive° to my life and soul
    That, as the star moves not but in his sphere,°   15
    I could not but by her. The other motive,
    Why to a public count° I might not go,
    Is the great love the general gender° bear him,
    Who, dipping all his faults in their affection,

___

21. **bore:** Caliber, i.e., importance.   IV, VII. **Location:** The castle.   1. **my acquittance seal:** Confirm or acknowledge my innocence.   6. **feats:** Acts.   7. **capital:**
Punishable by death.   9. **mainly:** Greatly.   10. **unsinew'd:** Weak.   14. **con-
junctive:** Closely united.   15. **sphere:** The hollow sphere in which, according to
Ptolemaic astronomy, the planets moved.   17. **count:** Account, reckoning.
18. **general gender:** Common people.

Would, like the spring° that turneth wood to stone,   20
Convert his gyves° to graces, so that my arrows,
Too slightly timber'd° for so loud° a wind,
Would have reverted to my bow again
And not where I had aim'd them.
LAERTES: And so have I a noble father lost,   25
A sister driven into desp'rate terms,°
Whose worth, if praises may go back° again,
Stood challenger on mount° of all the age
For her perfections. But my revenge will come.
KING: Break not your sleeps for that. You must not think   30
That we are made of stuff so flat and dull
That we can let our beard be shook with danger
And think it pastime. You shortly shall hear more.
I lov'd your father, and we love ourself;
And that, I hope, will teach you to imagine—   35

(*Enter a Messenger with letters.*)

[How now? What news?]
MESSENGER: [Letters, my lord, from Hamlet:]
These to your Majesty, this to the Queen.

                                        [*Gives letters.*]

KING: From Hamlet? Who brought them?
MESSENGER: Sailors, my lord, they say; I saw them not.
They were given me by Claudio. He receiv'd them   40
Of him that brought them.
KING: Laertes, you shall hear them.
Leave us.   [*Exit Messenger.*]
[*Reads.*] "High and mighty, you shall know I am set naked° on your
kingdom. Tomorrow shall I beg leave to see your kingly eyes, when I
shall, first asking your pardon° thereunto, recount the occasion of my 45
sudden and more strange return.   Hamlet."
What should this mean? Are all the rest come back?
Or is it some abuse,° and no such thing?

---

20. spring: A spring with such a concentration of lime that it coats a piece of
wood with limestone, in effect gilding it.   **21. gyves:** Fetters (which, gilded by
the people's praise, would look like badges of honor).   **22. slightly timber'd:**
Light.   **loud:** Strong.   **26. terms:** State, condition.   **27. go back:** Recall
Ophelia's former virtues.   **28. on mount:** On high.   **43. naked:** Destitute,
unarmed, without following.   **45. pardon:** Permission.   **48. abuse:** Deceit.

LAERTES: Know you the hand?
KING: 'Tis Hamlet's character.° "Naked!"
    And in a postscript here, he says "alone."   50
    Can you devise° me?
LAERTES: I am lost in it, my lord. But let him come.
    It warms the very sickness in my heart
    That I shall live and tell him to his teeth,
    "Thus didst thou."
KING: If it be so, Laertes—   55
    As how should it be so? How otherwise?°—
    Will you be ruled by me?
LAERTES: Ay, my lord,
    So° you will not o'errule me to a peace.
KING: To thine own peace. If he be now returned,
    As checking at° his voyage, and that he means   60
    No more to undertake it, I will work him
    To an exploit, now ripe in my device,
    Under the which he shall not choose but fall;
    And for his death no wind of blame shall breathe,
    But even his mother shall uncharge the practice°   65
    And call it accident.
LAERTES: My lord, I will be rul'd,
    The rather if you could devise it so
    That I might be the organ.°
KING: It falls right.
    You have been talk'd of since your travel much,
    And that in Hamlet's hearing, for a quality   70
    Wherein, they say, you shine. Your sum of parts°
    Did not together pluck such envy from him
    As did that one, and that, in my regard,
    Of the unworthiest siege.°
LAERTES: What part is that, my lord?   75
KING: A very riband in the cap of youth,
    Yet needful too, for youth no less becomes
    The light and careless livery that it wears

49. **character:** Handwriting.   51. **devise:** Explain to.   56. **As . . . otherwise:**
How can this (Hamlet's return) be true? Yet how otherwise than true (since we
have the evidence of his letter).   58. **So:** Provided that.   60. **checking at:**
Turning aside from (like a falcon leaving the quarry to fly at a chance bird).
65. **uncharge the practice:** Acquit the stratagem of being a plot.   68. **organ:**
Agent, instrument.   71. **Your . . . parts:** All your other virtues.   74. **unworthi-
est siege:** Least important rank.

Than settled age his sables° and his weeds,°
Importing health° and graveness. Two months since   80
Here was a gentleman of Normandy.
I have seen myself, and serv'd against, the French,
And they can well° on horseback, but this gallant
Had witchcraft in 't; he grew unto his seat,
And to such wondrous doing brought his horse   85
As had he been incorps'd and demi-natured°
With the brave beast. So far he topp'd° my thought
That I, in forgery° of shapes and tricks,
Come short of what he did.
LAERTES: A Norman was 't?
KING: A Norman.   90
LAERTES: Upon my life, Lamord.
KING: The very same.
LAERTES: I know him well. He is the brooch° indeed
And gem of all the nation.
KING: He made confession° of you,
And gave you such a masterly report   95
For art and exercise in your defense,
And for your rapier most especial,
That he cried out, 'twould be a sight indeed,
If one could match you. The scrimers° of their nation,
He swore, had neither motion, guard, nor eye,   100
If you oppos'd them. Sir, this report of his
Did Hamlet so envenom with his envy
That he could nothing do but wish and beg
Your sudden coming o'er to play° with you.
Now, out of this—
LAERTES: What out of this, my lord?   105
KING: Laertes, was your father dear to you?
Or are you like the painting of a sorrow,
A face without a heart?
LAERTES: Why ask you this?
KING: Not that I think you did not love your father,
But that I know love is begun by time,°   110

79. **sables:** Rich robes furred with sable. **weeds:** Garments. **80. Importing health:** Indicating prosperity. **83. can well:** Are skilled. **86. incorps'd and demi-natured:** Of one body and nearly of one nature (like the centaur). **87. topp'd:** Surpassed. **88. forgery:** Invention. **92. brooch:** Ornament. **94. confession:** Admission of superiority. **99. scrimers:** Fencers. **104. play:** Fence. **110. begun by time:** Subject to change.

And that I see, in passages of proof,°
Time qualifies° the spark and fire of it.
There lives within the very flame of love
A kind of wick or snuff° that will abate it,
And nothing is at a like goodness still,°   115
For goodness, growing to a plurisy,°
Dies in his own too much.° That° we would do,
We should do when we would; for this "would" changes
And hath abatements° and delays as many
As there are tongues, are hands, are accidents,°   120
And then this "should" is like a spendthrift's sigh,°
That hurts by easing.° But, to the quick o' th' ulcer;
Hamlet comes back. What would you undertake
To show yourself your father's son in deed
More than in words?
LAERTES: To cut his throat i' th' church!   125
KING: No place, indeed, should murder sanctuarize;°
Revenge should have no bounds. But, good Laertes,
Will you do this,° keep close within your chamber.
Hamlet return'd shall know you are come home.
We'll put on those° shall praise your excellence   130
And set a double varnish on the fame
The Frenchman gave you, bring you in fine° together,
And wager on your heads. He, being remiss,°
Most generous,° and free from all contriving,
Will not peruse the foils, so that, with ease,   135
Or with a little shuffling, you may choose
A sword unbated,° and in a pass of practice°
Requite him for your father.

---

111. **passages of proof:** Actual instances.   112. **qualifies:** Weakens.   114. **snuff:**
The charred part of a candlewick.   115. **nothing . . . still:** Nothing remains at a
constant level of perfection.   116. **plurisy:** Excess, plethora.   117. **in . . . much:**
Of its own excess.   **That:** That which.   119. **abatements:** Diminutions.
120. **accidents:** Occurrences, incidents.   121. **spendthrift's sigh:** An allusion to
the belief that each sigh cost the heart a drop of blood.   122. **hurts by easing:**
Costs the heart blood even while it affords emotional relief.   126. **sanctuarize:**
Protect from punishment (alludes to the right of sanctuary with which certain
religious places were invested).   128. **Will you do this:** If you wish to do this.
130. **put on those:** Instigate those who.   132. **in fine:** Finally.   133. **remiss:**
Negligently unsuspicious.   134. **generous:** Noble-minded.   137. **unbated:** Not
blunted, having no button.   **pass of practice:** Treacherous thrust.

LAERTES: I will do 't.
And for that purpose I'll anoint my sword.
I bought an unction° of a mountebank°   140
So mortal that, but dip a knife in it,
Where it draws blood no cataplasm° so rare,
Collected from all simples° that have virtue
Under the moon, can save the thing from death
That is but scratch'd withal. I'll touch my point   145
With this contagion, that, if I gall° him slightly,
It may be death.
KING: Let's further think of this,
Weigh what convenience both of time and means
May fit us to our shape.° If this should fail,
And that our drift look through our bad performance,°   150
'Twere better not assay'd. Therefore this project
Should have a back or second, that might hold
If this did blast in proof.° Soft, let me see.
We'll make a solemn wager on your cunnings —
I ha 't!   155
When in your motion you are hot and dry —
As° make your bouts more violent to that end —
And that he calls for drink, I'll have prepar'd him
A chalice for the nonce,° whereon but sipping,
If he by chance escape your venom'd stuck,°   160
Our purpose may hold there. [A cry within.] But stay, what noise?

(*Enter Queen.*)

QUEEN: One woe doth tread upon another's heel,
So fast they follow. Your sister's drowned, Laertes.
LAERTES: Drown'd! O, where?
QUEEN: There is a willow grows askant° the brook   165
That shows his hoar° leaves in the glassy stream;
Therewith fantastic garlands did she make
Of crow-flowers, nettles, daisies, and long purples°
That liberal° shepherds give a grosser name,

---

140. unction: Ointment. **mountebank:** Quack doctor. **142. cataplasm:** Plaster
or poultice. **143. simples:** Herbs. **146. gall:** Graze, wound. **149. shape:**
Part that we propose to act. **150. drift . . . performance:** I.e., intention be disclosed by our bungling. **153. blast in proof:** Burst in the test (like a cannon).
157. As: And you should. **159. nonce:** Occasion. **160. stuck:** Thrust (from
stoccado, a fencing term). **165. askant:** Aslant. **166. hoar:** White or gray.
168. long purples: Early purple orchids. **169. liberal:** Free-spoken.

But our cold° maids do dead men's fingers call them.   170
There on the pendent boughs her crownet° weeds
Clamb'ring to hang, an envious sliver° broke,
When down her weedy° trophies and herself
Fell in the weeping brook. Her clothes spread wide,
And mermaid-like awhile they bore her up,   175
Which time she chanted snatches of old lauds,°
As one incapable° of her own distress,
Or like a creature native and indued°
Unto that element. But long it could not be
Till that her garments, heavy with their drink,   180
Pull'd the poor wretch from her melodious lay
To muddy death.
LAERTES: Alas, then she is drown'd?
QUEEN: Drown'd, drown'd.
LAERTES: Too much of water hast thou, poor Ophelia,
And therefore I forbid my tears. But yet   185
It is our trick;° nature her custom holds,
Let shame say what it will. [*He weeps.*] When these are gone,
The woman will be out.° Adieu, my lord.
I have a speech of fire, that fain would blaze,
But that this folly drowns it.   (*Exit.*)
KING: Let's follow, Gertrude.   190
How much I had to do to calm his rage!
Now fear I this will give it start again;
Therefore let's follow.   (*Exeunt.*)

{ACT V   *Scene 1*}°

(*Enter two Clowns*° [*with spades, etc.*])

FIRST CLOWN: Is she to be buried in Christian burial when she willfully
seeks her own salvation?
SECOND CLOWN: I tell thee she is; therefore make her grave straight.° The
crowner° hath sat on her, and finds it Christian burial.

---

170. cold: Chaste.   171. crownet: Made into a chaplet or coronet.   172. envious sliver: Malicious branch.   173. weedy: I.e., of plants.   176. lauds: Hymns.
177. incapable: Lacking capacity to apprehend.   178. indued: Adapted by
nature.   186. It is our trick: Weeping is our natural way (when sad).
187–88. When . . . out: When my tears are all shed, the woman in me will be
expended, satisfied.   V, 1. Location: A churchyard.   [s.d.] *Clowns:* Rustics.
3. straight: Straightway, immediately.   4. crowner: Coroner.

FIRST CLOWN: How can that be, unless she drown'd herself in her own   5
defense?

SECOND CLOWN: Why, 'tis found so.

FIRST CLOWN: It must be "se offendendo";° it cannot be else. For here lies
the point: if I drown myself wittingly, it argues an act, and an act hath
three branches—it is to act, to do, and to perform. Argal,° she   10
drown'd herself wittingly.

SECOND CLOWN: Nay, but hear you, goodman delver—

FIRST CLOWN: Give me leave. Here lies the water; good. Here stands the
man; good. If the man go to this water, and drown himself, it is, will
he,° nill he, he goes, mark you that. But if the water come to him and   15
drown him, he drowns not himself. Argal, he that is not guilty of his
own death shortens not his own life.

SECOND CLOWN: But is this law?

FIRST CLOWN: Ay, marry, is 't—crowner's quest° law.

SECOND CLOWN: Will you ha' the truth on 't? If this had not been a gentle-   20
woman, she should have been buried out o' Christian burial.

FIRST CLOWN: Why, there thou say'st.° And the more pity that great folk
should have count'nance° in this world to drown or hang themselves,
more than their even-Christen.° Come, my spade. There is no ancient
gentlemen but gard'ners, ditchers, and grave-makers. They hold up   25
Adam's profession.

SECOND CLOWN: Was he a gentleman?

FIRST CLOWN: 'A was the first that ever bore arms.

[SECOND CLOWN: Why, he had none.

FIRST CLOWN: What, art a heathen? How dost thou understand the   30
Scripture? The Scripture says "Adam digg'd." Could he dig without
arms?] I'll put another question to thee. If thou answerest me not to
the purpose, confess thyself°—

SECOND CLOWN: Go to.

FIRST CLOWN: What is he that builds stronger than either the mason, the   35
shipwright, or the carpenter?

SECOND CLOWN: The gallows-maker, for that frame outlives a thousand
tenants.

FIRST CLOWN: I like thy wit well, in good faith. The gallows does well, but
how does it well? It does well to those that do ill. Now thou dost ill to   40

---

8. se offendendo: A comic mistake for *se defendendo,* term used in verdicts of jus-
tifiable homicide.   **10. Argal:** Corruption of *ergo,* therefore.   **14–15. will he:**
Will he not.   **19. quest:** Inquest.   **22. there thou say'st:** That's right.
23. count'nance: Privilege.   **24. even-Christen:** Fellow Christian.   **33. confess
thyself:** The saying continues, "and be hanged."

say the gallows is built stronger than the church. Argal, the gallows
may do well to thee. To 't again, come.
SECOND CLOWN: "Who builds stronger than a mason, a shipwright, or a
carpenter?"
FIRST CLOWN: Ay, tell me that, and unyoke.°   45
SECOND CLOWN: Marry, now I can tell.
FIRST CLOWN: To 't.
SECOND CLOWN: Mass,° I cannot tell.

(*Enter Hamlet and Horatio [at a distance].*)

FIRST CLOWN: Cudgel thy brains no more about it, for your dull ass will
not mend his pace with beating; and, when you are ask'd this question 50
next, say "a grave-maker." The houses he makes lasts till doomsday.
Go, get thee in, and fetch me a stoup° of liquor.

[*Exit Second Clown. First Clown digs.*]

(*Song.*)

"In youth, when I did love, did love,°
    Methought it was very sweet,
To contract—O—the time for—a—my behove,°   55
    O, methought there—a—was nothing—a—meet."°
HAMLET: Has this fellow no feeling of his business, that 'a sings at grave-
making?
HORATIO: Custom hath made it in him a property of easiness.°
HAMLET: 'Tis e'en so. The hand of little employment hath the daintier 60
sense.°

(*Song.*)

FIRST CLOWN: "But age, with his stealing steps,
    Hath claw'd me in his clutch,
And hath shipped me into the land,°
    As if I had never been such."   65

[*Throws up a skull.*]

45. **unyoke:** After this great effort you may unharness the team of your wits.
48. **Mass:** By the Mass.   52. **stoup:** Two-quart measure.   53. **In . . . love:** This
and the two following stanzas, with nonsensical variations, are from a poem
attributed to Lord Vaux and printed in *Tottel's Miscellany* (1557). The O and a
(for "ah") seemingly are the grunts of the digger.   55. **To contract . . . behove:**
To make a betrothal agreement for my benefit (?).   56. **meet:** Suitable, i.e., more
suitable.   59. **property of easiness:** Something he can do easily and without
thinking.   60–61. **daintier sense:** More delicate sense of feeling.   64. **into the
land:** Toward my grave (?) (but note the lack of rhyme in *steps, land*).

HAMLET: That skull had a tongue in it, and could sing once. How the
knave jowls° it to the ground, as if 'twere Cain's jaw-bone, that did the
first murder! This might be the pate of a politician,° which this ass
now o'erreaches,° one that would circumvent God, might it not?
HORATIO: It might, my lord.   70
HAMLET: Or of a courtier, which could say "Good morrow, sweet lord!
How dost thou, sweet lord?" This might be my Lord Such-a-one, that
prais'd my Lord Such-a-one's horse when 'a meant to beg it, might
it not?
HORATIO: Ay, my lord.   75
HAMLET: Why, e'en so, and now my Lady Worm's, chapless,° and knock'd
about the mazzard° with a sexton's spade. Here's fine revolution,° an°
we had the trick to see 't. Did these bones cost no more the breeding,°
but to play at loggats° with them? Mine ache to think on 't.

(Song.)

FIRST CLOWN: "A pick-axe, and a spade, a spade,   80
       For and° a shrouding sheet;
O, a pit of clay for to be made
       For such a guest is meet."

[Throws up another skull.]

HAMLET: There's another. Why may not that be the skull of a lawyer?
Where be his quiddities° now, his quillities,° his cases, his tenures,° 85
and his tricks? Why does he suffer this mad knave now to knock him
about the sconce° with a dirty shovel, and will not tell him of his
action of battery? Hum! This fellow might be in 's time a great buyer
of land, with his statutes, his recognizances,° his fines, his double°
vouchers,° his recoveries.° [Is this the fine of his fines, and the recov- 90

---

67. jowls: Dashes.   **68. politician:** Schemer, plotter.   **69. o'erreaches:** Circum-
vents, gets the better of (with a quibble on the literal sense).   **76. chapless:**
Having no lower jaw.   **77. mazzard:** Head (literally, a drinking vessel).   **revolution:** Change.   **an:** If.   **78. the breeding:** In the breeding, raising.   **79. loggats:**
A game in which pieces of hardwood are thrown to lie as near as possible to a
stake.   **81. For and:** And moreover.   **85. quiddities:** Subtleties, quibbles (from
Latin *quid*, a thing).   **quillities:** Verbal niceties, subtle distinctions (variation
of *quiddities*).   **tenures:** The holding of a piece of property or office, or the con-
ditions or period of such holding.   **87. sconce:** Head.   **89. statutes, recognizances:** Legal documents guaranteeing a debt by attaching land and property.
89–90. fines, recoveries: Ways of converting entailed estates into "fee simple" or
freehold.   **89. double:** Signed by two signatories.   **90. vouchers:** Guarantees of
the legality of a title to real estate.

ery of his recoveries,] to have his fine pate full of fine dirt?° Will his
vouchers vouch him no more of his purchases, and double [ones too],
than the length and breadth of a pair of indentures?° The very con-
veyances° of his lands will scarcely lie in this box,° and must th' inher-
itor° himself have no more, ha?   95
HORATIO: Not a jot more, my lord.
HAMLET: Is not parchment made of sheep-skins?
HORATIO: Ay, my lord, and of calf-skins too.
HAMLET: They are sheep and calves which seek out assurance in that.° I
will speak to this fellow.—Whose grave's this, sirrah?°   100
FIRST CLOWN: Mine, sir.
[Sings.] "O, a pit of clay for to be made
[For such a guest is meet]."
HAMLET: I think it be thine, indeed, for thou liest in 't.
FIRST CLOWN: You lie out on 't, sir, and therefore 'tis not yours. For my   105
part, I do not lie in 't, yet it is mine.
HAMLET: Thou dost lie in 't, to be in 't and say it is thine. 'Tis for the dead,
not for the quick;° therefore thou liest.
FIRST CLOWN: 'Tis a quick lie, sir; 'twill away again from me to you.
HAMLET: What man dost thou dig it for?   110
FIRST CLOWN: For no man, sir.
HAMLET: What woman, then?
FIRST CLOWN: For none, neither.
HAMLET: Who is to be buried in 't?
FIRST CLOWN: One that was a woman, sir, but, rest her soul, she's dead.   115
HAMLET: How absolute° the knave is! We must speak by the card,° or
equivocation° will undo us. By the Lord, Horatio, this three years I
have taken note of it: the age is grown so pick'd° that the toe of the
peasant comes so near the heel of the courtier, he galls his kibe.° How
long hast thou been a grave-maker?   120

90–91. fine of his fines . . . fine pate . . . fine dirt: End of his legal maneuvers . . .
elegant head . . . minutely sifted dirt.   93. pair of indentures: Legal document
drawn up in duplicate on a single sheet and then cut apart on a zigzag line so that
each pair was uniquely matched. (Hamlet may refer to two rows of teeth, or den-
tures.)   93–94. conveyances: Deeds.   94. this box: The skull.   94–95. inheri-
tor: Possessor, owner.   99. assurance in that: Safety in legal parchments.
100. sirrah: Term of address to inferiors.   108. quick: Living.   116. absolute:
Positive, decided.   by the card: By the mariner's card on which the points of the
compass were marked, i.e., with precision.   117. equivocation: Ambiguity
in the use of terms.   118. pick'd: Refined, fastidious.   119. galls his kibe:
Chafes the courtier's chilblain (a swelling or sore caused by cold).

FIRST CLOWN: Of all the days i' th' year, I came to 't that day that our last
  king Hamlet overcame Fortinbras.
HAMLET: How long is that since?
FIRST CLOWN: Cannot you tell that? Every fool can tell that. It was that
  very day that young Hamlet was born—he that is mad, and sent into   125
  England.
HAMLET: Ay, marry, why was he sent into England?
FIRST CLOWN: Why, because 'a was mad. 'A shall recover his wits there,
  or, if 'a do not, 'tis no great matter there.
HAMLET: Why?   130
FIRST CLOWN: 'Twill not be seen in him there. There the men are as mad
  as he.
HAMLET: How came he mad?
FIRST CLOWN: Very strangely, they say.
HAMLET: How strangely?   135
FIRST CLOWN: Faith, e'en with losing his wits.
HAMLET: Upon what ground?
FIRST CLOWN: Why, here in Denmark. I have been sexton here, man and
  boy, thirty years.
HAMLET: How long will a man lie i' th' earth ere he rot?   140
FIRST CLOWN: Faith, if 'a be not rotten before 'a die—as we have many
  pocky° corses [now-a-days], that will scarce hold the laying in—'a will
  last you some eight year or nine year. A tanner will last you nine year.
HAMLET: Why he more than another?
FIRST CLOWN: Why, sir, his hide is so tann'd with his trade that 'a will   145
  keep out water a great while, and your water is a sore decayer of your
  whoreson dead body. [Picks up a skull.] Here's a skull now hath lain
  you° i' th' earth three and twenty years.
HAMLET: Whose was it?
FIRST CLOWN: A whoreson mad fellow's it was. Whose do you think it   150
  was?
HAMLET: Nay, I know not.
FIRST CLOWN: A pestilence on him for a mad rogue! 'A pour'd a flagon of
  Rhenish° on my head once. This same skull, sir, was Yorick's skull, the
  King's jester.   155
HAMLET: This?
FIRST CLOWN: E'en that.
HAMLET: [Let me see.] [Takes the skull.] Alas, poor Yorick! I knew him,
  Horatio, a fellow of infinite jest, of most excellent fancy. He hath borne

142. pocky: Rotten, diseased (literally, with the pox, or syphilis).   147–48. lain
you: Lain.   154. Rhenish: Rhine wine.

me on his back a thousand times; and now, how abhorr'd in my imagi-   160
nation it is! My gorge rises at it. Here hung those lips that I have kiss'd
I know not how oft. Where be your gibes now? Your gambols, your
songs, your flashes of merriment that were wont to set the table on a
roar? Not one now, to mock your own grinning? Quite chap-fall'n?°
Now get you to my lady's chamber, and tell her, let her paint an inch   165
thick, to this favor° she must come; make her laugh at that. Prithee,
Horatio, tell me one thing.
HORATIO: What's that, my lord?
HAMLET: Dost thou think Alexander look'd o' this fashion i' th' earth?
HORATIO: E'en so.   170
HAMLET: And smelt so? Pah! [*Puts down the skull.*]
HORATIO: E'en so, my lord.
HAMLET: To what base uses we may return, Horatio! Why may not imag-
ination trace the noble dust of Alexander, till 'a find it stopping a bung-
hole?   175
HORATIO: 'twere to consider too curiously,° to consider so.
HAMLET: No, faith, not a jot, but to follow him thither with modesty°
enough, and likelihood to lead it. [As thus]: Alexander died, Alexander
was buried, Alexander returneth to dust; the dust is earth; of earth we
make loam;° and why of that loam, whereto he was converted, might   180
they not stop a beer-barrel?
Imperious° Caesar, dead and turn'd to clay,
Might stop a hole to keep the wind away.
O, that that earth which kept the world in awe
Should patch a wall t' expel the winter's flaw!°   185
But soft, but soft awhile! Here comes the King.

(*Enter King, Queen, Laertes, and the Corse* [*of Ophelia, in procession, with
Priest, Lords etc.*].)

The Queen, the courtiers. Who is this they follow?
And with such maimed rites? This doth betoken
The corse they follow did with desp'rate hand
Fordo it° own life. 'Twas of some estate.°   190
Couch° we awhile, and mark.

[*He and Horatio conceal themselves.
Ophelia's body is taken to the grave.*]

164. chap-fall'n: (1) Lacking the lower jaw; (2) dejected.   166. favor: Aspect,
appearance.   176. curiously: Minutely.   177. modesty: Moderation.   180. loam:
Clay mixture for brickmaking or other clay use.   182. Imperious: Imperial.
185. flaw: Gust of wind.   190. Fordo it: Destroy its.   estate: Rank.   191. Couch:
Hide, lurk.

LAERTES: What ceremony else?
HAMLET [*to Horatio*]: That is Laertes, a very noble youth. Mark.
LAERTES: What ceremony else?
PRIEST: Her obsequies have been as far enlarg'd   195
  As we have warranty. Her death was doubtful,
  And, but that great command o'ersways the order,
  She should in ground unsanctified been lodg'd
  Till the last trumpet. For° charitable prayers,
  Shards,° flints, and pebbles should be thrown on her.   200
  Yet here she is allow'd her virgin crants,°
  Her maiden strewments,° and the bringing home
  Of bell and burial.°
LAERTES: Must there no more be done?
PRIEST: No more be done.
  We should profane the service of the dead   205
  To sing a requiem and such rest to her
  As to peace-parted souls.
LAERTES: Lay her i' th' earth,
  And from her fair and unpolluted flesh
  May violets° spring! I tell thee, churlish priest,
  A minist'ring angel shall my sister be   210
  When thou liest howling!
HAMLET [*to Horatio*]:   What, the fair Ophelia!
QUEEN [*scattering flowers*]: Sweets to the sweet! Farewell.
  I hoped thou shouldst have been my Hamlet's wife.
  I thought thy bride-bed to have deck'd, sweet maid,
  And not have strew'd thy grave.
LAERTES: O, treble woe   215
  Fall ten times treble on that cursed head
  Whose wicked deed thy most ingenious sense°
  Depriv'd thee of! Hold off the earth awhile,
  Till I have caught her once more in mine arms.

            [*Leaps into the grave and embraces Ophelia.*]

  Now pile your dust upon the quick and dead,   220
  Till of this flat a mountain you have made

---

199. **For:** In place of.   200. **Shards:** Broken bits of pottery.   201. **crants:**
Garland.   202. **strewments:** Traditional strewing of flowers.   202–03. **bringing . . . burial:** Laying to rest of the body in consecrated ground, to the sound of
the bell.   209. **violets:** See IV, v, 181 and note.   217. **ingenious sense:** Mind
endowed with finest qualities.

T 'o'ertop old Pelion,° or the skyish head
Of blue Olympus.°
HAMLET [*coming forward*]: What is he whose grief
  Bears such an emphasis, whose phrase of sorrow   225
  Conjures the wand'ring stars,° and makes them stand
  Like wonder-wounded hearers? This is I,
  Hamlet the Dane.°
LAERTES: The devil take thy soul!

                                        [*Grappling with him.*]

HAMLET: Thou pray'st not well.
  I prithee, take thy fingers from my throat;   230
  For, though I am not splenitive° and rash,
  Yet have I in me something dangerous,
  Which let thy wisdom fear. Hold off thy hand.
KING: Pluck them asunder.
QUEEN: Hamlet, Hamlet!
ALL: Gentlemen!
HORATIO: Good my lord, be quiet.   235

                      [*Hamlet and Laertes are parted.*]

HAMLET: Why, I will fight with him upon this theme
  Until my eyelids will no longer wag.
QUEEN: O my son, what theme?
HAMLET: I lov'd Ophelia. Forty thousand brothers
  Could not with all their quantity of love   240
  Make up my sum. What wilt thou do for her?
KING: O, he is mad, Laertes.
QUEEN: For love of God, forbear him.
HAMLET: 'Swounds,° show me what thou' do.
  Woo 't° weep? Woo 't fight? Woo 't fast? Woo 't tear thyself?   245
  Woo 't drink up eisel?° Eat a crocodile?
  I'll do 't. Dost thou come here to whine?
  To outface me with leaping in her grave?
  Be buried quick° with her, and so will I.
  And, if thou prate of mountains, let them throw   250
  Millions of acres on us, till our ground,

222, 223. Pelion, Olympus: Mountains in the north of Thessaly; see also *Ossa* at line 253.   **226. wand'ring stars:** Planets.   **228. the Dane:** This title normally signifies the king; see I, I, 15 and note.   **231. splenitive:** Quick-tempered. **244. 'Swounds:** By His (Christ's) wounds.   **245. Woo 't:** Wilt thou.   **246. eisel:** Vinegar.   **249. quick:** Alive.

Singeing his pate° against the burning zone,°
Make Ossa° like a wart! Nay, an thou 'lt mouth,°
I'll rant as well as thou.
QUEEN: This is mere° madness,
And thus a while the fit will work on him;   255
Anon, as patient as the female dove
When that her golden couplets° are disclos'd,°
His silence will sit drooping.
HAMLET: Hear you, sir.
What is the reason that you use me thus?
I lov'd you ever. But it is no matter.   ·   260
Let Hercules himself do what he may,
The cat will mew, and dog will have his day.°
KING: I pray thee, good Horatio, wait upon him.

                                   (*Exit Hamlet and Horatio.*)

[*To Laertes.*] Strengthen your patience in° our last night's speech;
We'll put the matter to the present push.°—   265
Good Gertrude, set some watch over your son.—
This grave shall have a living° monument.
An hour of quiet shortly shall we see;
Till then, in patience our proceeding be.   (*Exeunt.*)

                        {*Scene II*}°

(*Enter Hamlet and Horatio.*)

HAMLET: So much for this, sir; now shall you see the other.°
    You do remember all the circumstance?
HORATIO: Remember it, my lord!
HAMLET: Sir, in my heart there was a kind of fighting
    That would not let me sleep. Methought I lay   5

---

252. his pate: Its head, i.e., top.   burning zone: Sun's orbit.   253. Ossa: Another
mountain in Thessaly. (In their war against the Olympian gods, the giants
attempted to heap Ossa, Pelion, and Olympus on one another to scale heaven.)
mouth: Rant.   254. mere: Utter.   257. golden couplets: Two baby pigeons, covered with yellow down.   disclos'd: Hatched.   261–62. Let . . . day: Despite any
blustering attempts at interference every person will sooner or later do what he
must do.   264. in: By recalling.   265. present push: Immediate test.   267. living: Lasting; also refers (for Laertes' benefit) to the plot against Hamlet.   V, II.
Location: The castle.   1. see the other: Hear the other news.

Worse than the mutines° in the bilboes.° Rashly,°
And prais'd be rashness for it—let us know,°
Our indiscretion sometime serves us well
When our deep plots do pall,° and that should learn° us
There's a divinity that shapes our ends,   10
Rough-hew° them how we will—
HORATIO: That is most certain.
HAMLET: Up from my cabin,
  My sea-gown scarf'd about me, in the dark
  Grop'd I to find out them, had my desire,
  Finger'd° their packet, and in fine° withdrew   15
  To mine own room again, making so bold,
  My fears forgetting manners, to unseal
  Their grand commission; where I found, Horatio—
  Ah, royal knavery!—an exact command,
  Larded° with many several sorts of reasons   20
  Importing° Denmark's health and England's too,
  With, ho, such bugs° and goblins in my life,°
  That, on the supervise,° no leisure bated,°
  No, not to stay the grinding of the axe,
  My head should be struck off.
HORATIO: Is 't possible?   25
HAMLET: Here's the commission; read it at more leisure.

                                         [*Gives document.*]

  But wilt thou hear now how I did proceed?
HORATIO: I beseech you.
HAMLET: Being thus benetted round with villainies,
  Or I could make a prologue to my brains,   30
  They had begun the play.° I sat me down,
  Devis'd a new commission, wrote it fair.°
  I once did hold it, as our statists° do,
  A baseness° to write fair, and labor'd much

6. mutines: Mutineers. bilboes: Shackles. Rashly: On impulse (this adverb goes with lines 12ff.). 7. know: Acknowledge. 9. pall: Fail. learn: Teach. 11. Rough-hew: Shape roughly. 15. Finger'd: Pilfered, pinched. in fine: Finally, in conclusion. 20. Larded: Enriched. 21. Importing: Relating to. 22. bugs: Bugbears, hobgoblins. in my life: To be feared if I were allowed to live. 23. supervise: Reading. leisure bated: Delay allowed. 30–31. Or . . . play: Before I could consciously turn my brain to the matter, it had started working on a plan. (*Or* means *ere*.) 32. fair: In a clear hand. 33. statists: Statesmen. 34. baseness: Lower-class trait.

How to forget that learning, but, sir, now   35
It did me yeoman's° service. Wilt thou know
Th' effect° of what I wrote?
HORATIO: Ay, good my lord.
HAMLET: An earnest conjuration from the King,
   As England was his faithful tributary,
   As love between them like the palm might flourish,   40
   As peace should still her wheaten garland° wear
   And stand a comma° 'tween their amities,
   And many such-like as's° of great charge,°
   That, on the view and knowing of these contents,
   Without debasement further, more or less,   45
   He should those bearers put to sudden death,
   Not shriving time° allow'd.
HORATIO: How was this seal'd?
HAMLET: Why, even in that was heaven ordinant.°
   I had my father's signet° in my purse,
   Which was the model of that Danish seal;   50
   Folded the writ up in the form of th' other,
   Subscrib'd° it, gave 't th' impression,° plac'd it safely,
   The changeling° never known. Now, the next day
   Was our sea-fight, and what to this was sequent
   Thou knowest already.   55
HORATIO: So Guildenstern and Rosencrantz go to 't.
HAMLET: [Why, man, they did make love to this employment.]
   They are not near my conscience. Their defeat
   Does by their own insinuation° grow.
   'Tis dangerous when the baser nature comes   60
   Between the pass° and fell° incensed points
   Of mighty opposites.
HORATIO: Why, what a king is this!
HAMLET: Does it not, think thee, stand° me now upon—
   He that hath killed my king and whor'd my mother,

36. **yeoman's:** Substantial, workmanlike. **37. effect:** Purport. **41. wheaten garland:** Symbolic of fruitful agriculture, of peace. **42. comma:** Indicating continuity, link. **43. as's:** (1) The "whereases" of formal document, (2) asses. **charge:** (1) Import, (2) burden. **47. shriving time:** Time for confession and absolution. **48. ordinant:** Directing. **49. signet:** Small seal. **52. Subscrib'd:** Signed. **impression:** With a wax seal. **53. changeling:** The substituted letter (literally, a fairy child substituted for a human one). **59. insinuation:** Interference. **61. pass:** Thrust. **fell:** Fierce. **63. stand:** Become incumbent.

Popp'd in between th' election° and my hopes,   65
Thrown out his angle° for my proper° life,
And with such coz'nage° — is 't not perfect conscience
[To quit° him with this arm? And is 't not to be damn'd
To let this canker° of our nature come
In further evil?   70
HORATIO: It must be shortly known to him from England
What is the issue of the business there.
HAMLET: It will be short. The interim is mine,
And a man's life 's no more than to say "One."°
But I am very sorry, good Horatio,   75
That to Laertes I forgot myself,
For by the image of my cause I see
The portraiture of his. I'll court his favors.
But, sure, the bravery° of his grief did put me
Into a tow'ring passion.
HORATIO: Peace, who comes here?]   80

(*Enter a Courtier* [*Osric*].)

OSRIC: Your lordship is right welcome back to Denmark.
HAMLET: I humbly thank you, sir. [*To Horatio.*] Dost know this water-fly?
HORATIO: No, my good lord.
HAMLET: Thy state is the more gracious, for 'tis a vice to know him. He
hath much land, and fertile. Let a beast be lord of beasts, and his crib   85
shall stand at the King's mess.° 'Tis a chough,° but, as I say, spacious in
the possession of dirt.
OSRIC: Sweet lord, if your lordship were at leisure, I should impart a
thing to you from his Majesty.
HAMLET: I will receive it, sir, with all diligence of spirit. Put your bonnet 90
to his right use; 'tis for the head.
OSRIC: I thank your lordship, it is very hot.
HAMLET: No, believe me, 'tis very cold; the wind is northerly.
OSRIC: It is indifferent° cold, my lord, indeed.
HAMLET: But yet methinks it is very sultry and hot for my complexion.°   95

---

65. **election:** The Danish monarch was "elected" by a small number of high-
ranking electors. 66. **angle:** Fishing line. **proper:** Very. 67. **coz'nage:**
Trickery. 68. **quit:** Repay. 69. **canker:** Ulcer. 74. **a man's . . . "One":** To take
a man's life requires no more than to count to one as one duels. 79. **bravery:**
Bravado. 85–86. **Let . . . mess:** If a man, no matter how beastlike, is as rich
in possessions as Osric, he may eat at the king's table. 86. **chough:** Chattering
jackdaw. 94. **indifferent:** Somewhat. 95. **complexion:** Temperament.

OSRIC: Exceedingly, my lord; it is very sultry, as 'twere—I cannot tell how. My lord, his Majesty bade me signify to you that 'a has laid a great wager on your head. Sir, this is the matter—
HAMLET: I beseech you, remember—

[Hamlet moves him to put on his hat.]

OSRIC: Nay, good my lord; for my ease,° in good faith. Sir, here is newly   100
come to court Laertes—believe me, an absolute gentleman, full of most
excellent differences,° of very soft society° and great showing.° Indeed,
to speak feelingly° of him, he is the card° or calendar° of gentry,° for you
shall find in him the continent of what part° a gentleman would see.
HAMLET: Sir, his definement° suffers no perdition° in you, though, I   105
know, to divide him inventorially° would dozy° th' arithmetic of memory, and yet but yaw° neither° in respect of° his quick sail. But, in the
verity of extolment,° I take him to be a soul of great article,° and his
infusion° of such dearth and rareness,° as, to make true diction° of
him, his semblable° is his mirror, and who else would trace° him, his   110
umbrage,° nothing more.
OSRIC: Your lordship speaks most infallibly of him.
HAMLET: The concernancy,° sir? Why do we wrap the gentleman in our
more rawer breath?°
OSRIC: Sir?   115
HORATIO: Is 't not possible to understand in another tongue?° You will do
't,° sir, really.

100. for my ease: A conventional reply declining the invitation to put his hat back on.   **102. differences:** Special qualities.   **soft society:** Agreeable manners.   **great showing:** Distinguished appearance.   **103. feelingly:** With just perception.   **card:** Chart, map.   **calendar:** Guide.   **gentry:** Good breeding.   **104. the continent . . . part:** One who contains in him all the qualities (a *continent* is that which contains).   **105. definement:** Definition. (Hamlet proceeds to mock Osric by using his lofty diction back at him.)   **perdition:** Loss, diminution.   **106. divide him inventorially:** Enumerate his graces.   **dozy:** Dizzy.   **107. yaw:** To move unsteadily (said of a ship).   **neither:** For all that.   **in respect of:** In comparison with.   **107–08. in . . . extolment:** In true praise (of him).   **108. article:** Moment or importance.   **109. infusion:** Essence, character imparted by nature.   **dearth and rareness:** Rarity.   **make true diction:** Speak truly.   **110. semblable:** Only true likeness.   **who . . . trace:** Any other person who would wish to follow.   **111. umbrage:** Shadow.   **113. concernancy:** Import, relevance.   **114. breath:** Speech.   **116. to understand . . . tongue:** For Osric to understand when someone else speaks in his manner. (Horatio twits Osric for not being able to understand the kind of flowery speech he himself uses when Hamlet speaks in such a vein.)   **116–17. You will do 't:** You can if you try.

HAMLET: What imports the nomination° of this gentleman?

OSRIC: Of Laertes?

HORATIO [*to Hamlet*]: His purse is empty already; all 's golden words are   120
spent.

HAMLET: Of him, sir.

OSRIC: I know you are not ignorant—

HAMLET: I would you did, sir; yet, in faith, if you did, it would not much
approve° me. Well, sir?   125

OSRIC: You are not ignorant of what excellence Laertes is—

HAMLET: I dare not confess that, lest I should compare° with him in
excellence; but to know a man well were to know himself.°

OSRIC: I mean, sir, for his weapon; but in the imputation laid on him by
them,° in his meed° he's unfellow'd.°   130

HAMLET: What's his weapon?

OSRIC: Rapier and dagger.

HAMLET: That's two of his weapons—but well.

OSRIC: The King, sir, hath wager'd with him six Barbary horses, against
the which he has impawn'd,° as I take it, six French rapiers and   135
poniards, with their assigns,° as girdle, hangers,° and so. Three of the
carriages,° in faith, are very dear to fancy,° very responsive° to the
hilts, most delicate° carriages, and of very liberal conceit.°

HAMLET: What call you the carriages?

HORATIO [*to Hamlet*]: I knew you must be edified by the margent° ere you   140
had done.

OSRIC: The carriages, sir, are the hangers.

HAMLET: The phrase would be more germane to the matter if we could
carry a cannon by our sides; I would it might be hangers till then. But,
on: six Barb'ry horses against six French swords, their assigns, and   145
three liberal-conceited carriages; that's the French bet against the
Danish. Why is this impawn'd, as you call it?

118. **nomination:** Naming.   125. **approve:** Commend.   127. **compare:** Seem
to compete.   128. **but . . . himself:** For, to recognize excellence in another man,
one must know oneself.   129–30. **imputation . . . them:** Reputation given him
by others.   130. **meed:** Merit.   **unfellow'd:** Unmatched.   135. **impawn'd:**
Staked, wagered.   136. **assigns:** Appurtenances.   **hangers:** Straps on the sword
belt (*girdle*) from which the sword hung.   137. **carriages:** An affected way of saying *hangers;* literally, gun-carriages.   **dear to fancy:** Fancifully designed, taste-
ful.   **responsive:** Corresponding closely,   matching.   138. **delicate:** I.e., in
workmanship.   **liberal conceit:** Elaborate design.   140. **margent:** Margin of a
book, place for explanatory notes.

OSRIC: The King, sir, hath laid,° sir, that in a dozen passes° between yourself and him, he shall not exceed you three hits. He hath laid on twelve for nine, and it would come to immediate trial, if your lordship 150 would vouchsafe the answer.

HAMLET: How if I answer no?

OSRIC: I mean, my lord, the opposition of your person in trial.

HAMLET: Sir, I will walk here in the hall. If it please his Majesty, it is the breathing time° of day with me. Let the foils be brought, the gentle- 155 man willing, and the King hold his purpose, I will win for him an I can; if not, I will gain nothing but my shame and the odd hits.

OSRIC: Shall I deliver you so?

HAMLET: To this effect, sir—after what flourish your nature will.

OSRIC: I commend my duty to your lordship. 160

HAMLET: Yours, yours. [*Exit Osric.*] He does well to commend it himself; there are no tongues else for 's turn.

HORATIO: This lapwing° runs away with the shell on his head.

HAMLET: 'A did comply, sir, with his dug,° before 'a suck'd it. Thus has he—and many more of the same breed that I know the drossy° age 165 dotes on—only got the tune° of the time and, out of an habit of encounter,° a kind of yesty° collection,° which carries them through and through the most fann'd and winnow'd° opinions; and do but blow them to their trial, the bubbles are out.°

(*Enter a Lord.*)

LORD: My lord, his Majesty commended him to you by young Osric, who 170 brings back to him that you attend him in the hall. He sends to know if your pleasure hold to play with Laertes, or that you will take longer time.

HAMLET: I am constant to my purposes; they follow the King's pleasure. If his fitness speaks,° mine is ready; now or whensoever, provided I be 175 so able as now.

---

148. laid: Wagered. passes: Bouts. (The odds of the betting are hard to explain. Possibly the king bets that Hamlet will win at least five out of twelve, at which point Laertes raises the odds against himself by betting he will win nine.) 155. breathing time: Exercise period. 163. lapwing: A bird that draws intruders away from its nest and was thought to run about when newly hatched with its head in the shell; a seeming reference to Osric's hat. 164. comply . . . dug: Observe ceremonious formality toward his mother's teat. 165. drossy: Frivolous. 166. tune: Temper, mood, manner of speech. 166–67. habit of encounter: Demeanor of social intercourse. 167. yesty: Yeasty, frothy. collection: I.e., of current phrases. 168. fann'd and winnow'd: Select and refined. 169. blow . . . out: Put them to the test, and their ignorance is exposed. 175. If . . . speaks: If his readiness answers to the time.

LORD: The King and Queen and all are coming down.
HAMLET: In happy time.°
LORD: The Queen desires you to use some gentle entertainment° to
Laertes before you fall to play.   180
HAMLET: She well instructs me.   [*Exit Lord.*]
HORATIO: You will lose, my lord.
HAMLET: I do not think so. Since he went into France, I have been in
continual practice; I shall win at the odds. But thou wouldst not think
how ill all's here about my heart; but it is no matter.   185
HORATIO: Nay, good my lord—
HAMLET: It is but foolery, but it is such a kind of gain-giving,° as would
perhaps trouble a woman.
HORATIO: If your mind dislike anything, obey it. I will forestall their
repair hither, and say you are not fit.   190
HAMLET: Not a whit, we defy augury. There is special providence in the
fall of a sparrow. If it be now, 'tis not to come; if it be not to come, it
will be now, if it be not now, yet it will come. The readiness is all. Since
no man of aught he leaves knows what is 't to leave betimes,° let be.

(*A table prepar'd.* [*Enter*] *trumpets, drums, and Officers with cushions; King,
Queen,* [*Osric,*] *and all the State; foils, daggers,* [*and wine borne in;*] *and
Laertes.*)

KING: Come, Hamlet, come, and take this hand from me.   195

[*The King puts Laertes' hand into Hamlet's.*]

HAMLET: Give me your pardon, sir. I have done you wrong,
But pardon 't, as you are a gentleman.
This presence° knows,
And you must needs have heard, how I am punish'd
With a sore distraction. What I have done   200
That might your nature, honor, and exception°
Roughly awake, I here proclaim was madness.
Was 't Hamlet wrong'd Laertes? Never Hamlet.
If Hamlet from himself be ta'en away,
And when he's not himself does wrong Laertes,   205
Then Hamlet does it not, Hamlet denies it.
Who does it, then? His madness. If 't be so,
Hamlet is of the faction that is wrong'd;

---

178. **In happy time:** A phrase of courtesy indicating acceptance.   179. **entertainment:** Greeting.   187.   **gain-giving:** Misgiving.   194.   **what . . . betimes:**
What is the best time to leave it.   198. **presence:** Royal assembly.   201. **excep-
tion:** Disapproval.

His madness is poor Hamlet's enemy.
[Sir, in this audience,]   210
Let my disclaiming from a purpos'd evil
Free me so far in your most generous thoughts
That I have shot my arrow o'er the house
And hurt my brother.
LAERTES: 'I am satisfied in nature,°
Whose motive in this case should stir me most   215
To my revenge. But in my terms of honor
I stand aloof, and will no reconcilement
Till by some elder masters of known honor
I have a voice° and precedent of peace
To keep my name ungor'd. But till that time,   220
I do receive your offer'd love like love,
And will not wrong it.
HAMLET: I embrace it freely,
And will this brothers' wager frankly play.
Give us the foils. Come on.
LAERTES: Come, one for me.
HAMLET: I'll be your foil,° Laertes. In mine ignorance   225
Your skill shall, like a star i' th' darkest night,
Stick fiery off° indeed.
LAERTES: You mock me, sir.
HAMLET: No, by this hand.
KING: Give them the foils, young Osric. Cousin Hamlet,
You know the wager?
HAMLET: Very well, my lord.   230
Your Grace has laid the odds o' th' weaker side.
KING: I do not fear it; I have seen you both.
But since he is better'd,° we have therefore odds.
LAERTES: This is too heavy, let me see another.

                    [*Exchanges his foil for another.*]

HAMLET: This likes me well. These foils have all a length?   235

                    [*They prepare to play.*]

OSRIC: Ay, my good lord.
KING: Set me the stoups of wine upon that table.

214. in nature: As to my personal feelings.   **219. voice:** Authoritative pronouncement.   **225. foil:** Thin metal background which sets a jewel off (with pun on the blunted rapier for fencing).   **227. Stick fiery off:** Stand out brilliantly.   **233. is better'd:** Has improved; is the odds-on favorite.

If Hamlet give the first or second hit,
Or quit° in answer of the third exchange,
Let all the battlements their ordnance fire.   240
The King shall drink to Hamlet's better breath,
And in the cup an union° shall he throw,
Richer than that which four successive kings
In Denmark's crown have worn. Give me the cups,
And let the kettle° to the trumpet speak,   245
The trumpet to the cannoneer without,
The cannons to the heavens, the heaven to earth,
"Now the King drinks to Hamlet." Come, begin.

                                   (*Trumpets the while.*)

And you, the judges, bear a wary eye.
HAMLET: Come on sir.   250
LAERTES: Come, my lord.   [*They play. Hamlet scores a hit.*]
HAMLET: One.
LAERTES: No.
HAMLET: Judgment.
OSRIC: A hit, a very palpable hit.

                         (*Drum, trumpets, and shot. Flourish.*
                                      A piece goes off.)

LAERTES: Well, again.   255
KING: Stay, give me drink. Hamlet, this pearl is thine.

            [*He throws a pearl in Hamlet's cup and drinks.*]

    Here's to thy health. Give him the cup.
HAMLET: I'll play this bout first, set it by awhile.
    Come. [*They play.*] Another hit; what say you?
LAERTES: A touch, a touch. I do confess 't.   260
KING: Our son shall win.
QUEEN: He's fat,° and scant of breath.
    Here, Hamlet, take my napkin,° rub thy brows.
    The Queen carouses° to thy fortune, Hamlet.
HAMLET: Good madam!
KING: Gertrude, do not drink.   265
QUEEN: I will, my lord; I pray you pardon me.

---

239. **quit:** Repay (with a hit).   242. **union:** Pearl (so called, according to Pliny's *Natural History*, IX, because pearls are *unique*, never identical).   245. **kettle:** Kettledrum.   261. **fat:** Not physically fit, out of training.   262. **napkin:** Handkerchief.   263. **carouses:** Drinks a toast.

[Drinks.]

KING *[aside]*: It is the pois'ned cup. It is too late.
HAMLET: I dare not drink yet, madam; by and by.
QUEEN: Come, let me wipe thy face.
LAERTES *[to King]*: My lord, I'll hit him now.
KING: I do not think 't.   270
LAERTES *[aside]*: And yet it is almost against my conscience.
HAMLET: Come, for the third Laertes. You do but dally.
  I pray you, pass with your best violence;
  I am afeard you make a wanton of me.°
LAERTES: Say you so? Come on.   *[They play.]* 275
OSRIC: Nothing, neither way.
LAERTES: Have at you now!

                *[Laertes wounds Hamlet; then, in scuffling,
                they change rapiers,° and Hamlet wounds Laertes.]*

KING: Part them! They are incens'd.
HAMLET: Nay, come, again.   *[The Queen falls.]*
OSRIC: Look to the Queen there, ho!
HORATIO: They bleed on both sides. How is it, my lord?
OSRIC: How is 't, Laertes?   280
LAERTES: Why, as a woodcock° to mine own springe,° Osric;
  I am justly kill'd with mine own treachery.
HAMLET: How does the Queen?
KING: She swoons to see them bleed.
QUEEN: No, no, the drink, the drink—O my dear Hamlet—
  The drink, the drink! I am pois'ned.   *[Dies.]* 285
HAMLET: O villainy! Ho, let the door be lock'd!
  Treachery! Seek it out.   *[Laertes falls.]*
LAERTES: It is here, Hamlet. Hamlet, thou art slain.
  No med'cine in the world can do thee good;
  In thee there is not half an hour's life.   290
  The treacherous instrument is in thy hand,
  Unbated° and envenom'd. The foul practice
  Hath turn'd itself on me. Lo, here I lie,

---

274. make . . . me: Treat me like a spoiled child, holding back to give me an advantage. **[S.D.]** *in scuffling, they change rapiers:* This stage direction occurs in the Folio. According to a widespread stage tradition, Hamlet receives a scratch, realizes that Laertes' sword is unbated, and accordingly forces an exchange. **281. woodcock:** A bird, a type of stupidity or as a decoy. **springe:** Trap, snare. **292. Unbated:** Not blunted with a button.

Never to rise again. Thy mother's pois'ned.
I can no more. The King, the King's to blame.   295
HAMLET: The point envenom'd too? Then, venom, to thy work.

[*Stabs the King.*]

ALL: Treason! Treason!
KING: O, yet defend me, friends; I am but hurt.
HAMLET: Here, thou incestuous, murd'rous, damned Dane,

[*He forces the King to drink the poisoned cup.*]

Drink off this potion. Is thy union° here?   300
Follow my mother.   [*King dies.*]
LAERTES: He is justly serv'd.
It is a poison temper'd° by himself.
Exchange forgiveness with me, noble Hamlet.
Mine and my father's death come not upon thee,
Nor thine on me!   [*Dies.*] 305
HAMLET: Heaven make thee free of it! I follow thee.
I am dead, Horatio. Wretched Queen, adieu!
You that look pale and tremble at this chance,
That are but mutes° or audience to this act,
Had I but time—as this fell° sergeant,° Death,   310
Is strict in his arrest—O, I could tell you—
But let it be. Horatio, I am dead;
Thou livest. Report me and my cause aright
To the unsatisfied.
HORATIO: Never believe it.
I am more an antique Roman° than a Dane.   315
Here's yet some liquor left.

[*He attempts to drink from the poisoned cup.*
Hamlet prevents him.]

HAMLET: As th' art a man,
Give me the cup! Let go! By heaven, I'll ha 't.
O God, Horatio, what a wounded name,
Things standing thus unknown, shall I leave behind me!
If thou didst ever hold me in thy heart,   320
Absent thee from felicity awhile,

---

300. **union:** Pearl (see line 242; with grim puns on the word's other meanings: marriage, shared death[?]). **302. temper'd:** Mixed. **309. mutes:** Silent observers. **310. fell:** Cruel. **sergeant:** Sheriff's officer. **315. Roman:** It was the Roman custom to follow masters in death.

And in this harsh world draw thy breath in pain
To tell my story.

                        (*A march afar off* [*and a volley within*].)

              What warlike noise is this?
OSRIC: Young Fortinbras, with conquest come from Poland,
  To the ambassadors of England gives   325
  This warlike volley.
HAMLET: O, I die, Horatio!
  The potent poison quite o'ercrows° my spirit.
  I cannot live to hear the news from England,
  But I do prophesy th' election lights
  On Fortinbras. He has my dying voice.°   330
  So tell him, with th' occurrents° more and less
  Which have solicited° — the rest is silence.   [*Dies.*]
HORATIO: Now cracks a noble heart. Good night, sweet prince;
  And flights of angels sing thee to thy rest!

                            [*March within.*]

  Why does the drum come hither?   335

(*Enter Fortinbras, with the* [*English*] *Ambassadors* [*with drum, colors, and attendants*].)

FORTINBRAS: Where is this sight?
HORATIO: What is it you would see?
  If aught of woe or wonder, cease your search.
FORTINBRAS: This quarry° cries on havoc.° O proud Death.
  What feast is toward° in thine eternal cell,
  That thou so many princes at a shot   340
  So bloodily hast struck?
FIRST AMBASSADOR: The sight is dismal;
  And our affairs from England come too late.
  The ears are senseless that should give us hearing,
  To tell him his commandment is fulfill'd,
  That Rosencrantz and Guildenstern are dead.   345
  Where should we have our thanks?
HORATIO: Not from his° mouth,
  Had it th' ability of life to thank you.

---

327. o'ercrows: Triumphs over. **330. voice:** Vote. **331. occurrents:** Events,
incidents. **332. solicited:** Moved, urged. **338. quarry:** Heap of dead. **cries on
havoc:** Proclaims a general slaughter. **339. toward:** In preparation. **346. his:**
Claudius's.

He never gave commandment for their death.
But since, so jump° upon this bloody question,°
You from the Polack wars, and you from England,   350
Are here arriv'd, give order that these bodies
High on a stage° be placed to the view,
And let me speak to th' yet unknowing world
How these things came about. So shall you hear
Of carnal, bloody, and unnatural acts,   355
Of accidental judgments,° casual° slaughters,
Of deaths put on° by cunning and forc'd cause,
And, in this upshot, purposes mistook
Fall'n on th' inventors' heads. All this can I
Truly deliver.
FORTINBRAS: Let us haste to hear it,   360
And call the noblest to the audience.
For me, with sorrow I embrace my fortune.
I have some rights of memory° in this kingdom,
Which now to claim my vantage° doth invite me.
HORATIO: Of that I shall have also cause to speak,   365
And from his mouth whose voice will draw on more.°
But let this same be presently° perform'd,
Even while men's minds are wild, lest more mischance
On° plots and errors happen.
FORTINBRAS: Let four captains
Bear Hamlet, like a soldier, to the stage,   370
For he was likely, had he been put on,°
To have prov'd most royal; and, for his passage,°
The soldiers' music and the rite of war
Speak loudly for him.
Take up the bodies. Such a sight as this   375
Becomes the field,° but here shows much amiss.
Go, bid the soldiers shoot.

(*Exeunt* [*marching, bearing off the dead bodies;
a peal of ordnance is shot off*].)

[c. 1600]

349. jump: Precisely.   question: Dispute.   352. stage: Platform.   356. judgments: Retributions.   casual: Occurring by chance.   357. put on: Instigated.
363. of memory: Traditional, remembered.   364. vantage: Presence at this
opportune moment.   366. voice . . . more: Vote will influence still others.
367. presently: Immediately.   369. On: On the basis of.   371. put on: Invested in
royal office and so put to the test.   372. passage: Death.   376. field: I.e., of battle.

WILLIAM SHAKESPEARE [1564–1616]

Sonnet 116

William Shakespeare (1564–1616) was born in Stratford-upon-Avon, England, where his father was a glovemaker and bailiff, and he presumably went to grammar school there. He married Anne Hathaway in 1582 and sometime before 1592 left for London to work as a playwright and actor. Shakespeare joined the Lord Chamberlain's Men (later the King's Men), an acting company for which he wrote thirty-seven plays—comedies, tragedies, histories, and romances—upon which his reputation as the finest dramatist in the English language is based. He was also arguably the finest lyric poet of his day, as exemplified by songs scattered throughout his plays, two early nondramatic poems (*Venus and Adonis* and *The Rape of Lucrece*), and the sonnet sequence expected of all noteworthy writers in the Elizabethan age. Shakespeare's sonnets were probably written in the 1590s, although they were not published until 1609. Shakespeare retired to Stratford around 1612, and by the time he died at the age of fifty-two, he was acknowledged as a leading light of the Elizabethan stage and had become successful enough to have purchased a coat of arms for his family home.

Let me not to the marriage of true minds
Admit impediments. Love is not love
Which alters when it alteration finds,
Or bends with the remover to remove.
O, no, it is an ever-fixèd mark   5
That looks on tempests and is never shaken;
It is the star to every wandering bark,°   *ship*
Whose worth's unknown, although his height be taken.°   *is measured*
Love's not time's fool, though rosy lips and cheeks
Within his bending sickle's compass come;   10
Love alters not with his brief hours and weeks,
But bears it out even to the edge of doom.°   *Judgment Day*
   If this be error and upon me proved,
   I never writ, nor no man ever loved.

[1609]

WILLIAM SHAKESPEARE [1564–1616]

Sonnet 130

William Shakespeare (1564–1616) was born in Stratford-upon-Avon, England, where his father was a glovemaker and bailiff, and he presumably went to grammar school there. He married Anne Hathaway in 1582 and sometime before 1592 left for London to work as a playwright and actor. Shakespeare joined the Lord Chamberlain's Men (later the King's Men), an acting company for which he wrote thirty-seven plays—comedies, tragedies, histories, and romances—upon which his reputation as the finest dramatist in the English language is based. He was also arguably the finest lyric poet of his day, as exemplified by songs scattered throughout his plays, two early nondramatic poems (*Venus and Adonis* and *The Rape of Lucrece*), and the sonnet sequence expected of all noteworthy writers in the Elizabethan age. Shakespeare's sonnets were probably written in the 1590s, although they were not published until 1609. Shakespeare retired to Stratford around 1612, and by the time he died at the age of fifty-two, he was acknowledged as a leading light of the Elizabethan stage and had become successful enough to have purchased a coat of arms for his family home.

My mistress' eyes are nothing like the sun;
Coral is far more red than her lips' red;
If snow be white, why then her breasts are dun;°   *dull grayish brown*
If hairs be wires, black wires grow on her head.
I have seen roses damasked,° red and white,   *variegated*   5
But no such roses see I in her cheeks;
And in some perfumes is there more delight
Than in the breath that from my mistress reeks.
I love to hear her speak, yet well I know
That music hath a far more pleasing sound.   10
I grant I never saw a goddess go;°   *walk*
My mistress, when she walks, treads on the ground.
    And yet, by heaven, I think my love as rare
    As any she° belied° with false compare.   *woman/misrepresented*

[1609]

WILLIAM SHAKESPEARE [1564–1616]

Sonnet 18

William Shakespeare (1564–1616) was born in Stratford-upon-Avon, England, where his father was a glovemaker and bailiff, and he presumably went to grammar school there. He married Anne Hathaway in 1582 and sometime before 1592 left for London to work as a playwright and actor. Shakespeare joined the Lord Chamberlain's Men (later the King's Men), an acting company for which he wrote thirty-seven plays—comedies, tragedies, histories, and romances—upon which his reputation as the finest dramatist in the English language is based. He was also arguably the finest lyric poet of his day, as exemplified by songs scattered throughout his plays, two early nondramatic poems (*Venus and Adonis* and *The Rape of Lucrece*), and the sonnet sequence expected of all noteworthy writers in the Elizabethan age. Shakespeare's sonnets were probably written in the 1590s, although they were not published until 1609. Shakespeare retired to Stratford around 1612, and by the time he died at the age of fifty-two, he was acknowledged as a leading light of the Elizabethan stage and had become successful enough to have purchased a coat of arms for his family home.

Shall I compare thee to a summer's day?
Thou art more lovely and more temperate:
Rough winds do shake the darling buds of May,
And summer's lease° hath all too short a date;°   *allotted time/duration*
Sometime too hot the eye of heaven shines,
And often is his gold complexion dimmed;   5
And every fair° from fair° sometimes declines,   *beautiful thing/beauty*
By chance or nature's changing course untrimmed;°   *stripped of its beauty*
But thy eternal summer shall not fade,
Nor lose possession of that fair thou ow'st;°   *beauty you own*
Nor shall death brag thou wand'rest in his shade,   10
When in eternal lines° to time thou grow'st:°
   So long as men can breathe, or eyes can see,
   So long lives this,° and this gives life to thee.   *this sonnet*

[1609]

12. **lines:** (Of poetry); **grow'st:** You are grafted to time.

217

WILLIAM SHAKESPEARE [1564–1616]

Sonnet 73

William Shakespeare (1564–1616) was born in Stratford-upon-Avon, England, where his father was a glovemaker and bailiff, and he presumably went to grammar school there. He married Anne Hathaway in 1582 and sometime before 1592 left for London to work as a playwright and actor. Shakespeare joined the Lord Chamberlain's Men (later the King's Men), an acting company for which he wrote thirty-seven plays—comedies, tragedies, histories, and romances—upon which his reputation as the finest dramatist in the English language is based. He was also arguably the finest lyric poet of his day, as exemplified by songs scattered throughout his plays, two early nondramatic poems (*Venus and Adonis* and *The Rape of Lucrece*), and the sonnet sequence expected of all noteworthy writers in the Elizabethan age. Shakespeare's sonnets were probably written in the 1590s, although they were not published until 1609. Shakespeare retired to Stratford around 1612, and by the time he died at the age of fifty-two, he was acknowledged as a leading light of the Elizabethan stage and had become successful enough to have purchased a coat of arms for his family home.

That time of year thou mayst in me behold
When yellow leaves, or none, or few, do hang
Upon those boughs which shake against the cold,
Bare ruined choirs,° where late° the sweet birds sang.   *choirstalls/lately*
In me thou seest the twilight of such day   5
As after sunset fadeth in the west,
Which by and by black night doth take away,
Death's second self, that seals up all in rest.
In me thou seest the glowing of such fire
That on the ashes of his youth doth lie,   10
As the deathbed whereon it must expire,
Consumed with that which it was nourished by.
　　This thou perceiv'st, which makes thy love more strong,
　　To love that well which thou must leave ere long.

[1609]

PERCY BYSSHE SHELLEY [1792–1822]

Ode to the West Wind

Born into a wealthy aristocratic family in Sussex County, England, **Percy Bysshe Shelley** (1792–1822) was educated at Eton and then went on to Oxford University, where he was expelled after six months for writing a defense of atheism, the first price he would pay for his non-conformity and radical (for his time) commitment to social justice. The following year he eloped with Harriet Westbrook, daughter of a tavern keeper, despite his belief that marriage was a tyrannical and de-grading social institution (she was sixteen, he eighteen). He became a disciple of the radical social philosopher William Godwin, fell in love with Godwin's daughter, Mary Wollstonecraft Godwin (the author, later, of *Frankenstein*), and went to live with her in France. Two years later, after Harriet had committed suicide, the two married and moved to Italy, where they shifted about restlessly and Shelley was generally short on money and in poor health. In such trying circumstances he wrote his greatest works. He died at age thirty, when the boat he was in was overturned by a sudden storm.

1

O wild West Wind, thou breath° of Autumn's being,
Thou, from whose unseen presence the leaves dead
Are driven, like ghosts from an enchanter fleeing,

Yellow, and black, and pale, and hectic red,
Pestilence-stricken multitudes: O thou,   5
Who chariotest to their dark wintry bed

The wingèd seeds, where they lie cold and low,
Each like a corpse within its grave, until
Thine azure sister of the Spring shall blow

Her clarion o'er the dreaming earth, and fill   10
(Driving sweet buds like flocks to feed in air)
With living hues and odors plain and hill:

---

1. breath: In many ancient languages, the words for *breath, wind, soul,* and *inspiration* are the same or closely related: in Latin, *spiritus.* Shelley uses this to interconnect nature and artistic inspiration (poetry) in his poem.

Wild Spirit, which art moving everywhere;
Destroyer and preserver; hear, oh, hear!

2

Thou on whose stream, mid the steep sky's commotion,   15
Loose clouds like earth's decaying leaves are shed,
Shook from the tangled boughs of Heaven and Ocean,

Angels of rain and lightning: there are spread
On the blue surface of thine airy surge,
Like the bright hair uplifted from the head   20

Of some fierce Maenad,° even from the dim verge
Of the horizon to the zenith's height,
The locks of the approaching storm. Thou dirge

Of the dying year, to which this closing night
Will be the dome of a vast sepulcher,   25
Vaulted with all thy congregated might

Of vapors, from whose solid atmosphere
Black rain, and fire, and hail will burst: oh, hear!

3

Thou who didst waken from his summer dreams
The blue Mediterranean, where he lay,   30
Lulled by the coil of his crystàlline streams,

Beside a pumice isle in Baiae's bay,°
And saw in sleep old palaces° and towers
Quivering within the wave's intenser day,

All overgrown with azure moss and flowers   35
So sweet, the sense faints picturing them! Thou
For whose path the Atlantic's level powers

Cleave themselves into chasms, while far below
The sea-blooms and the oozy woods which wear
The sapless foliage of the ocean, know   40

Thy voice, and suddenly grow gray with fear,
And tremble and despoil themselves: oh, hear!

---

21. **Maenad:** A female votary of Dionysus, Greek god of wine and vegetation, who took part in the wild, orgiastic rites that characterize his worship.
32. **pumice:** Porous volcanic stone; **Baiae's bay:** West of Naples, Italy.
33. **old palaces:** Villas built by the Roman emperors.

4

If I were a dead leaf thou mightest bear;
If I were a swift cloud to fly with thee;
A wave to pant beneath thy power, and share   45

The impulse of thy strength, only less free
Than thou, O uncontrollable! If even
I were as in my boyhood, and could be

The comrade of thy wanderings over Heaven,
As then, when to outstrip thy skyey speed   50
Scarce seemed a vision; I would ne'er have striven

As thus with thee in prayer in my sore need.
Oh, lift me as a wave, a leaf, a cloud!
I fall upon the thorns of life! I bleed!

A heavy weight of hours has chained and bowed   55
One too like thee: tameless, and swift, and proud.

5

Make me thy lyre,° even as the forest is:
What if my leaves are falling like its own!
The tumult of thy mighty harmonies

Will take from both a deep, autumnal tone,   60
Sweet though in sadness. Be thou, Spirit fierce,
My spirit! Be thou me, impetuous one!

Drive my dead thoughts over the universe
Like withered leaves to quicken a new birth!
And, by the incantation of this verse,   65

Scatter, as from an unextinguished hearth
Ashes and sparks, my words among mankind!
Be through my lips to unawakened earth

The trumpet of a prophecy! O Wind,
If Winter comes, can Spring be far behind?   70

[1820]

---

57. lyre: An Aeolian harp, whose strings produce a sequence of rising and falling harmonies as air blows over them.

221

PERCY BYSSHE SHELLEY [1792–1822]

Ozymandias°

Born into a wealthy aristocratic family in Sussex County, England, **Percy Bysshe Shelley** (1792–1822) was educated at Eton and then went on to Oxford University, where he was expelled after six months for writing a defense of atheism, the first price he would pay for his nonconformity and radical (for his time) commitment to social justice. The following year he eloped with Harriet Westbrook, daughter of a tavern keeper, despite his belief that marriage was a tyrannical and degrading social institution (she was sixteen, he eighteen). He became a disciple of the radical social philosopher William Godwin, fell in love with Godwin's daughter, Mary Wollstonecraft Godwin (the author, later, of *Frankenstein*), and went to live with her in France. Two years later, after Harriet had committed suicide, the two married and moved to Italy, where they shifted about restlessly and Shelley was generally short on money and in poor health. In such trying circumstances he wrote his greatest works. He died at age thirty, when the boat he was in was overturned by a sudden storm.

I met a traveler from an antique land
Who said: Two vast and trunkless legs of stone
Stand in the desert. Near them, on the sand,
Half sunk, a shattered visage lies, whose frown,
And wrinkled lip, and sneer of cold command,   5
Tell that its sculptor well those passions read
Which yet survive, stamped on these lifeless things,
The hand that mocked them, and the heart that fed:
And on the pedestal these words appear:
"My name is Ozymandias, king of kings: 10
Look on my works, ye Mighty, and despair!"
Nothing beside remains. Round the decay
Of that colossal wreck, boundless and bare
The lone and level sands stretch far away.

[1818]

Ozymandias: The Greek name for Ramses II of Egypt (thirteenth century B.C.E.), who erected the largest statue in Egypt as a memorial to himself.

SOPHOCLES   [c. 496–c. 406 B.C.]

Antigone

TRANSLATED BY DUDLEY FITTS AND ROBERT FITZGERALD

An accomplished tragic dramatist and an icon of Athenian theater, **Sophocles** was born to a wealthy family and educated in the arts. Venerated by his countrymen as a man of wisdom and valor, over the course of his life he served as a priest, a treasurer for Athens, and an elected Athenian general. As a dramatist, Sophocles was exceptional, composing outstanding plays for the Dionysia, drama festivals honoring Dionysus, the Greek god of wine. During the Dionysia, revelries spanning several days spotlighted a series of theatrical performances written by Athens's most acclaimed dramatists. On a given day, in an outdoor amphitheater, a playwright would present a series of four plays — three tragedies and a comedy—before a panel of judges and thousands of audience members. In 468 B.C., in his first competition, Sophocles took first place. Sources indicate that Sophocles wrote more than 120 plays in his dramatic career; always produced in fours, his stagings proved victorious in at least eighteen Dionysia and never placed lower than second. Unfortunately, only seven complete plays have survived: *Ajax, Antigone, Oedipus Rex, Electra, Trachiniae, Philoctetes,* and *Oedipus at Colonus.* Several innovations in classical Greek theater have been attributed to Sophocles' influence, including the utilization of three masked actors rather than the traditional two, and painted scenery.

   Antigone, which would eventually accompany the tragedies *Oedipus Rex* and *Oedipus at Colonus* at the Dionysia, was likely first performed in 441 B.C. As with other Greek dramas, *Antigone* flows from one scene to the next and is not divided into acts; as events occur, audiences are expected to presuppose the passage of time and follow the plot contextually. The play opens in Thebes with Antigone believing her family to be tainted by the sins of Oedipus, her father. She is eventually condemned to

death by Kreon, Antigone's uncle and the Theban king, for going against
his command and mourning the death of her brother Polyneices, whom
Kreon deemed a traitor. Kreon repeatedly thwarts the efforts of Antigone
to bury her brother. Kreon's son, Haimon, along with the chorus and a
seer, convince him to swallow his pride and honor the gods and the traditional ways by authorizing the burial and mourning of Polyneices.
Kreon's hubris clouds his judgment and his procrastination results in a
grim turn of events. It takes an unbearable loss and insurmountable grief
to teach Kreon that "proud men in old age learn to be wise."

Characters

ANTIGONE,
ISMENE, } *daughters of Oedipus*
EURYDICE, *wife of Kreon*
KREON, *King of Thebes*
HAIMON, *son of Kreon*
TEIRESIAS, *a blind seer*
A SENTRY
A MESSENGER
CHORUS

Scene: *Before the palace of Kreon, King of Thebes. A central double door, and two
lateral doors. A platform extends the length of the facade, and from this platform
three steps lead down into the orchestra, or chorus-ground.*

Time: *Dawn of the day after the repulse of the Argive army from the assault on Thebes.*

PROLOGUE°

(*Antigone and Ismene enter from the central door of the palace.*)

ANTIGONE: Ismene, dear sister,
 You would think that we had already suffered enough
 For the curse on Oedipus.°

Prologue: Portion of the play explaining the background and current action.
3. curse on Oedipus: Oedipus, king of Thebes and the father of Antigone and
Ismene, was abandoned by his parents as an infant after the oracle foretold that
he would one day kill his father and marry his mother. Rescued by a shepherd
and raised by the king of Corinth, Oedipus returned years later to Thebes and
unknowingly lived out the oracle's prophecy by killing Laios and marrying
Iokaste. After his two sons, Eteocles and Polyneices, killed each other in combat,
the throne went to Kreon, Iokaste's brother.

I cannot imagine any grief
That you and I have not gone through. And now—   5
Have they told you of the new decree of our King Kreon?
ISMENE: I have heard nothing: I know
    That two sisters lost two brothers, a double death
    In a single hour; and I know that the Argive army
    Fled in the night; but beyond this, nothing.   10
ANTIGONE: I thought so. And that is why I wanted you
To come out here with me. There is something we must do.
ISMENE: Why do you speak so strangely?
ANTIGONE: Listen, Ismene: ·
    Kreon buried our brother Eteocles   15
    With military honors, gave him a soldier's funeral,
    And it was right that he should; but Polyneices,
    Who fought as bravely and died as miserably,—
    They say that Kreon has sworn
    No one shall bury him, no one mourn for him,   20
    But his body must lie in the fields, a sweet treasure
    For carrion birds to find as they search for food.
    That is what they say, and our good Kreon is coming here
    To announce it publicly; and the penalty—
    Stoning to death in the public square!
                                        There it is,   25
    And now you can prove what you are:
    A true sister, or a traitor to your family.
ISMENE: Antigone, you are mad! What could I possibly do?
ANTIGONE: You must decide whether you will help me or not.
ISMENE: I do not understand you. Help you in what?   30
ANTIGONE: Ismene, I am going to bury him. Will you come?
ISMENE: Bury him! You have just said the new law forbids it.
ANTIGONE: He is my brother. And he is your brother, too.
ISMENE: But think of the danger! Think what Kreon will do!
ANTIGONE: Kreon is not strong enough to stand in my way.   35
ISMENE: Ah sister!
    Oedipus died, everyone hating him
    For what his own search brought to light, his eyes
    Ripped out by his own hand; and Iocaste died,
    His mother and wife at once: she twisted the cords   40
    That strangled her life; and our two brothers died,
    Each killed by the other's sword. And we are left:
    But oh, Antigone,
    Think how much more terrible than these
    Our own death would be if we should go against Kreon   45

And do what he has forbidden! We are only women,
We cannot fight with men, Antigone!
The law is strong, we must give in to the law
In this thing, and in worse. I beg the Dead
To forgive me, but I am helpless: I must yield   50
To those in authority. And I think it is dangerous business
To be always meddling.

ANTIGONE: If that is what you think,
I should not want you, even if you asked to come.
You have made your choice, you can be what you want to be.
But I will bury him; and if I must die,   55
I say that this crime is holy: I shall lie down
With him in death, and I shall be as dear
To him as he to me.
                        It is the dead,
Not the living, who make the longest demands:
We die for ever...
                        You may do as you like,   60
Since apparently the laws of the gods mean nothing to you.

ISMENE: They mean a great deal to me; but I have no strength
To break laws that were made for the public good.

ANTIGONE: That must be your excuse, I suppose. But as for me,
I will bury the brother I love.

ISMENE: Antigone,   65
I am so afraid for you!

ANTIGONE: You need not be:
You have yourself to consider, after all.

ISMENE: But no one must hear of this, you must tell no one!
I will keep it a secret, I promise!

ANTIGONE: O tell it! Tell everyone!
Think how they'll hate you when it all comes out   70
If they learn that you knew about it all the time!

ISMENE: So fiery! You should be cold with fear.

ANTIGONE: Perhaps. But I am doing only what I must.

ISMENE: But can you do it? I say that you cannot.

ANTIGONE: Very well: when my strength gives out,   75
I shall do no more.

ISMENE: Impossible things should not be tried at all.

ANTIGONE: Go away, Ismene:
I shall be hating you soon, and the dead will too,
For your words are hateful. Leave me my foolish plan: 80
I am not afraid of the danger; if it means death,
It will not be the worst of deaths — death without honor.

SOPHOCLES / Antigone   Parodos

ISMENE: Go then, if you feel that you must.
   You are unwise,
   But a loyal friend indeed to those who love you.   85

(*Exit into the palace. Antigone goes off, left. Enter the Chorus.*)

PARODOS°   *Strophe° 1*

CHORUS: Now the long blade of the sun, lying
   Level east to west, touches with glory
   Thebes of the Seven Gates. Open, unlidded
   Eye of golden day! O marching light
   Across the eddy and rush of Dirce's stream,°   5
   Striking the white shields of the enemy
   Thrown headlong backward from the blaze of morning!
CHORAGOS:° Polyneices their commander
   Roused them with windy phrases,
   He the wild eagle screaming   10
   Insults above our land,
   His wings their shields of snow,
   His crest their marshalled helms.

Antistrophe° 1

CHORUS: Against our seven gates in a yawning ring
   The famished spears came onward in the night;   15
   But before his jaws were sated with our blood,
   Or pinefire took the garland of our towers,
   He was thrown back, and as he turned, great Thebes—
   No tender victim for his noisy power—
   Rose like a dragon behind him, shouting war.   20
CHORAGOS: For God hates utterly
   The bray of bragging tongues;
   And when he beheld their smiling,
   Their swagger of golden helms,
   The frown of his thunder blasted   25
   Their first man from our walls.

Parodos: The song or ode chanted by the Chorus on its entry.   **Strophe:** Song sung by the Chorus as it danced from stage right to stage left.   **5. Dirce's stream:** River near Thebes.   **8. Choragos:** Leader of the Chorus.   **Antistrophe:** Song sung by the Chorus following the Strophe, as it danced back from stage left to stage right.

Strophe 2

CHORUS: We heard his shout of triumph high in the air
   Turn to a scream; far out in a flaming arc
   He fell with his windy torch, and the earth struck him.
   And others storming in fury no less than his   30
   Found shock of death in the dusty joy of battle.
CHORAGOS: Seven captains at seven gates
   Yielded their clanging arms to the god
   That bends the battle-line and breaks it.
   These two only, brothers in blood,   35
   Face to face in matchless rage,
   Mirroring each the other's death
   Clashed in long combat.

Antistrophe 2

CHORUS: But now in the beautiful morning of victory
   Let Thebes of the many chariots sing for joy!   40
   With hearts for dancing we'll take leave of war:
   Our temples shall be sweet with hymns of praise,
   And the long nights shall echo with our chorus.

SCENE 1

CHORAGOS: But now at last our new King is coming:
   Kreon of Thebes, Menoikeus' son.
   In this auspicious dawn of his reign
   What are the new complexities
   That shifting Fate has woven for him?   5
   What is his counsel? Why has he summoned
   The old men to hear him?

(*Enter Kreon from the palace, center. He addresses the Chorus from the top
step.*)

KREON: Gentlemen: I have the honor to inform you that our Ship of State,
   which recent storms have threatened to destroy, has come safely to harbor at last, guided by the merciful wisdom of Heaven. I have summoned 10
   you here this morning because I know that I can depend upon you: your
   devotion to King Laios was absolute; you never hesitated in your duty to
   our late ruler Oedipus; and when Oedipus died, your loyalty was transferred to his children. Unfortunately, as you know, his two sons, the

princes Eteocles and Polyneices, have killed each other in battle; and I, as 15
the next in blood, have succeeded to the full power of the throne.

I am aware, of course, that no Ruler can expect complete loyalty
from his subjects until he has been tested in office. Nevertheless, I say
to you at the very outset that I have nothing but contempt for the kind
of Governor who is afraid, for whatever reason, to follow the course 20
that he knows is best for the State; and as for the man who sets private
friendship above the public welfare,—I have no use for him, either. I
call God to witness that if I saw my country headed for ruin, I should
not be afraid to speak out plainly; and I need hardly remind you that I
would never have any dealings with an enemy of the people. No one 25
values friendship more highly than I; but we must remember that
friends made at the risk of wrecking our Ship are not real friends at all.

These are my principles, at any rate, and that is why I have made the
following decision concerning the sons of Oedipus: Eteocles, who died
as a man should die, fighting for his country, is to be buried with full 30
military honors, with all the ceremony that is usual when the greatest
heroes die; but his brother Polyneices, who broke his exile to come
back with fire and sword against his native city and the shrines of his
fathers' gods, whose one idea was to spill the blood of his blood and
sell his own people into slavery—Polyneices, I say, is to have no bur- 35
ial: no man is to touch him or say the least prayer for him; he shall lie
on the plain, unburied; and the birds and the scavenging dogs can do
with him whatever they like.

This is my command, and you can see the wisdom behind it. As long
as I am King, no traitor is going to be honored with the loyal man. But 40
whoever shows by word and deed that he is on the side of the State,—
he shall have my respect while he is living and my reverence when he
is dead.

CHORAGOS: If that is your will, Kreon son of Menoikeus,
   You have the right to enforce it: we are yours.   45
KREON: That is my will. Take care that you do your part.
CHORAGOS: We are old men: let the younger ones carry it out.
KREON: I do not mean that: the sentries have been appointed.
CHORAGOS: Then what is it that you would have us do?
KREON: You will give no support to whoever breaks this law.   50
CHORAGOS: Only a crazy man is in love with death!
KREON: And death it is; yet money talks, and the wisest
   Have sometimes been known to count a few coins too many.

(*Enter Sentry from left.*)

SENTRY: I'll not say that I'm out of breath from running, King, because
   every time I stopped to think about what I have to tell you, I felt like 55

229

going back. And all the time a voice kept saying, "You fool, don't you
know you're walking straight into trouble?"; and then another voice:
"Yes, but if you let somebody else get the news to Kreon first, it will be
even worse than that for you!" But good sense won out, at least I hope
it was good sense, and here I am with a story that makes no sense at   60
all; but I'll tell it anyhow, because, as they say, what's going to happen's
going to happen and—
KREON: Come to the point. What have you to say?
SENTRY: I did not do it. I did not see who did it.
    You must not punish me for what someone else has done.   65
KREON: A comprehensive defense! More effective, perhaps,
    If I knew its purpose. Come: what is it?
SENTRY: A dreadful thing...I don't know how to put it—
KREON: Out with it!
SENTRY: Well, then;
    The dead man—
                Polyneices—

(*Pause. The Sentry is overcome, fumbles for words. Kreon waits impassively.*)

                out there—
                            someone,—   70
    New dust on the slimy flesh!

(*Pause. No sign from Kreon.*)

    Someone has given it burial that way, and
    Gone...

(*Long pause. Kreon finally speaks with deadly control.*)

KREON: And the man who dared do this?
SENTRY: I swear I
    Do not know! You must believe me!
                            Listen: 75
    The ground was dry, not a sign of digging, no,
    Not a wheeltrack in the dust, no trace of anyone.
    It was when they relieved us this morning: and one of them,
    The corporal, pointed to it.
                        There it was,
    The strangest—
                Look: 80
    The body, just mounded over with light dust: you see?
    Not buried really, but as if they'd covered it
    Just enough for the ghost's peace. And no sign
    Of dogs or any wild animal that had been there.

230

And then what a scene there was! Every man of us   85
Accusing the other: we all proved the other man did it.
We all had proof that we could not have done it.
We were ready to take hot iron in our hands,
Walk through fire, swear by all the gods,
It was not I!   90
I do not know who it was, but it was not I!

(*Kreon's rage has been mounting steadily, but the Sentry is too intent upon his
story to notice it.*)

And then, when this came to nothing, someone said
A thing that silenced us and made us stare
Down at the ground: you had to be told the news,
And one of us had to do it! We threw the dice,   95
And the bad luck fell to me. So here I am,
No happier to be here than you are to have me:
Nobody likes the man who brings bad news.
CHORAGOS: I have been wondering, King: can it be that the gods have
done this?
KREON (*furiously*): Stop!   100
Must you doddering wrecks
Go out of your heads entirely? "The gods"!
Intolerable!
The gods favor this corpse? Why? How had he served them?
Tried to loot their temples, burn their images,   105
Yes, and the whole State, and its laws with it!
Is it your senile opinion that the gods love to honor bad men?
A pious thought! —
                         No, from the very beginning
There have been those who have whispered together,
Stiff-necked anarchists, putting their heads together,   110
Scheming against me in alleys. These are the men,
And they have bribed my own guard to do this thing.
(*Sententiously.*) Money!
There's nothing in the world so demoralizing as money.
Down go your cities,   115
Homes gone, men gone, honest hearts corrupted,
Crookedness of all kinds, and all for money!
(*To Sentry.*)   But you —
I swear by God and by the throne of God,
The man who has done this thing shall pay for it!
Find that man, bring him here to me, or your death   120
Will be the least of your problems: I'll string you up

231

Alive, and there will be certain ways to make you
Discover your employer before you die;
And the process may teach you a lesson you seem to have missed:
The dearest profit is sometimes all too dear: 125
That depends on the source. Do you understand me?
A fortune won is often misfortune.
SENTRY: King, may I speak?
KREON: Your very voice distresses me.
SENTRY: Are you sure that it is my voice, and not your conscience?
KREON: By God, he wants to analyze me now!   130
SENTRY: It is not what I say, but what has been done, that hurts you.
KREON: You talk too much.
SENTRY: Maybe; but I've done nothing.
KREON: Sold your soul for some silver: that's all you've done.
SENTRY: How dreadful it is when the right judge judges wrong!
KREON: Your figures of speech   135
May entertain you now; but unless you bring me the man,
You will get little profit from them in the end.

(*Exit Kreon into the palace.*)

SENTRY: "Bring me the man" — !
I'd like nothing better than bringing him the man!
But bring him or not, you have seen the last of me here.   140
At any rate, I am safe!   (*Exit Sentry.*)

ODE° 1   *Strophe 1*

CHORUS: Numberless are the world's wonders, but none
More wonderful than man; the stormgray sea
Yields to his prows, the huge crests bear him high;
Earth, holy and inexhaustible, is graven
With shining furrows where his plows have gone
Year after year, the timeless labor of stallions.   5

Antistrophe 1

The lightboned birds and beasts that cling to cover,
The lithe fish lighting their reaches of dim water,
All are taken, tamed in the net of his mind;
The lion on the hill, the wild horse windy-maned,

10

Ode: Song sung by the Chorus.

232

Resign to him; and his blunt yoke has broken
The sultry shoulders of the mountain bull.

Strophe 2

Words also, and thought as rapid as air,
He fashions to his good use; statecraft is his
And his the skill that deflects the arrows of snow,   15
The spears of winter rain: from every wind
He has made himself secure—from all but one:
In the late wind of death he cannot stand.

Antistrophe 2

O clear intelligence, force beyond all measure!
O fate of man, working both good and evil!   20
When the laws are kept, how proudly his city stands!
When the laws are broken, what of his city then?
Never may the anarchic man find rest at my hearth,
Never be it said that my thoughts are his thoughts.

SCENE 2

(*Reenter Sentry leading Antigone.*)

CHORAGOS: What does this mean? Surely this captive woman
   Is the Princess, Antigone. Why should she be taken?
SENTRY: Here is the one who did it! We caught her
   In the very act of burying him.—Where is Kreon?
CHORAGOS: Just coming from the house.

(*Enter Kreon, center.*)

KREON: What has happened?   5
   Why have you come back so soon?
SENTRY (*expansively*):   O King,
   A man should never be too sure of anything:
   I would have sworn
   That you'd not see me here again: your anger
   Frightened me so, and the things you threatened me with;   10
   But how could I tell then
   That I'd be able to solve the case so soon?

233

No dice-throwing this time: I was only too glad to come!
Here is this woman. She is the guilty one:
We found her trying to bury him.   15
Take her, then; question her; judge her as you will.
I am through with the whole thing now, and glad of it.
KREON: But this is Antigone! Why have you brought her here?
SENTRY: She was burying him, I tell you!
KREON (*severely*):   Is this the truth?
SENTRY: I saw her with my own eyes. Can I say more?   20
KREON: The details: come, tell me quickly!
SENTRY: It was like this:
    After those terrible threats of yours, King,
    We went back and brushed the dust away from the body.
    The flesh was soft by now, and stinking,
    So we sat on a hill to windward and kept guard.   25
    No napping this time! We kept each other awake.
    But nothing happened until the white round sun
    Whirled in the center of the round sky over us:
    Then, suddenly,
    A storm of dust roared up from the earth, and the sky   30
    Went out, the plain vanished with all its trees
    In the stinging dark. We closed our eyes and endured it.
    The whirlwind lasted a long time, but it passed;
    And then we looked, and there was Antigone!
    I have seen   35
    A mother bird come back to a stripped nest, heard
    Her crying bitterly a broken note or two
    For the young ones stolen. Just so, when this girl
    Found the bare corpse, and all her love's work wasted,
    She wept, and cried on heaven to damn the hands   40
    That had done this thing.
                         And then she brought more dust
    And sprinkled wine three times for her brother's ghost.
    We ran and took her at once. She was not afraid,
    Not even when we charged her with what she had done.
    She denied nothing.
                         And this was a comfort to me,   45
    And some uneasiness: for it is a good thing
    To escape from death, but it is no great pleasure
    To bring death to a friend.
                         Yet I always say
    There is nothing so comfortable as your own safe skin!
KREON (*slowly, dangerously*): And you, Antigone,   50

You with your head hanging, —do you confess this thing?
ANTIGONE: I do. I deny nothing.
KREON (*to Sentry*):   You may go.

                                        (*Exit Sentry.*)

(*To Antigone.*) Tell me, tell me briefly:
Had you heard my proclamation touching this matter?
ANTIGONE: It was public. Could I help hearing it?   55
KREON: And yet you dared defy the law.
ANTIGONE: I dared.
It was not God's proclamation. That final Justice
That rules the world below makes no such laws.

Your edict, King, was strong,
But all your strength is weakness itself against   60
The immortal unrecorded laws of God.
They are not merely now: they were, and shall be,
Operative for ever, beyond man utterly.

I knew I must die, even without your decree:
I am only mortal. And if I must die   65
Now, before it is my time to die,
Surely this is no hardship: can anyone
Living, as I live, with evil all about me,
Think Death less than a friend? This death of mine
Is of no importance; but if I had left my brother   70
Lying in death unburied, I should have suffered.
Now I do not.
                You smile at me. Ah Kreon,
Think me a fool, if you like; but it may well be
That a fool convicts me of folly.
CHORAGOS: Like father, like daughter: both headstrong, deaf to reason!   75
She has never learned to yield.
KREON: She has much to learn.
The inflexible heart breaks first, the toughest iron
Cracks first, and the wildest horses bend their necks
At the pull of the smallest curb.
                          Pride? In a slave?
This girl is guilty of a double insolence,   80
Breaking the given laws and boasting of it.
Who is the man here,
She or I, if this crime goes unpunished?
Sister's child, or more than sister's child,

235

Or closer yet in blood—she and her sister   85
Win bitter death for this!
(*To Servants.*)   Go, some of you,
Arrest Ismene. I accuse her equally.
Bring her: you will find her sniffling in the house there.

Her mind's a traitor: crimes kept in the dark
Cry for light, and the guardian brain shudders;   90
But how much worse than this
Is brazen boasting of barefaced anarchy!
ANTIGONE: Kreon, what more do you want than my death?
KREON: Nothing.
   That gives me everything.
ANTIGONE: Then I beg you: kill me.
   This talking is a great weariness: your words   95
   Are distasteful to me, and I am sure that mine
   Seem so to you. And yet they should not seem so:
   I should have praise and honor for what I have done.
   All these men here would praise me
   Were their lips not frozen shut with fear of you.   100
   (*Bitterly.*) Ah the good fortune of kings,
   Licensed to say and do whatever they please!
KREON: You are alone here in that opinion.
ANTIGONE: No, they are with me. But they keep their tongues in leash.
KREON: Maybe. But you are guilty, and they are not.   105
ANTIGONE: There is no guilt in reverence for the dead.
KREON: But Eteocles—was he not your brother too?
ANTIGONE: My brother too.
KREON: And you insult his memory?
ANTIGONE (*softly*): The dead man would not say that I insult it.
KREON: He would: for you honor a traitor as much as him.   110
ANTIGONE: His own brother, traitor or not, and equal in blood.
KREON: He made war on his country. Eteocles defended it.
ANTIGONE: Nevertheless, there are honors due all the dead.
KREON: But not the same for the wicked as for the just.
ANTIGONE: Ah Kreon, Kreon,   115
   Which of us can say what the gods hold wicked?
KREON: An enemy is an enemy, even dead.
ANTIGONE: It is my nature to join in love, not hate.
KREON (*finally losing patience*): Go join them then; if you must have your love,
   Find it in hell!   120
CHORAGOS: But see, Ismene comes:

(*Enter Ismene, guarded.*)

Those tears are sisterly, the cloud
That shadows her eyes rains down gentle sorrow.
KREON: You too, Ismene,
  Snake in my ordered house, sucking my blood   125
  Stealthily—and all the time I never knew
  That these two sisters were aiming at my throne!
                                  Ismene,
  Do you confess your share in this crime, or deny it?
  Answer me.
ISMENE: Yes, if she will let me say so. I am guilty.   130
ANTIGONE (*coldly*): No, Ismene. You have no right to say so.
  You would not help me, and I will not have you help me.
ISMENE: But now I know what you meant; and I am here
  To join you, to take my share of punishment.
ANTIGONE: The dead man and the gods who rule the dead   135
  Know whose act this was. Words are not friends.
ISMENE: Do you refuse me, Antigone? I want to die with you:
  I too have a duty that I must discharge to the dead.
ANTIGONE: You shall not lessen my death by sharing it.
ISMENE: What do I care for life when you are dead?   140
ANTIGONE: Ask Kreon. You're always hanging on his opinions.
ISMENE: You are laughing at me. Why, Antigone?
ANTIGONE: It's a joyless laughter, Ismene.
ISMENE: But can I do nothing?
ANTIGONE: Yes. Save yourself. I shall not envy you.
  There are those who will praise you; I shall have honor, too.   145
ISMENE: But we are equally guilty!
ANTIGONE: No more, Ismene.
  You are alive, but I belong to Death.
KREON (*to the Chorus*): Gentlemen, I beg you to observe these girls:
  One has just now lost her mind; the other,
  It seems, has never had a mind at all.   150
ISMENE: Grief teaches the steadiest minds to waver, King.
KREON: Yours certainly did, when you assumed guilt with the guilty!
ISMENE: But how could I go on living without her?
KREON: You are.
  She is already dead.
ISMENE: But your own son's bride!
KREON: There are places enough for him to push his plow.   155
  I want no wicked women for my sons!
ISMENE: O dearest Haimon, how your father wrongs you!
KREON: I've had enough of your childish talk of marriage!
CHORAGOS: Do you really intend to steal this girl from your son?

KREON: No; Death will do that for me.
CHORAGOS: Then she must die?   160
KREON (*ironically*): You dazzle me.
   —But enough of this talk!
   (*To Guards.*) You, there, take them away and guard them well:
   For they are but women, and even brave men run
   When they see Death coming.

                    (*Exeunt° Ismene, Antigone, and Guards.*)

ODE 2   *Strophe 1*

CHORUS: Fortunate is the man who has never tasted God's vengeance!
   Where once the anger of heaven has struck, that house is shaken
   For ever: damnation rises behind each child
   Like a wave cresting out of the black northeast,
   When the long darkness under sea roars up   5
   And bursts drumming death upon the windwhipped sand.

Antistrophe 1

I have seen this gathering sorrow from time long past
Loom upon Oedipus' children: generation from generation
Takes the compulsive rage of the enemy god.
So lately this last flower of Oedipus' line   10
Drank the sunlight! but now a passionate word
And a handful of dust have closed up all its beauty.

Strophe 2

   What mortal arrogance
   Transcends the wrath of Zeus?
Sleep cannot lull him nor the effortless long months   15
Of the timeless gods: but he is young for ever,
And his house is the shining day of high Olympos.
   All that is and shall be,
   And all the past, is his.
No pride on earth is free of the curse of heaven.   20

Antistrophe 2

   The straying dreams of men
     May bring them ghosts of joy:

165. [S.D.] *Exeunt*: Latin for "they go out."

But as they drowse, the waking embers burn them;
Or they walk with fixed eyes, as blind men walk.
But the ancient wisdom speaks for our own time: 25
   Fate works most for woe
   With Folly's fairest show.
Man's little pleasure is the spring of sorrow.

SCENE 3

CHORAGOS: But here is Haimon, King, the last of all your sons.
   Is it grief for Antigone that brings him here,
   And bitterness at being robbed of his bride?

(*Enter Haimon.*)

KREON: We shall soon see, and no need of diviners.
                                —Son,
   You have heard my final judgment on that girl: 5
   Have you come here hating me, or have you come
   With deference and with love, whatever I do?
HAIMON: I am your son, father. You are my guide.
   You make things clear for me, and I obey you.
   No marriage means more to me than your continuing wisdom.   10
KREON: Good. That is the way to behave: subordinate
   Everything else, my son, to your father's will.
   This is what a man prays for, that he may get
   Sons attentive and dutiful in his house,
   Each one hating his father's enemies,   15
   Honoring his father's friends. But if his sons
   Fail him, if they turn out unprofitably,
   What has he fathered but trouble for himself
   And amusement for the malicious?
                          So you are right
   Not to lose your head over this woman.   20
   Your pleasure with her would soon grow cold, Haimon,
   And then you'd have a hellcat in bed and elsewhere.
   Let her find her husband in Hell!
   Of all the people in this city, only she
   Has had contempt for my law and broken it.   25

Do you want me to show myself weak before the people?
   Or to break my sworn word? No, and I will not.
   The woman dies.
   I suppose she'll plead "family ties." Well, let her.

If I permit my own family to rebel,   30
How shall I earn the world's obedience?
Show me the man who keeps his house in hand,
He's fit for public authority.
                    I'll have no dealings
With lawbreakers, critics of the government:
Whoever is chosen to govern should be obeyed—   35
Must be obeyed, in all things, great and small,
Just and unjust! O Haimon,
The man who knows how to obey, and that man only,
Knows how to give commands when the time comes.
You can depend on him, no matter how fast   40
The spears come: he's a good soldier, he'll stick it out.
Anarchy, anarchy! Show me a greater evil!
This is why cities tumble and the great houses rain down,
This is what scatters armies!
No, no: good lives are made so by discipline.   45
We keep the laws then, and the lawmakers,
And no woman shall seduce us. If we must lose,
Let's lose to a man, at least! Is a woman stronger than we?
CHORAGOS: Unless time has rusted my wits,
    What you say, King, is said with point and dignity.   50
HAIMON (*boyishly earnest*): Father:
    Reason is God's crowning gift to man, and you are right
    To warn me against losing mine. I cannot say—
    I hope that I shall never want to say!—that you
    Have reasoned badly. Yet there are other men   55
    Who can reason, too; and their opinions might be helpful.
    You are not in a position to know everything
    That people say or do, or what they feel:
    Your temper terrifies—everyone
    Will tell you only what you like to hear.   60
    But I, at any rate, can listen; and I have heard them
    Muttering and whispering in the dark about this girl.
    They say no woman has ever, so unreasonably,
    Died so shameful a death for a generous act:
    "She covered her brother's body. Is this indecent?   65
    She kept him from dogs and vultures. Is this a crime?
    Death?—She should have all the honor that we can give her!"

    This is the way they talk out there in the city.
    You must believe me:
    Nothing is closer to me than your happiness.   70

What could be closer? Must not any son
Value his father's fortune as his father does his?
I beg you, do not be unchangeable:
Do not believe that you alone can be right.
The man who thinks that,   75
The man who maintains that only he has the power
To reason correctly, the gift to speak, the soul—
A man like that, when you know him, turns out empty.
It is not reason never to yield to reason!

In flood time you can see how some trees bend,   80
And because they bend, even their twigs are safe,
While stubborn trees are torn up, roots and all.
And the same thing happens in sailing:
Make your sheet fast, never slacken,—and over you go,
Head over heels and under: and there's your voyage.   85
Forget you are angry! Let yourself be moved!
I know I am young; but please let me say this:
The ideal condition
Would be, I admit, that men should be right by instinct;
But since we are all too likely to go astray,   90
The reasonable thing is to learn from those who can teach.
CHORAGOS: You will do well to listen to him, King,
    If what he says is sensible. And you, Haimon,
    Must listen to your father.—Both speak well.
KREON: You consider it right for a man of my years and experience   95
    To go to school to a boy?
HAIMON: It is not right
    If I am wrong. But if I am young, and right,
    What does my age matter?
KREON: You think it right to stand up for an anarchist?
HAIMON: Not at all. I pay no respect to criminals.   100
KREON: Then she is not a criminal?
HAIMON: The City would deny it, to a man.
KREON: And the City proposes to teach me how to rule?
HAIMON: Ah. Who is it that's talking like a boy now?
KREON: My voice is the one voice giving orders in this City!   105
HAIMON: It is no City if it takes orders from one voice.
KREON: The State is the King!
HAIMON: Yes, if the State is a desert.

(*Pause.*)

KREON: This boy, it seems, has sold out to a woman.

241

HAIMON: If you are a woman: my concern is only for you.
KREON: So? Your "concern"! In a public brawl with your father!   110
HAIMON: How about you, in a public brawl with justice?
KREON: With justice, when all that I do is within my rights?
HAIMON: You have no right to trample on God's right.
KREON (*completely out of control*): Fool, adolescent fool! Taken in by a
    woman!
HAIMON: You'll never see me taken in by anything vile.   115
KREON: Every word you say is for her!
HAIMON (*quietly, darkly*):   And for you.
    And for me. And for the gods under the earth.
KREON: You'll never marry her while she lives.
HAIMON: Then she must die. — But her death will cause another.
KREON: Another?   120
    Have you lost your senses? Is this an open threat?
HAIMON: There is no threat in speaking to emptiness.
KREON: I swear you'll regret this superior tone of yours!
    You are the empty one!
HAIMON: If you were not my father,
    I'd say you were perverse.   125
KREON: You girl-struck fool, don't play at words with me!
HAIMON: I am sorry. You prefer silence.
KREON: Now, by God—
    I swear, by all the gods in heaven above us,
    You'll watch it, I swear you shall!
    (*To the Servants.*)   Bring her out!
    Bring the woman out! Let her die before his eyes!   130
    Here, this instant, with her bridegroom beside her!
HAIMON: Not here, no; she will not die here, King.
    And you will never see my face again.
    Go on raving as long as you've a friend to endure you. (*Exit Haimon.*)
CHORAGOS: Gone, gone.   135
    Kreon, a young man in a rage is dangerous!
KREON: Let him do, or dream to do, more than a man can.
    He shall not save these girls from death.
CHORAGOS: These girls?
    You have sentenced them both?
KREON: No, you are right.
    I will not kill the one whose hands are clean.   140
CHORAGOS: But Antigone?
KREON (*somberly*):   I will carry her far away
    Out there in the wilderness, and lock her
    Living in a vault of stone. She shall have food,

242

As the custom is, to absolve the State of her death.
And there let her pray to the gods of hell: 145
They are her only gods:
Perhaps they will show her an escape from death,
Or she may learn,
                    though late,
That piety shown the dead is pity in vain.

                                        (*Exit Kreon.*)

ODE 3   *Strophe*

CHORUS: Love, unconquerable
Waster of rich men, keeper
Of warm lights and all-night vigil
In the soft face of a girl:
Sea-wanderer, forest-visitor!   5
Even the pure Immortals cannot escape you,
And mortal man, in his one day's dusk,
Trembles before your glory.

Antistrophe

Surely you swerve upon ruin
The just man's consenting heart,   10
As here you have made bright anger
Strike between father and son—
And none has conquered but Love!
A girl's glance working the will of heaven:
Pleasure to her alone who mocks us,   15
Merciless Aphrodite.°

SCENE 4

CHORAGOS (*as Antigone enters guarded*): But I can no longer stand in awe
    of this,
Nor, seeing what I see, keep back my tears.
Here is Antigone, passing to that chamber
Where all find sleep at last.

16. **Aphrodite:** Goddess of love and beauty.

Strophe 1

ANTIGONE: Look upon me, friends, and pity me   5
   Turning back at the night's edge to say
   Good-by to the sun that shines for me no longer;
   Now sleepy Death
   Summons me down to Acheron,° that cold shore:
   There is no bridesong there, nor any music.   10
CHORUS: Yet not unpraised, not without a kind of honor,
   You walk at last into the underworld
   Untouched by sickness, broken by no sword.
   What woman has ever found your way to death?

Antistrophe 1

ANTIGONE: How often I have heard the story of Niobe,°   15
   Tantalos' wretched daughter, how the stone
   Clung fast about her, ivy-close: and they say
   The rain falls endlessly
   And sifting soft snow; her tears are never done.
   I feel the loneliness of her death in mine.   20
CHORUS: But she was born of heaven, and you
   Are woman, woman-born. If her death is yours,
   A mortal woman's, is this not for you
   Glory in our world and in the world beyond?

Strophe 2

ANTIGONE: You laugh at me. Ah, friends, friends,   25
   Can you not wait until I am dead? O Thebes,
   O men many-charioted, in love with Fortune,
   Dear springs of Dirce, sacred Theban grove,
   Be witnesses for me, denied all pity,
   Unjustly judged! and think a word of love   30
   For her whose path turns
   Under dark earth, where there are no more tears.
CHORUS: You have passed beyond human daring and come at last
   Into a place of stone where Justice sits.

9. **Acheron:** River in Hades, domain of the dead.   15. **Niobe:** When Niobe's many children (up to twenty in some accounts) were slain in punishment for their mother's boastfulness, Niobe was turned into a stone on Mount Sipylus. Her tears became the mountain's streams.

I cannot tell   35
What shape of your father's guilt appears in this.

Antistrophe 2

ANTIGONE: You have touched it at last: that bridal bed
    Unspeakable, horror of son and mother mingling:
    Their crime, infection of all our family!
    O Oedipus, father and brother!   40
    Your marriage strikes from the grave to murder mine.
    I have been a stranger here in my own land:
    All my life
    The blasphemy of my birth has followed me.
CHORUS: Reverence is a virtue, but strength   45
    Lives in established law: that must prevail.
    You have made your choice,
    Your death is the doing of your conscious hand.

Epode°

ANTIGONE: Then let me go, since all your words are bitter,
    And the very light of the sun is cold to me.   50
    Lead me to my vigil, where I must have
    Neither love nor lamentation; no song, but silence.

(*Kreon interrupts impatiently.*)

KREON: If dirges and planned lamentations could put off death,
    Men would be singing for ever.
    (*To the Servants.*)   Take her, go!
    You know your orders: take her to the vault   55
    And leave her alone there. And if she lives or dies,
    That's her affair, not ours: our hands are clean.
ANTIGONE: O tomb, vaulted bride-bed in eternal rock,
    Soon I shall be with my own again
    Where Persephone° welcomes the thin ghosts underground: 60
    And I shall see my father again, and you, mother,
    And dearest Polyneices—
                            dearest indeed
    To me, since it was my hand

Epode: Song sung by the Chorus while standing still after singing the strophe and antistrophe.   **60. Persephone:** Abducted by Pluto, god of the underworld, to be his queen.

245

That washed him clean and poured the ritual wine:
And my reward is death before my time!   65

And yet, as men's hearts know, I have done no wrong,
I have not sinned before God. Or if I have,
I shall know the truth in death. But if the guilt
Lies upon Kreon who judged me, then, I pray,
May his punishment equal my own.
CHORAGOS: O passionate heart,   70
  Unyielding, tormented still by the same winds!
KREON: Her guards shall have good cause to regret their delaying.
ANTIGONE: Ah! That voice is like the voice of death!
KREON: I can give you no reason to think you are mistaken.
ANTIGONE: Thebes, and you my fathers' gods,   75
  And rulers of Thebes, you see me now, the last
  Unhappy daughter of a line of kings,
  Your kings, led away to death. You will remember
  What things I suffer, and at what men's hands,
  Because I would not transgress the laws of heaven.   80
  (*To the Guards, simply.*) Come: let us wait no longer.

                                    (*Exit Antigone, left, guarded.*)

ODE 4   *Strophe 1*

CHORUS: All Danae's beauty was locked away
  In a brazen cell where the sunlight could not come:
  A small room still as any grave, enclosed her.
  Yet she was a princess too,
  And Zeus in a rain of gold poured love upon her.°   5
  O child, child,
  No power in wealth or war
  Or tough sea-blackened ships
  Can prevail against untiring Destiny!

1–5. **All Danae's beauty...poured love upon her:** Locked away to prevent the fulfillment of a prophecy that she would bear a son who would kill her father, Danae was nonetheless impregnated by Zeus, who came to her in a shower of gold. The prophecy was fulfilled by the son that came of their union.

Antistrophe 1

And Dryas's, son° also, that furious king,   10
Bore the god's prisoning anger for his pride:
Sealed up by Dionysos in deaf stone,
His madness died among echoes.
So at the last he learned what dreadful power
His tongue had mocked: 15
For he had profaned the revels,
And fired the wrath of the nine
Implacable Sisters° that love the sound of the flute.

Strophe 2

And old men tell a half-remembered tale
Of horror° where a dark ledge splits the sea   20
And a double surf beats on the gray shores:
How a king's new woman, sick
With hatred for the queen he had imprisoned,
Ripped out his two sons' eyes with her bloody hands
While grinning Ares° watched the shuttle plunge   25
Four times: four blind wounds crying for revenge,

Antistrophe 2

Crying, tears and blood mingled. — Piteously born,
Those sons whose mother was of heavenly birth!
Her father was the god of the North Wind
And she was cradled by gales,   30
She raced with young colts on the glittering hills
And walked untrammeled in the open light:
But in her marriage deathless Fate found means
To build a tomb like yours for all her joy.

---

10. Dryas's son: King Lycurgus of Thrace, whom Dionysus, god of wine, caused to
be stricken with madness.   **18. Sisters:** The Muses, nine sister goddesses who
presided over poetry and music, arts and sciences.   **19–20. half-remembered
tale of horror:** The second wife of King Phineas blinded the sons of his first wife,
Cleopatra, whom Phineas had imprisoned in a cave.   **25. Ares:** God of war.

SCENE 5

(*Enter blind Teiresias, led by a boy. The opening speeches of Teiresias should be in singsong contrast to the realistic lines of Kreon.*)

TEIRESIAS: This is the way the blind man comes, Princes, Princes,
  Lockstep, two heads lit by the eyes of one.
KREON: What new thing have you to tell us, old Teiresias?
TEIRESIAS: I have much to tell you: listen to the prophet, Kreon.
KREON: I am not aware that I have ever failed to listen.   5
TEIRESIAS: Then you have done wisely, King, and ruled well.
KREON: I admit my debt to you. But what have you to say?
TEIRESIAS: This, Kreon: you stand once more on the edge of fate.
KREON: What do you mean? Your words are a kind of dread.
TEIRESIAS: Listen, Kreon: 10
  I was sitting in my chair of augury, at the place
  Where the birds gather about me. They were all a-chatter,
  As is their habit, when suddenly I heard
  A strange note in their jangling, a scream, a
  Whirring fury; I knew that they were fighting,   15
  Tearing each other, dying
  In a whirlwind of wings clashing. And I was afraid.
  I began the rites of burnt-offering at the altar
  But Hephaistos° failed me: instead of bright flame,
  There was only the sputtering slime of the fat thigh-flesh   20
  Melting: the entrails dissolved in gray smoke,
  The bare bone burst from the welter. And no blaze!

  This was a sign from heaven. My boy described it,
  Seeing for me as I see for others.
  I tell you, Kreon, you yourself have brought   25
  This new calamity upon us. Our hearths and altars
  Are stained with the corruption of dogs and carrion birds
  That glut themselves on the corpse of Oedipus's son.
  The gods are deaf when we pray to them, their fire
  Recoils from our offering, their birds of omen   30
  Have no cry of comfort, for they are gorged
  With the thick blood of the dead.
                          O my son,
  These are no trifles! Think: all men make mistakes,
  But a good man yields when he knows his course is wrong,

19. **Hephaistos:** God of fire.

248

And repairs the evil. The only crime is pride.   35

Give in to the dead man, then: do not fight with a corpse—
What glory is it to kill a man who is dead?
Think, I beg you:
It is for your own good that I speak as I do.
You should be able to yield for your own good.   40
KREON: It seems that prophets have made me their especial province.
All my life long
I have been a kind of butt for the dull arrows
Of doddering fortune-tellers!
                    No, Teiresias:
If your birds—if the great eagles of God himself   45
Should carry him stinking bit by bit to heaven,
I would not yield. I am not afraid of pollution:
No man can defile the gods.
                    Do what you will,
Go into business, make money, speculate
In India gold or that synthetic gold from Sardis,   50
Get rich otherwise than by my consent to bury him.
Teiresias, it is a sorry thing when a wise man
Sells his wisdom, lets out his words for hire!
TEIRESIAS: Ah Kreon! Is there no man left in the world—
KREON: To do what?—Come, let's have the aphorism!   55
TEIRESIAS: No man who knows that wisdom outweighs any wealth?
KREON: As surely as bribes are baser than any baseness.
TEIRESIAS: You are sick, Kreon! You are deathly sick!
KREON: As you say: it is not my place to challenge a prophet.
TEIRESIAS: Yet you have said my prophecy is for sale.   60
KREON: The generation of prophets has always loved gold.
TEIRESIAS: The generation of kings has always loved brass.
KREON: You forget yourself! You are speaking to your King.
TEIRESIAS: I know it. You are a king because of me.
KREON: You have a certain skill; but you have sold out.   65
TEIRESIAS: King, you will drive me to words that—
KREON: Say them, say them!
Only remember: I will not pay you for them.
TEIRESIAS: No, you will find them too costly.
KREON: No doubt. Speak:
Whatever you say, you will not change my will.
TEIRESIAS: Then take this, and take it to heart!   70
The time is not far off when you shall pay back
Corpse for corpse, flesh of your own flesh.

You have thrust the child of this world into living night,
You have kept from the gods below the child that is theirs:
The one in a grave before her death, the other,   75
Dead, denied the grave. This is your crime:
And the Furies° and the dark gods of Hell
Are swift with terrible punishment for you.

Do you want to buy me now, Kreon?

                              Not many days,
And your house will be full of men and women weeping,   80
And curses will be hurled at you from far
Cities grieving for sons unburied, left to rot
Before the walls of Thebes.

These are my arrows, Kreon: they are all for you.

(*To Boy.*) But come, child: lead me home.   85
Let him waste his fine anger upon younger men.
Maybe he will learn at last
To control a wiser tongue in a better head.

                                        (*Exit Teiresias.*)

CHORAGOS: The old man has gone, King, but his words
    Remain to plague us. I am old, too,   90
    But I cannot remember that he was ever false.
KREON: That is true.... It troubles me.
    Oh it is hard to give in! but it is worse
    To risk everything for stubborn pride.
CHORAGOS: Kreon: take my advice.
KREON: What shall I do?   95
CHORAGOS: Go quickly: free Antigone from her vault
    And build a tomb for the body of Polyneices.
KREON: You would have me do this!
CHORAGOS: Kreon, yes!
    And it must be done at once: God moves
    Swiftly to cancel the folly of stubborn men.   100
KREON: It is hard to deny the heart! But I
    Will do it: I will not fight with destiny.
CHORAGOS: You must go yourself, you cannot leave it to others.
KREON: I will go.
                —Bring axes, servants:

77. **Furies:** Spirits called on to avenge crimes, especially those against kin.

Come with me to the tomb. I buried her, I   105
Will set her free.
              Oh quickly!
My mind misgives —
The laws of the gods are mighty, and a man must serve them
To the last day of his life!   (*Exit Kreon.*)

                        PAEAN°   *Strophe 1*

CHORAGOS: God of many names   .
CHORUS: O Iacchos
                                   son
      of Kadmeian Semele
                   O born of the Thunder!
      Guardian of the West
                        Regent
      of Eleusis' plain
                   O Prince of maenad Thebes
      and the Dragon Field by rippling Ismenos:°   5

                        Antistrophe 1

CHORAGOS: God of many names
CHORUS: the flame of torches
      flares on our hills
                   the nymphs of Iacchos
      dance at the spring of Castalia:°
      from the vine-close mountain
                        come ah come in ivy:
      Evohe evohe!° sings through the streets of Thebes   10

                        Strophe 2

CHORAGOS: God of many names
CHORUS: Iacchos of Thebes

Paean: A song of praise or prayer. **1–5. God of many names...rippling
Ismenos:** The following is a litany of names for Dionysus (Iacchos): he was son of
Zeus ("Thunder") and Semele; he was honored in secret rites at Eleusis; and he
was worshiped by the Maenads of Thebes. Kadmos, Semele's father, sowed
dragon's teeth in a field beside the river Ismenos from which sprang warriors who
became the first Thebans. **8. spring of Castalia:** A spring on Mount Parnassus
used by priestesses of Dionysus in rites of purification. **10.** *Evohe evohe!:* Cry of
the Maenads to Dionysus.

                        251

heavenly Child
     of Semele bride of the Thunderer!
The shadow of plague is upon us:
           come
with clement feet
     oh come from Parnasos
down the long slopes
       across the lamenting water   15

Antistrophe 2

CHORAGOS: Io Fire! Chorister of the throbbing stars!
  O purest among the voices of the night!
  Thou son of God, blaze for us!
CHORUS: Come with choric rapture of circling Maenads
  Who cry *Io Iacche!*°
       God of many names!   20

EXODOS°

(Enter Messenger from left.)

MESSENGER: Men of the line of Kadmos, you who live
  Near Amphion's citadel,°
        I cannot say
Of any condition of human life "This is fixed,
This is clearly good, or bad." Fate raises up,
And Fate casts down the happy and unhappy alike: 5
No man can foretell his Fate.
        Take the case of Kreon:
Kreon was happy once, as I count happiness:
Victorious in battle, sole governor of the land,
Fortunate father of children nobly born.
And now it has all gone from him! Who can say   10
That a man is still alive when his life's joy fails?
He is a walking dead man. Grant him rich,
Let him live like a king in his great house:
If his pleasure is gone, I would not give
So much as the shadow of smoke for all he owns.   15

20. *Io Iacche!*: Ritual cry. **Exodos:** Final scene. **2. Amphion's citadel:** A name for Thebes.

CHORAGOS: Your words hint at sorrow: what is your news for us?
MESSENGER: They are dead. The living are guilty of their death.
CHORAGOS: Who is guilty? Who is dead? Speak!
MESSENGER: Haimon.
   Haimon is dead; and the hand that killed him
   Is his own hand.
CHORAGOS: His father's? or his own?   20
MESSENGER: His own, driven mad by the murder his father had done.
CHORAGOS: Teiresias, Teiresias, how clearly you saw it all!
MESSENGER: This is my news: you must draw what conclusions you can
   from it.
CHORAGOS: But look: Eurydice, our Queen:
   Has she overheard us?   25

(*Enter Eurydice from the palace, center.*)

EURYDICE: I have heard something, friends:
   As I was unlocking the gate of Pallas'° shrine,
   For I needed her help today, I heard a voice
   Telling of some new sorrow. And I fainted
   There at the temple with all my maidens about me.   30
   But speak again: whatever it is, I can bear it:
   Grief and I are no strangers.
MESSENGER: Dearest Lady,
   I will tell you plainly all that I have seen.
   I shall not try to comfort you: what is the use,
   Since comfort could lie only in what is not true?   35
   The truth is always best.
                             I went with Kreon
   To the outer plain where Polyneices was lying,
   No friend to pity him, his body shredded by dogs.
   We made our prayers in that place to Hecate
   And Pluto,° that they would be merciful. And we bathed   40
   The corpse with holy water, and we brought
   Fresh-broken branches to burn what was left of it,
   And upon the urn we heaped up a towering barrow
   Of the earth of his own land.
                                When we were done, we ran
   To the vault where Antigone lay on her couch of stone.   45
   One of the servants had gone ahead,
   And while he was yet far off he heard a voice

---

27. Pallas: Pallas Athene, goddess of wisdom.   **39–40. Hecate and Pluto:**
Goddess of witchcraft and sorcery and King of Hades, the underworld.

Grieving within the chamber, and he came back
And told Kreon. And as the King went closer,
The air was full of wailing, the words lost,   50
And he begged us to make all haste. "Am I a prophet?"
He said, weeping, "And must I walk this road,
The saddest of all that I have gone before?
My son's voice calls me on. Oh quickly, quickly!
Look through the crevice there, and tell me   55
If it is Haimon, or some deception of the gods!"

We obeyed; and in the cavern's farthest corner
We saw her lying:
She had made a noose of her fine linen veil
And hanged herself. Haimon lay beside her,   60
His arms about her waist, lamenting her,
His love lost under ground, crying out
That his father had stolen her away from him.

When Kreon saw him the tears rushed to his eyes
And he called to him: "What have you done, child? speak to me.   65
What are you thinking that makes your eyes so strange?
O my son, my son, I come to you on my knees!"
But Haimon spat in his face. He said not a word,
Staring—
           And suddenly drew his sword
And lunged. Kreon shrank back, the blade missed; and the boy,   70
Desperate against himself, drove it half its length
Into his own side, and fell. And as he died
He gathered Antigone close in his arms again,
Choking, his blood bright red on her white cheek.
And now he lies dead with the dead, and she is his   75
At last, his bride in the house of the dead.

                                    (*Exit Eurydice into the palace.*)

CHORAGOS: She has left us without a word. What can this mean?
MESSENGER: It troubles me, too; yet she knows what is best,
     Her grief is too great for public lamentation,
     And doubtless she has gone to her chamber to weep   80
     For her dead son, leading her maidens in his dirge.

(*Pause.*)

CHORAGOS: It may be so: but I fear this deep silence.
MESSENGER: I will see what she is doing. I will go in.

(Exit Messenger into the palace.)

(Enter Kreon with attendants, bearing Haimon's body.)

CHORAGOS: But here is the king himself: oh look at him,
　Bearing his own damnation in his arms.　　　　　　　　　85
KREON: Nothing you say can touch me any more.
　My own blind heart has brought me
　From darkness to final darkness. Here you see
　The father murdering, the murdered son—
　And all my civic wisdom!　　　　　　　　　　　　　　90

　Haimon my son, so young, so young to die,
　I was the fool, not you; and you died for me.
CHORAGOS: That is the truth; but you were late in learning it.
KREON: This truth is hard to bear. Surely a god
　Has crushed me beneath the hugest weight of heaven,　　95
　And driven me headlong a barbaric way
　To trample out the thing I held most dear.

　The pains that men will take to come to pain!

(Enter Messenger from the palace.)

MESSENGER: The burden you carry in your hands is heavy,
　But it is not all: you will find more in your house.　　　100
KREON: What burden worse than this shall I find there?
MESSENGER: The Queen is dead.
KREON: O port of death, deaf world,
　Is there no pity for me? And you, Angel of evil,
　I was dead, and your words are death again.　　　　　105
　Is it true, boy? Can it be true?
　Is my wife dead? Has death bred death?
MESSENGER: You can see for yourself.

(The doors are opened and the body of Eurydice is disclosed within.)

KREON: Oh pity!
　All true, all true, and more than I can bear!　　　　　110
　O my wife, my son!
MESSENGER: She stood before the altar, and her heart
　Welcomed the knife her own hand guided,
　And a great cry burst from her lips for Megareus° dead,

114. Megareus: Son of Kreon and brother of Haimon, Megareus sacrificed himself in the unsuccessful attack upon Thebes, believing that his death was necessary to save Thebes.

And for Haimon dead, her sons; and her last breath   115
Was a curse for their father, the murderer of her sons.
And she fell, and the dark flowed in through her closing eyes.
KREON: O God, I am sick with fear.
Are there no swords here? Has no one a blow for me?
MESSENGER: Her curse is upon you for the deaths of both.   120
KREON: It is right that it should be. I alone am guilty.
I know it, and I say it. Lead me in,
Quickly, friends.
I have neither life nor substance. Lead me in.
CHORAGOS: You are right, if there can be right in so much wrong.   125
The briefest way is best in a world of sorrow.
KREON: Let it come,
Let death come quickly, and be kind to me.
I would not ever see the sun again.
CHORAGOS: All that will come when it will; but we, meanwhile,   130
Have much to do. Leave the future to itself.
KREON: All my heart was in that prayer!
CHORAGOS: Then do not pray any more: the sky is deaf.
KREON: Lead me away. I have been rash and foolish.
I have killed my son and my wife.   135
I look for comfort; my comfort lies here dead.
Whatever my hands have touched has come to nothing.
Fate has brought all my pride to a thought of dust.

(*As Kreon is being led into the house, the Choragos advances and speaks directly to the audience.*)

CHORAGOS: There is no happiness where there is no wisdom;
No wisdom but in submission to the gods.   140
Big words are always punished,
And proud men in old age learn to be wise.

[441 B.C.]

256

SOPHOCLES   [c. 496–c. 406 B.C.E.]

Oedipus Rex

TRANSLATED BY DUDLEY FITTS AND ROBERT FITZGERALD

Sophocles (c. 496–c. 406 B.C.E.) was not the first important voice to emerge in drama, but as a representative of classical Greek tragedy, it is hard to imagine a more important figure. Indeed, his works were considered such models of the craft that Aristotle based much of his *Poetics* on an analysis of *Oedipus Rex*. Sophocles was born to a wealthy Athenian family and became active in many aspects of civic life as a soldier, a priest, and a statesman. Today, however, he is remembered principally for his achievements as a playwright. During a long and distinguished career, he won first prize in Greek drama competitions more often than any other writer. Though there is evidence that he wrote more than 120 plays, only seven have survived in their entirety, along with fragments of many others. In his plays, Sophocles wrestled with some of the most important issues of his time and indeed of all time — the conflict between fate and free will; between public and private morality; and between duty to one's family, the state, and the gods — giving his work enduring appeal. *Oedipus Rex* (*Oedipus the King*, first performed in 430 B.C.E.) is one of Sophocles' three Theban plays, the others being *Antigone* (441 B.C.E.) and *Oedipus at Colonus* (401 B.C.E., first performed posthumously).

Characters

OEDIPUS, *King of Thebes, supposed son of Polybos and Merope, King and Queen of Corinth*
IOKASTE,° *wife of Oedipus and widow of the late King Laios*
KREON,° *brother of Iokaste, a prince of Thebes*
TEIRESIAS, *a blind seer who serves Apollo*
PRIEST

Iokaste: Traditional Western spelling is *Jocasta*.   **Kreon:** Traditional Western spelling is *Creon*.

257

MESSENGER, *from Corinth*
SHEPHERD, *former servant of Laios*
SECOND MESSENGER, *from the palace*
CHORUS OF THEBAN ELDERS
CHORAGOS, *leader of the Chorus*
ANTIGONE *and* ISMENE, *young daughters of Oedipus and Iokaste. They appear*
  in the Exodos but do not speak.
SUPPLIANTS, GUARDS, SERVANTS

Scene: *Before the palace of Oedipus, King of Thebes. A central door and two lateral*
doors open onto a platform which runs the length of the facade. On the platform,
right and left, are altars; and three steps lead down into the orchestra, or chorus-
ground. At the beginning of the action these steps are crowded by suppliants who
have brought branches and chaplets of olive leaves and who sit in various attitudes
of despair. Oedipus enters.

PROLOGUE°

OEDIPUS: My children, generations of the living
  In the line of Kadmos,° nursed at his ancient hearth:
  Why have you strewn yourselves before these altars
  In supplication, with your boughs and garlands?
  The breath of incense rises from the city   5
  With a sound of prayer and lamentation.
        Children,
  I would not have you speak through messengers,
  And therefore I have come myself to hear you—
  I, Oedipus, who bear the famous name.
  (*To a Priest.*) You, there, since you are eldest in the company,   10
  Speak for them all, tell me what preys upon you,
  Whether you come in dread, or crave some blessing:
  Tell me, and never doubt that I will help you
  In every way I can; I should be heartless
  Were I not moved to find you suppliant here.   15
PRIEST: Great Oedipus, O powerful king of Thebes!
  You see how all the ages of our people
  Cling to your altar steps: here are boys
  Who can barely stand alone, and here are priests
  By weight of age, as I am a priest of God,   20
  And young men chosen from those yet unmarried;

Prologue: First part of the play explaining the background and introducing the
scene. 2. Kadmos: Founder of Thebes.

As for the others, all that multitude,
They wait with olive chaplets in the squares,
At the two shrines of Pallas,° and where Apollo°
Speaks in the glowing embers.
                    Your own eyes   25
Must tell you: Thebes is tossed on a murdering sea
And can not lift her head from the death surge.
A rust consumes the buds and fruits of the earth;
The herds are sick; children die unborn,
And labor is vain. The god of plague and pyre   30
Raids like detestable lightning through the city,
And all the house of Kadmos is laid waste,
All emptied, and all darkened: Death alone
Battens upon the misery of Thebes.

You are not one of the immortal gods, we know;   35
Yet we have come to you to make our prayer
As to the man surest in mortal ways
And wisest in the ways of God. You saved us
From the Sphinx,° that flinty singer, and the tribute
We paid to her so long; yet you were never   40
Better informed than we, nor could we teach you:
A god's touch, it seems, enabled you to help us.

Therefore, O mighty power, we turn to you:
Find us our safety, find us a remedy,
Whether by counsel of the gods or of men.   45
A king of wisdom tested in the past
Can act in a time of troubles, and act well.
Noblest of men, restore
Life to your city! Think how all men call you
Liberator for your boldness long ago;   50
Ah, when your years of kingship are remembered,
Let them not say We rose, but later fell—
Keep the State from going down in the storm!
Once, years ago, with happy augury,
You brought us fortune; be the same again!   55

24. **Pallas:** Daughter of Zeus, goddess of wisdom, and protectress of Athens.
Apollo: Son of Zeus and god of the sun, of light, and of healing.   **39. Sphinx:** A
winged monster with the body of a lion and the face of a woman. The Sphinx tormented Thebes with a riddle—"What goes on four legs in the morning, two at
noon, and three in the evening?"—and killed those who could not answer correctly. When Oedipus solved the riddle, the Sphinx killed herself.

No man questions your power to rule the land:
But rule over men, not over a dead city!
Ships are only hulls, high walls are nothing,
When no life moves in the empty passageways.
OEDIPUS: Poor children! You may be sure I know   60
All that you longed for in your coming here.
I know that you are deathly sick; and yet,
Sick as you are, not one is as sick as I.
Each of you suffers in himself alone
His anguish, not another's; but my spirit   65
Groans for the city, for myself, for you.

I was not sleeping, you are not waking me.
No, I have been in tears for a long while
And in my restless thought walked many ways.
In all my search I found one remedy,   70
And I have adopted it: I have sent Kreon,
Son of Menoikeus, brother of the queen,
To Delphi,° Apollo's place of revelation,
To learn there, if he can,
What act or pledge of mine may save the city.   75
I have counted the days, and now, this very day,
I am troubled, for he has overstayed his time.
What is he doing? He has been gone too long.
Yet whenever he comes back, I should do ill
Not to take any action the god orders.   80
PRIEST: It is a timely promise. At this instant
They tell me Kreon is here.
OEDIPUS: O Lord Apollo!
May his news be fair as his face is radiant!
PRIEST: Good news, I gather! he is crowned with bay,
The chaplet is thick with berries.
OEDIPUS: We shall soon know;   85
He is near enough to hear us now. (*Enter Kreon.*) O prince:
Brother: son of Menoikeus:
What answer do you bring us from the god?
KREON: A strong one. I can tell you, great afflictions
Will turn out well, if they are taken well.   90
OEDIPUS: What was the oracle? These vague words
Leave me still hanging between hope and fear.
KREON: Is it your pleasure to hear me with all these

73. **Delphi:** Site of the oracle, the preeminent shrine of Apollo.

Gathered around us? I am prepared to speak,
But should we not go in?
OEDIPUS: Speak to them all,   95
It is for them I suffer, more than for myself.
KREON: Then I will tell you what I heard at Delphi.
In plain words   ₁
The god commands us to expel from the land of Thebes
An old defilement we are sheltering.   100
It is a deathly thing, beyond cure;
We must not let it feed upon us longer.
OEDIPUS: What defilement? How shall we rid ourselves of it?
KREON: By exile or death, blood for blood. It was
Murder that brought the plague-wind on the city.   105
OEDIPUS: Murder of whom? Surely the god has named him?
KREON: My Lord: Laios once ruled this land,
Before you came to govern us.
OEDIPUS: I know;
I learned of him from others; I never saw him.
KREON: He was murdered; and Apollo commands us now   110
To take revenge upon whoever killed him.
OEDIPUS: Upon whom? Where are they? Where shall we find a clue
To solve that crime, after so many years?
KREON: Here in this land, he said. Search reveals
Things that escape an inattentive man.   115
OEDIPUS: Tell me: Was Laios murdered in his house,
Or in the fields, or in some foreign country?
KREON: He said he planned to make a pilgrimage.
He did not come home again.
OEDIPUS: And was there no one,
No witness, no companion, to tell what happened?   120
KREON: They were all killed but one, and he got away
So frightened that he could remember one thing only.
OEDIPUS: What was that one thing? One may be the key
To everything, if we resolve to use it.
KREON: He said that a band of highwaymen attacked them,   125
Outnumbered them, and overwhelmed the king.
OEDIPUS: Strange, that a highwayman should be so daring—
Unless some faction here bribed him to do it.
KREON: We thought of that. But after Laios' death
New troubles arose and we had no avenger.   130
OEDIPUS: What troubles could prevent your hunting down the killers?
KREON: The riddling Sphinx's song
Made us deaf to all mysteries but her own.

261

OEDIPUS: Then once more I must bring what is dark to light.
It is most fitting that Apollo shows,   135
As you do, this compunction for the dead.
You shall see how I stand by you, as I should,
Avenging this country and the god as well,
And not as though it were for some distant friend,
But for my own sake, to be rid of evil.   140
Whoever killed King Laios might — who knows? —
Lay violent hands even on me — and soon.
I act for the murdered king in my own interest.

Come, then, my children: leave the altar steps,
Lift up your olive boughs!
                              One of you go   145
And summon the people of Kadmos to gather here.
I will do all that I can; you may tell them that.   (*Exit a Page.*)
So, with the help of God,
We shall be saved — or else indeed we are lost.
PRIEST: Let us rise, children. It was for this we came,   150
And now the king has promised it.
Phoibos° has sent us an oracle; may he descend
Himself to save us and drive out the plague.

(*Exeunt° Oedipus and Kreon into the palace by the central door. The Priest and
the Suppliants disperse right and left. After a short pause the Chorus enters the
orchestra.*)

PARODOS°   *Strophe° 1*

CHORUS: What is God singing in his profound
    Delphi of gold and shadow?
    What oracle for Thebes, the Sunwhipped city?
    Fear unjoints me, the roots of my heart tremble.
    Now I remember, O Healer, your power, and wonder: 5
    Will you send doom like a sudden cloud, or weave it
    Like nightfall of the past?
    Speak to me, tell me, O
    Child of golden Hope, immortal Voice.

152. Phoibos: Apollo.   [S.D.] *Exeunt:* Latin for "they go out."   **Parodos:** The
song chanted by the Chorus on their entry.   **Strophe:** Song sung by the Chorus
as they danced from stage right to stage left.

Antistrophe° 1

Let me pray to Athene, the immortal daughter of Zeus,   10
And to Artemis° her sister
Who keeps her famous throne in the market ring,
And to Apollo, archer from distant heaven—
O gods, descend! Like three streams leap against
The fires of our grief, the fires of darkness;   15
Be swift to bring us rest!
As in the old time from the brilliant house
Of air you stepped to save us, come again!

Strophe 2

Now our afflictions have no end,
Now all our stricken host lies down   20
And no man fights off death with his mind;
The noble plowland bears no grain,
And groaning mothers can not bear—
See, how our lives like birds take wing,
Like sparks that fly when a fire soars,   25
To the shore of the god of evening.

Antistrophe 2

The plague burns on, it is pitiless,
Though pallid children laden with death
Lie unwept in the stony ways,
And old gray women by every path   30
Flock to the strand about the altars
There to strike their breasts and cry
Worship of Phoibos in wailing prayers:
Be kind, God's golden child!

Strophe 3

There are no swords in this attack by fire,   35
No shields, but we are ringed with cries.
Send the besieger plunging from our homes

Antistrophe: Song sung by the Chorus as they danced from stage left back to stage right.   **11. Artemis:** Daughter of Zeus, twin sister of Apollo, goddess of the hunt and female chastity.

Into the vast sea-room of the Atlantic
Or into the waves that foam eastward of Thrace—
For the day ravages what the night spares—   40
Destroy our enemy, lord of the thunder!
Let him be riven by lightning from heaven!

Antistrophe 3

Phoibos Apollo, stretch the sun's bowstring,
That golden cord, until it sing for us,
Flashing arrows in heaven!
                    Artemis, Huntress,   45
Race with flaring lights upon our mountains!
O scarlet god,° O golden-banded brow,
O Theban Bacchos in a storm of Maenads,°

(*Enter Oedipus, center.*)

Whirl upon Death, that all the Undying hate!
Come with blinding torches, come in joy!   50

SCENE 1

OEDIPUS: Is this your prayer? It may be answered. Come,
  Listen to me, act as the crisis demands,
  And you shall have relief from all these evils.

Until now I was a stranger to this tale,
As I had been a stranger to the crime.   5
Could I track down the murderer without a clue?
But now, friends,
As one who became a citizen after the murder,
I make this proclamation to all Thebans:
If any man knows by whose hand Laios, son of Labdakos,   10
Met his death, I direct that man to tell me everything,
No matter what he fears for having so long withheld it.
Let it stand as promised that no further trouble
Will come to him, but he may leave the land in safety.
Moreover: If anyone knows the murderer to be foreign,   15
Let him not keep silent: he shall have his reward from me.

47. scarlet god: Bacchus, god of wine (also called Dionysus).   **48. Maenads:**
Bacchus's female devotees.

However, if he does conceal it; if any man
Fearing for his friend or for himself disobeys this edict,
Hear what I propose to do:

I solemnly forbid the people of this country,   20
Where power and throne are mine, ever to receive that man
Or speak to him, no matter who he is, or let him
Join in sacrifice, lustration, or in prayer.
I decree that he be driven from every house,
Being, as he is, corruption itself to us: the Delphic   25
Voice of Apollo has pronounced this revelation.
Thus I associate myself with the oracle
And take the side of the murdered king.

As for the criminal, I pray to God—
Whether it be a lurking thief, or one of a number—   30
I pray that that man's life be consumed in evil and wretchedness.
And as for me, this curse applies no less
If it should turn out that the culprit is my guest here,
Sharing my hearth.
                        You have heard the penalty.
I lay it on you now to attend to this   35
For my sake, for Apollo's, for the sick
Sterile city that heaven has abandoned.
Suppose the oracle had given you no command:
Should this defilement go uncleansed for ever?
You should have found the murderer: your king,   40
A noble king, had been destroyed!
                        Now I,
Having the power that he held before me,
Having his bed, begetting children there
Upon his wife, as he would have, had he lived—
Their son would have been my children's brother,   45
If Laios had had luck in fatherhood!
(And now his bad fortune has struck him down)—
I say I take the son's part, just as though
I were his son, to press the fight for him
And see it won! I'll find the hand that brought   50
Death to Labdakos' and Polydoros' child,
Heir of Kadmos' and Agenor's line.°

51–52. Labdakos, Polydoros, Kadmos, and Agenor: Father, grandfather, great-grandfather, and great-great-grandfather of Laios.

And as for those who fail me,
May the gods deny them the fruit of the earth,
Fruit of the womb, and may they rot utterly!   55
Let them be wretched as we are wretched, and worse!

For you, for loyal Thebans, and for all
Who find my actions right, I pray the favor
Of justice, and of all the immortal gods.
CHORAGOS:° Since I am under oath, my lord, I swear   60
   I did not do the murder, I can not name
   The murderer. Phoibos ordained the search;
   Why did he not say who the culprit was?
OEDIPUS: An honest question. But no man in the world
   Can make the gods do more than the gods will.   65
CHORAGOS: There is an alternative, I think—
OEDIPUS: Tell me.
   Any or all, you must not fail to tell me.
CHORAGOS: A lord clairvoyant to the lord Apollo,
   As we all know, is the skilled Teiresias.
   One might learn much about this from him, Oedipus.   70
OEDIPUS: I am not wasting time:
   Kreon spoke of this, and I have sent for him—
   Twice, in fact; it is strange that he is not here.
CHORAGOS: The other matter—that old report—seems useless.
OEDIPUS: What was that? I am interested in all reports.   75
CHORAGOS: The king was said to have been killed by highwaymen.
OEDIPUS: I know. But we have no witnesses to that.
CHORAGOS: If the killer can feel a particle of dread,
   Your curse will bring him out of hiding!
OEDIPUS: No.
   The man who dared that act will fear no curse.   80

(*Enter the blind seer Teiresias, led by a Page.*)

CHORAGOS: But there is one man who may detect the criminal.
   This is Teiresias, this is the holy prophet
   In whom, alone of all men, truth was born.
OEDIPUS: Teiresias: seer: student of mysteries,
   Of all that's taught and all that no man tells,   85
   Secrets of Heaven and secrets of the earth:
   Blind though you are, you know the city lies

---

60. **Choragos:** Chorus leader.

Sick with plague; and from this plague, my lord,
We find that you alone can guard or save us.

Possibly you did not hear the messengers?   90
Apollo, when we sent to him,
Sent us back word that this great pestilence
Would lift, but only if we established clearly
The identity of those who murdered Laios.
They must be killed or exiled.
                                   Can you use   95
Birdflight° or any art of divination
To purify yourself, and Thebes, and me
From this contagion? We are in your hands.
There is no fairer duty
Than that of helping others in distress.   100
TEIRESIAS: How dreadful knowledge of the truth can be
  When there's no help in truth! I knew this well,
  But did not act on it; else I should not have come.
OEDIPUS: What is troubling you? Why are your eyes so cold?
TEIRESIAS: Let me go home. Bear your own fate, and I'll   105
  Bear mine. It is better so: trust what I say.
OEDIPUS: What you say is ungracious and unhelpful
  To your native country. Do not refuse to speak.
TEIRESIAS: When it comes to speech, your own is neither temperate
  Nor opportune. I wish to be more prudent.   110
OEDIPUS: In God's name, we all beg you—
TEIRESIAS: You are all ignorant.
  No; I will never tell you what I know.
  Now it is my misery; then, it would be yours.
OEDIPUS: What! You do know something, and will not tell us?
  You would betray us all and wreck the State?   115
TEIRESIAS: I do not intend to torture myself, or you.
  Why persist in asking? You will not persuade me.
OEDIPUS: What a wicked old man you are! You'd try a stone's
  Patience! Out with it! Have you no feeling at all?
TEIRESIAS: You call me unfeeling. If you could only see   120
  The nature of your own feelings . . .
OEDIPUS: Why,
  Who would not feel as I do? Who could endure
  Your arrogance toward the city?

96. **Birdflight:** Prophets believed they could predict the future based on the flight
of birds.

267

TEIRESIAS: What does it matter?
  Whether I speak or not, it is bound to come.
OEDIPUS: Then, if "it" is bound to come, you are bound to tell me.   125
TEIRESIAS: No, I will not go on. Rage as you please.
OEDIPUS: Rage? Why not!
                And I'll tell you what I think:
  You planned it, you had it done, you all but
  Killed him with your own hands: if you had eyes,
  I'd say the crime was yours, and yours alone.   130
TEIRESIAS: So? I charge you, then,
  Abide by the proclamation you have made:
  From this day forth
  Never speak again to these men or to me;
  You yourself are the pollution of this country.   135
OEDIPUS: You dare say that! Can you possibly think you have
  Some way of going free, after such insolence?
TEIRESIAS: I have gone free. It is the truth sustains me.
OEDIPUS: Who taught you shamelessness? It was not your craft.
TEIRESIAS: You did. You made me speak. I did not want to.   140
OEDIPUS: Speak what? Let me hear it again more clearly.
TEIRESIAS: Was it not clear before? Are you tempting me?
OEDIPUS: I did not understand it. Say it again.
TEIRESIAS: I say that you are the murderer whom you seek.
OEDIPUS: Now twice you have spat out infamy. You'll pay for it!   145
TEIRESIAS: Would you care for more? Do you wish to be really angry?
OEDIPUS: Say what you will. Whatever you say is worthless.
TEIRESIAS: I say you live in hideous shame with those
  Most dear to you. You can not see the evil.
OEDIPUS: Can you go on babbling like this for ever?   150
TEIRESIAS: I can, if there is power in truth.
OEDIPUS: There is:
  But not for you, not for you,
  You sightless, witless, senseless, mad old man!
TEIRESIAS: You are the madman. There is no one here
  Who will not curse you soon, as you curse me.   155
OEDIPUS: You child of total night! I would not touch you;
  Neither would any man who sees the sun.
TEIRESIAS: True: it is not from you my fate will come.
  That lies within Apollo's competence,
  As it is his concern.
OEDIPUS: Tell me, who made   160
  These fine discoveries? Kreon? or someone else?
TEIRESIAS: Kreon is no threat. You weave your own doom.

OEDIPUS: Wealth, power, craft of statemanship!
  Kingly position, everywhere admired!
  What savage envy is stored up against these,   165
  If Kreon, whom I trusted, Kreon my friend,
  For this great office which the city once
  Put in my hands unsought—if for this power
  Kreon desires in secret to destroy me!

  He has bought this decrepit fortune-teller, this   170
  Collector of dirty pennies, this prophet fraud—
  Why, he is no more clairvoyant than I am!
                                        Tell us:
  Has your mystic mummery ever approached the truth?
  When that hellcat the Sphinx was performing here,
  What help were you to these people?   175
  Her magic was not for the first man who came along:
  It demanded a real exorcist. Your birds—
  What good were they? or the gods, for the matter of that?
  But I came by,
  Oedipus, the simple man, who knows nothing—   180
  I thought it out for myself, no birds helped me!
  And this is the man you think you can destroy,
  That you may be close to Kreon when he's king!
  Well, you and your friend Kreon, it seems to me,
  Will suffer most. If you were not an old man,   185
  You would have paid already for your plot.
CHORAGOS: We can not see that his words or yours
  Have been spoken except in anger, Oedipus,
  And of anger we have no need. How to accomplish
  The god's will best: that is what most concerns us.   190
TEIRESIAS: You are a king. But where argument's concerned
  I am your man, as much a king as you.
  I am not your servant, but Apollo's.
  I have no need of Kreon or Kreon's name.

  Listen to me. You mock my blindness, do you?   195
  But I say that you, with both your eyes, are blind:
  You can not see the wretchedness of your life,
  Nor in whose house you live, no, nor with whom.
  Who are your father and mother? Can you tell me?
  You do not even know the blind wrongs   200
  That you have done them, on earth and in the world below.
  But the double lash of your parents' curse will whip you

Out of this land some day, with only night
Upon your precious eyes.
Your cries then—where will they not be heard?   205
What fastness of Kithairon° will not echo them?
And that bridal-descant of yours—you'll know it then,
The song they sang when you came here to Thebes
And found your misguided berthing.
All this, and more, that you can not guess at now,   210
Will bring you to yourself among your children.

Be angry, then. Curse Kreon. Curse my words.
I tell you, no man that walks upon the earth
Shall be rooted out more horribly than you.
OEDIPUS: Am I to bear this from him?—Damnation   215
    Take you! Out of this place! Out of my sight!
TEIRESIAS: I would not have come at all if you had not asked me.
OEDIPUS: Could I have told that you'd talk nonsense, that
    You'd come here to make a fool of yourself, and of me?
TEIRESIAS: A fool? Your parents thought me sane enough.   220
OEDIPUS: My parents again!—Wait: who were my parents?
TEIRESIAS: This day will give you a father, and break your heart.
OEDIPUS: Your infantile riddles! Your damned abracadabra!
TEIRESIAS: You were a great man once at solving riddles.
OEDIPUS: Mock me with that if you like; you will find it true.   225
TEIRESIAS: It was true enough. It brought about your ruin.
OEDIPUS: But if it saved this town?
TEIRESIAS (*to the Page*):   Boy, give me your hand.
OEDIPUS: Yes, boy; lead him away.
                        —While you are here
    We can do nothing. Go; leave us in peace.
TEIRESIAS: I will go when I have said what I have to say.   230
    How can you hurt me? And I tell you again:
    The man you have been looking for all this time,
    The damned man, the murderer of Laios,
    That man is in Thebes. To your mind he is foreign-born,
    But it will soon be shown that he is a Theban,   235
    A revelation that will fail to please.
                        A blind man,
    Who has his eyes now; a penniless man, who is rich now;
    And he will go tapping the strange earth with his staff.

206. Kithairon: The mountain near Thebes where Oedipus was abandoned as an
infant.

To the children with whom he lives now he will be
Brother and father—the very same; to her   240
Who bore him, son and husband—the very same
Who came to his father's bed, wet with his father's blood.
Enough. Go think that over.
If later you find error in what I have said,
You may say that I have no skill in prophecy.   245

(*Exit Teiresias, led by his Page. Oedipus goes into the palace.*)

ODE° 1   *Strophe 1*

CHORUS: The Delphic stone of prophecies
Remembers ancient regicide
And a still bloody hand.
That killer's hour of flight has come.
He must be stronger than riderless   5
Coursers of untiring wind,
For the son of Zeus° armed with his father's thunder
Leaps in lightning after him;
And the Furies° hold his track, the sad Furies.

Antistrophe 1

Holy Parnassos'° peak of snow   10
Flashes and blinds that secret man,
That all shall hunt him down:
Though he may roam the forest shade
Like a bull gone wild from pasture
To rage through glooms of stone.   15
Doom comes down on him; flight will not avail him;
For the world's heart calls him desolate,
And the immortal voices follow, for ever follow.

Strophe 2

But now a wilder thing is heard
From the old man skilled at hearing Fate in the wing-beat of a bird.   20

Ode: Song sung by the Chorus.   **7. son of Zeus:** Apollo.   **9. Furies:** Powerful
avenging divinities.   **10. Parnassos:** Mountain sacred to Apollo.

271

Bewildered as a blown bird, my soul hovers and can not find
Foothold in this debate, or any reason or rest of mind.
But no man ever brought—none can bring
Proof of strife between Thebes' royal house,
Labdakos' line,° and the son of Polybos;°   25
And never until now has any man brought word
Of Laios' dark death staining Oedipus the King.

Antistrophe 2

Divine Zeus and Apollo hold
Perfect intelligence alone of all tales ever told;
And well though this diviner works, he works in his own night;   30
No man can judge that rough unknown or trust in second sight,
For wisdom changes hands among the wise.
Shall I believe my great lord criminal
At a raging word that a blind old man let fall?
I saw him, when the carrion woman° faced him of old,   35
Prove his heroic mind. These evil words are lies.

SCENE 2

KREON: Men of Thebes:
   I am told that heavy accusations
   Have been brought against me by King Oedipus.

   I am not the kind of man to bear this tamely.

   If in these present difficulties   5
   He holds me accountable for any harm to him
   Through anything I have said or done—why, then,
   I do not value life in this dishonor.
   It is not as though this rumor touched upon
   Some private indiscretion. The matter is grave.   10
   The fact is that I am being called disloyal
   To the State, to my fellow citizens, to my friends.
CHORAGOS: He may have spoken in anger, not from his mind.

---

25. **Labdakos' line:** Laios's family. **Polybos:** King of Corinth who adopted
Oedipus. 35. **woman:** The Sphinx.

272

KREON: But did you not hear him say I was the one
  Who seduced the old prophet into lying?   15
CHORAGOS: The thing was said; I do not know how seriously.
KREON: But you were watching him! Were his eyes steady?
  Did he look like a man in his right mind?
CHORAGOS: I do not know.
  I can not judge the behavior of great men.
  But here is the king himself.

(*Enter Oedipus.*)

OEDIPUS: So you dared come back.   20
  Why? How brazen of you to come to my house,
  You murderer!
                    Do you think I do not know
  That you plotted to kill me, plotted to steal my throne?
  Tell me, in God's name: am I coward, a fool,
  That you should dream you could accomplish this?   25
  A fool who could not see your slippery game?
  A coward, not to fight back when I saw it?
  You are the fool, Kreon, are you not? hoping
  Without support or friends to get a throne?
  Thrones may be won or bought: you could do neither.   30
KREON: Now listen to me. You have talked; let me talk, too.
  You can not judge unless you know the facts.
OEDIPUS: You speak well: there is one fact; but I find it hard
  To learn from the deadliest enemy I have.
KREON: That above all I must dispute with you.   35
OEDIPUS: That above all I will not hear you deny.
KREON: If you think there is anything good in being stubborn
  Against all reason, then I say you are wrong.
OEDIPUS: If you think a man can sin against his own kind
  And not be punished for it, I say you are mad.   40
KREON: I agree. But tell me: what have I done to you?
OEDIPUS: You advised me to send for that wizard, did you not?
KREON: I did. I should do it again.
OEDIPUS: Very well. Now tell me:
  How long has it been since Laios—
KREON: What of Laios?
OEDIPUS: Since he vanished in that onset by the road?   45
KREON: It was long ago, a long time.
OEDIPUS: And this prophet,
  Was he practicing here then?
KREON: He was; and with honor, as now.

273

OEDIPUS: Did he speak of me at that time?
KREON:　　　　　　　　　　　He never did,
　At least, not when I was present.
OEDIPUS:　　　　　　　But . . . the enquiry?
　I suppose you held one?
KREON:　　　　　　We did, but we learned nothing.　　50
OEDIPUS: Why did the prophet not speak against me then?
KREON: I do not know; and I am the kind of man
　Who holds his tongue when he has no facts to go on.
OEDIPUS: There's one fact that you know, and you could tell it.
KREON: What fact is that? If I know it, you shall have it.　　55
OEDIPUS: If he were not involved with you, he could not say
　That it was I who murdered Laios.
KREON: If he says that, you are the one that knows it!—
　But now it is my turn to question you.
OEDIPUS: Put your questions. I am no murderer.　　60
KREON: First, then: You married my sister?
OEDIPUS:　　　　　　　　　　I married your sister.
KREON: And you rule the kingdom equally with her?
OEDIPUS: Everything that she wants she has from me.
KREON: And I am the third, equal to both of you?
OEDIPUS: That is why I call you a bad friend.　　65
KREON: No. Reason it out, as I have done.
　Think of this first: would any sane man prefer
　Power, with all a king's anxieties,
　To that same power and the grace of sleep?
　Certainly not I.　　70
　I have never longed for the king's power—only his rights.
　Would any wise man differ from me in this?
　As matters stand, I have my way in everything
　With your consent, and no responsibilities.
　If I were king, I should be a slave to policy.　　75
　How could I desire a scepter more
　Than what is now mine—untroubled influence?
　No, I have not gone mad; I need no honors,
　Except those with the perquisites I have now.
　I am welcome everywhere; every man salutes me,　　80
　And those who want your favor seek my ear,
　Since I know how to manage what they ask.
　Should I exchange this ease for that anxiety?
　Besides, no sober mind is treasonable.
　I hate anarchy　　85
　And never would deal with any man who likes it.

Test what I have said. Go to the priestess
At Delphi, ask if I quoted her correctly.
And as for this other thing: if I am found
Guilty of treason with Teiresias,   90
Then sentence me to death. You have my word
It is a sentence I should cast my vote for—
But not without evidence!
                                        You do wrong
When you take good men for bad, bad men for good.
A true friend thrown aside—why, life itself   95
Is not more precious!   ·
                                        In time you will know this well:
For time, and time alone, will show the just man,
Though scoundrels are discovered in a day.
CHORAGOS: This is well said, and a prudent man would ponder it.
    Judgments too quickly formed are dangerous.   100
OEDIPUS: But is he not quick in his duplicity?
    And shall I not be quick to parry him?
    Would you have me stand still, hold my peace, and let
    This man win everything, through my inaction?
KREON: And you want—what is it, then? To banish me?   105
OEDIPUS: No, not exile. It is your death I want,
    So that all the world may see what treason means.
KREON: You will persist, then? You will not believe me?
OEDIPUS: How can I believe you?
KREON: Then you are a fool.
OEDIPUS: To save myself?
KREON: In justice, think of me.   110
OEDIPUS: You are evil incarnate.
KREON: But suppose that you are wrong?
OEDIPUS: Still I must rule.
KREON: But not if you rule badly.
OEDIPUS: O city, city!
KREON: It is my city, too!
CHORAGOS: Now, my lords, be still. I see the queen,
    Iokaste, coming from her palace chambers;   115
    And it is time she came, for the sake of you both.
    This dreadful quarrel can be resolved through her.

(*Enter Iokaste.*)

IOKASTE: Poor foolish men, what wicked din is this?
    With Thebes sick to death, is it not shameful
    That you should take some private quarrel up?   120

(*To Oedipus.*) Come into the house.
                         —And you, Kreon, go now:
Let us have no more of this tumult over nothing.
KREON: Nothing? No, sister: what your husband plans for me
  Is one of two great evils: exile or death.
OEDIPUS: He is right.
                    Why, woman I have caught him squarely   125
  Plotting against my life.
KREON: No! Let me die
  Accurst if ever I have wished you harm!
IOKASTE: Ah, believe it, Oedipus!
  In the name of the gods, respect this oath of his
  For my sake, for the sake of these people here!   130

Strophe 1

CHORAGOS: Open your mind to her, my lord. Be ruled by her, I beg you!
OEDIPUS: What would you have me do?
CHORAGOS: Respect Kreon's word. He has never spoken like a fool,
  And now he has sworn an oath.
OEDIPUS: You know what you ask?
CHORAGOS: I do.
OEDIPUS: Speak on, then.
CHORAGOS: A friend so sworn should not be baited so,   135
  In blind malice, and without final proof.
OEDIPUS: You are aware, I hope, that what you say
  Means death for me, or exile at the least.

Strophe 2

CHORAGOS: No, I swear by Helios, first in heaven!
    May I die friendless and accurst,   140
  The worst of deaths, if ever I meant that!
  It is the withering fields
    That hurt my sick heart:
  Must we bear all these ills,
  And now your bad blood as well?   145
OEDIPUS: Then let him go. And let me die, if I must,
  Or be driven by him in shame from the land of Thebes.
  It is your unhappiness, and not his talk,
  That touches me.
            As for him—
  Wherever he goes, hatred will follow him.   150

KREON: Ugly in yielding, as you were ugly in rage!
  Natures like yours chiefly torment themselves.
OEDIPUS: Can you not go? Can you not leave me?
KREON: I can.
  You do not know me; but the city knows me,
  And in its eyes I am just, if not in yours.   (*Exit Kreon.*)   155

Antistrophe 1

CHORAGOS: Lady Iokaste, did you not ask the King to go to his
  chambers?
IOKASTE: First tell me what has happened.
CHORAGOS: There was suspicion without evidence; yet it rankled
  As even false charges will.
IOKASTE: On both sides?
CHORAGOS: On both.
IOKASTE: But what was said?   160
CHORAGOS: Oh let it rest, let it be done with!
  Have we not suffered enough?
OEDIPUS: You see to what your decency has brought you:
  You have made difficulties where my heart saw none.

Antistrophe 2

CHORAGOS: Oedipus, it is not once only I have told you—   165
  You must know I should count myself unwise
  To the point of madness, should I now forsake you—
      You, under whose hand,
        In the storm of another time,
        Our dear land sailed out free.   170
        But now stand fast at the helm!
IOKASTE: In God's name, Oedipus, inform your wife as well:
  Why are you so set in this hard anger?
OEDIPUS: I will tell you, for none of these men deserves
  My confidence as you do. It is Kreon's work,   175
  His treachery, his plotting against me.
IOKASTE: Go on, if you can make this clear to me.
OEDIPUS: He charges me with the murder of Laios.
IOKASTE: Has he some knowledge? Or does he speak from
  hearsay?
OEDIPUS: He would not commit himself to such a charge,   180
  But he has brought in that damnable soothsayer
  To tell his story.

IOKASTE: Set your mind at rest.
If it is a question of soothsayers, I tell you
That you will find no man whose craft gives knowledge
Of the unknowable.
                    Here is my proof: 185
An oracle was reported to Laios once
(I will not say from Phoibos himself, but from
His appointed ministers, at any rate)
That his doom would be death at the hands of his own son—
His son, born of his flesh and of mine!   190

Now, you remember the story: Laios was killed
By marauding strangers where three highways meet;
But his child had not been three days in this world
Before the king had pierced the baby's ankles
And left him to die on a lonely mountainside.   195

Thus, Apollo never caused that child
To kill his father, and it was not Laios' fate
To die at the hands of his son, as he had feared.
This is what prophets and prophecies are worth!
Have no dread of them.
                    It is God himself   200
Who can show us what he wills, in his own way.
OEDIPUS: How strange a shadowy memory crossed my mind,
     Just now while you were speaking; it chilled my heart.
IOKASTE: What do you mean? What memory do you speak of?
OEDIPUS: If I understand you, Laios was killed   205
     At a place where three roads meet.
IOKASTE: So it was said;
     We have no later story.
OEDIPUS: Where did it happen?
IOKASTE: Phokis, it is called: at a place where the Theban Way
     Divides into the roads toward Delphi and Daulia.
OEDIPUS: When?
IOKASTE: We had the news not long before you came   210
     And proved the right to your succession here.
OEDIPUS: Ah, what net has God been weaving for me?
IOKASTE: Oedipus! Why does this trouble you?
OEDIPUS: Do not ask me yet.
     First, tell me how Laios looked, and tell me
     How old he was.

IOKASTE: He was tall, his hair just touched   215
  With white; his form was not unlike your own.
OEDIPUS: I think that I myself may be accurst
  By my own ignorant edict.
IOKASTE: You speak strangely.
  It makes me tremble to look at you, my king.
OEDIPUS: I am not sure that the blind man can not see.   220
  But I should know better if you were to tell me —
IOKASTE: Anything — though I dread to hear you ask it.
OEDIPUS: Was the king lightly escorted, or did he ride
  With a large company, as a ruler should?
IOKASTE: There were five men with him in all: one was a herald;   225
  And a single chariot, which he was driving.
OEDIPUS: Alas, that makes it plain enough!
                                But who —
  Who told you how it happened?
IOKASTE: A household servant,
  The only one to escape.
OEDIPUS: And is he still
  A servant of ours?
IOKASTE: No; for when he came back at last   230
  And found you enthroned in the place of the dead king,
  He came to me, touched my hand with his, and begged
  That I would send him away to the frontier district
  Where only the shepherds go —
  As far away from the city as I could send him.   235
  I granted his prayer; for although the man was a slave,
  He had earned more than this favor at my hands.
OEDIPUS: Can he be called back quickly?
IOKASTE: Easily.
  But why?
OEDIPUS: I have taken too much upon myself   240
  Without enquiry; therefore I wish to consult him.
IOKASTE: Then he shall come.
                      But am I not one also
  To whom you might confide these fears of yours?
OEDIPUS: That is your right; it will not be denied you,
  Now least of all; for I have reached a pitch   245
  Of wild foreboding. Is there anyone
  To whom I should sooner speak?

  Polybos of Corinth is my father.
  My mother is a Dorian: Merope.

I grew up chief among the men of Corinth   250
Until a strange thing happened—
Not worth my passion, it may be, but strange.
At a feast, a drunken man maundering in his cups
Cries out that I am not my father's son!
I contained myself that night, though I felt anger   255
And a sinking heart. The next day I visited
My father and mother, and questioned them. They stormed,
Calling it all the slanderous rant of a fool;
And this relieved me. Yet the suspicion
Remained always aching in my mind;   260
I knew there was talk; I could not rest;
And finally, saying nothing to my parents,
I went to the shrine at Delphi.

The god dismissed my question without reply;
He spoke of other things.
                        Some were clear,   265
Full of wretchedness, dreadful, unbearable:
As, that I should lie with my own mother, breed
Children from whom all men would turn their eyes;
And that I should be my father's murderer.

I heard all this, and fled. And from that day   270
Corinth to me was only in the stars
Descending in that quarter of the sky,
As I wandered farther and farther on my way
To a land where I should never see the evil
Sung by the oracle. And I came to this country   275
Where, so you say, King Laios was killed.

I will tell you all that happened there, my lady.
There were three highways
Coming together at a place I passed;
And there a herald came towards me, and a chariot   280
Drawn by horses, with a man such as you describe
Seated in it. The groom leading the horses
Forced me off the road at his lord's command;
But as this charioteer lurched over towards me
I struck him in my rage. The old man saw me   285
And brought his double goad down upon my head
As I came abreast.
                        He was paid back, and more!

Swinging my club in this right hand I knocked him
Out of his car, and he rolled on the ground.
                                      I killed him.

I killed them all.   290
Now if that stranger and Laios were—kin,
Where is a man more miserable than I?
More hated by the gods? Citizen and alien alike
Must never shelter me or speak to me—
I must be shunned by all.
                         And I myself   295
Pronounced this malediction upon myself!

Think of it: I have touched you with these hands,
These hands that killed your husband. What defilement!

Am I all evil, then? It must be so,
Since I must flee from Thebes, yet never again   300
See my own countrymen, my own country,
For fear of joining my mother in marriage
And killing Polybos, my father.
                              Ah,
If I was created so, born to this fate,
Who could deny the savagery of God?   305

O holy majesty of heavenly powers!
May I never see that day! Never!
Rather let me vanish from the race of men
Than know the abomination destined me!
CHORAGOS: We too, my lord, have felt dismay at this.   310
    But there is hope: you have yet to hear the shepherd.
OEDIPUS: Indeed, I fear no other hope is left me.
IOKASTE: What do you hope from him when he comes?
OEDIPUS: This much:
    If his account of the murder tallies with yours,
    Then I am cleared.
IOKASTE: What was it that I said   315
    Of such importance?
OEDIPUS: Why, "marauders," you said,
    Killed the king, according to this man's story.
    If he maintains that still, if there were several,
    Clearly the guilt is not mine: I was alone.
    But if he says one man, singlehanded, did it,   320
    Then the evidence all points to me.

IOKASTE: You may be sure that he said there were several;
   And can he call back that story now? He can not.
   The whole city heard it as plainly as I.
   But suppose he alters some detail of it: 325
   He can not ever show that Laios' death
   Fulfilled the oracle: for Apollo said
   My child was doomed to kill him; and my child—
   Poor baby!—it was my child that died first.

   No. From now on, where oracles are concerned,   330
   I would not waste a second thought on any.
OEDIPUS: You may be right.
                  But come: let someone go
   For the shepherd at once. This matter must be settled.
IOKASTE: I will send for him.
   I would not wish to cross you in anything,   335
   And surely not in this.—Let us go in.

                       (*Exeunt into the palace.*)

ODE 2   *Strophe 1*

CHORUS: Let me be reverent in the ways of right,
   Lowly the paths I journey on;
   Let all my words and actions keep
   The laws of the pure universe
   From highest Heaven handed down.   5
   For Heaven is their bright nurse,
   Those generations of the realms of light;
   Ah, never of mortal kind were they begot,
   Nor are they slaves of memory, lost in sleep:
   Their Father is greater than Time, and ages not.   10

Antistrophe 1

   The tyrant is a child of Pride
   Who drinks from his great sickening cup
   Recklessness and vanity,
   Until from his high crest headlong
   He plummets to the dust of hope.   15
   That strong man is not strong.
   But let no fair ambition be denied;

May God protect the wrestler for the State
In government, in comely policy,
Who will fear God, and on his ordinance wait.   20

Strophe 2

Haughtiness and the high hand of disdain
Tempt and outrage God's holy law;
And any mortal who dares hold
No immortal Power in awe
Will be caught up in a net of pain: 25
The price for which his levity is sold.
Let each man take due earnings, then,
And keep his hands from holy things,
And from blasphemy stand apart—
Else the crackling blast of heaven   30
Blows on his head, and on his desperate heart.
Though fools will honor impious men,
In their cities no tragic poet sings.

Antistrophe 2

Shall we lose faith in Delphi's obscurities,
We who have heard the world's core   35
Discredited, and the sacred wood
Of Zeus at Elis praised no more?
The deeds and the strange prophecies
Must make a pattern yet to be understood.
Zeus, if indeed you are lord of all,   40
Throned in light over night and day,
Mirror this in your endless mind:
Our masters call the oracle
Words on the wind, and the Delphic vision blind!
Their hearts no longer know Apollo,   45
And reverence for the gods has died away.

SCENE 3

(*Enter Iokaste.*)

IOKASTE: Princes of Thebes, it has occurred to me
    To visit the altars of the gods, bearing

These branches as a suppliant, and this incense.
Our king is not himself: his noble soul
Is overwrought with fantasies of dread,   5
Else he would consider
The new prophecies in the light of the old.
He will listen to any voice that speaks disaster,
And my advice goes for nothing. (*She approaches the
altar, right.*)
                To you, then, Apollo,
Lycean lord, since you are nearest, I turn in prayer   10
Receive these offerings, and grant us deliverance
From defilement. Our hearts are heavy with fear
When we see our leader distracted, as helpless sailors
Are terrified by the confusion of their helmsman.

(*Enter Messenger.*)

MESSENGER: Friends, no doubt you can direct me: 15
  Where shall I find the house of Oedipus,
  Or, better still, where is the king himself?
CHORAGOS: It is this very place, stranger; he is inside.
  This is his wife and mother of his children.
MESSENGER: I wish her happiness in a happy house,   20
  Blest in all the fulfillment of her marriage.
IOKASTE: I wish as much for you: your courtesy
  Deserves a like good fortune. But now, tell me:
  Why have you come? What have you to say to us?
MESSENGER: Good news, my lady, for your house and your husband. 25
IOKASTE: What news? Who sent you here?
MESSENGER: I am from Corinth.
  The news I bring ought to mean joy for you,
  Though it may be you will find some grief in it.
IOKASTE: What is it? How can it touch us in both ways?
MESSENGER: The word is that the people of the Isthmus   30
  Intend to call Oedipus to be their king.
IOKASTE: But old King Polybos—is he not reigning still?
MESSENGER: No. Death holds him in his sepulchre.
IOKASTE: What are you saying? Polybos is dead?
MESSENGER: If I am not telling the truth, may I die myself.   35
IOKASTE (*to a Maidservant*): Go in, go quickly; tell this to your master.
  O riddlers of God's will, where are you now!
  This was the man whom Oedipus, long ago,
  Feared so, fled so, in dread of destroying him—
  But it was another fate by which he died.   40

(*Enter Oedipus, center.*)

OEDIPUS: Dearest Iokaste, why have you sent for me?
IOKASTE: Listen to what this man says, and then tell me
  What has become of the solemn prophecies.
OEDIPUS: Who is this man? What is his news for me?
IOKASTE: He has come.from Corinth to announce your father's death!   45
OEDIPUS: Is it true, stranger? Tell me in your own words.
MESSENGER: I can not say it more clearly: the king is dead.
OEDIPUS: Was it by treason? Or by an attack of illness?
MESSENGER: A little thing brings old men to their rest.
OEDIPUS: It was sickness, then?
MESSENGER: Yes, and his many years.   50
OEDIPUS: Ah!
  Why should a man respect the Pythian hearth,° or
  Give heed to the birds that jangle above his head?
  They prophesied that I should kill Polybos,
  Kill my own father; but he is dead and buried,   55
  And I am here—I never touched him, never,
  Unless he died of grief for my departure,
  And thus, in a sense, through me. No. Polybos
  Has packed the oracles off with him underground.
  They are empty words.
IOKASTE: Had I not told you so?   60
OEDIPUS: You had; it was my faint heart that betrayed me.
IOKASTE: From now on never think of those things again.
OEDIPUS: And yet—must I not fear my mother's bed?
IOKASTE: Why should anyone in this world be afraid
  Since Fate rules us and nothing can be foreseen?   65
  A man should live only for the present day.

  Have no more fear of sleeping with your mother:
  How many men, in dreams, have lain with their mothers!
  No reasonable man is troubled by such things.
OEDIPUS: That is true, only—   70
  If only my mother were not still alive!
  But she is alive. I can not help my dread.
IOKASTE: Yet this news of your father's death is wonderful.
OEDIPUS: Wonderful. But I fear the living woman.
MESSENGER: Tell me, who is this woman that you fear?   75
OEDIPUS: It is Merope, man; the wife of King Polybos.

52. **Pythian hearth:** A site in Delphi where ritualistic offerings were made.

285

MESSENGER: Merope? Why should you be afraid of her?
OEDIPUS: An oracle of the gods, a dreadful saying.
MESSENGER: Can you tell me about it or are you sworn to silence?
OEDIPUS: I can tell you, and I will.   80
   Apollo said through his prophet that I was the man
   Who should marry his own mother, shed his father's blood
   With his own hands. And so, for all these years
   I have kept clear of Corinth, and no harm has come—
   Though it would have been sweet to see my parents again.   85
MESSENGER: And is this the fear that drove you out of Corinth?
OEDIPUS: Would you have me kill my father?
MESSENGER: As for that
   You must be reassured by the news I gave you.
OEDIPUS: If you could reassure me, I would reward you.
MESSENGER: I had that in mind, I will confess: I thought   90
   I could count on you when you returned to Corinth.
OEDIPUS: No: I will never go near my parents again.
MESSENGER: Ah, son, you still do not know what you are doing—
OEDIPUS: What do you mean? In the name of God tell me!
MESSENGER:—If these are your reasons for not going home.   95
OEDIPUS: I tell you, I fear the oracle may come true.
MESSENGER: And guilt may come upon you through your parents?
OEDIPUS: That is the dread that is always in my heart.
MESSENGER: Can you not see that all your fears are groundless?
OEDIPUS: Groundless? Am I not my parents' son?   100
MESSENGER: Polybos was not your father.
OEDIPUS: Not my father?
MESSENGER: No more your father than the man speaking to you.
OEDIPUS: But you are nothing to me!
MESSENGER: Neither was he.
OEDIPUS: Then why did he call me son?
MESSENGER: I will tell you:
   Long ago he had you from my hands, as a gift.   105
OEDIPUS: Then how could he love me so, if I was not his?
MESSENGER: He had no children, and his heart turned to you.
OEDIPUS: What of you? Did you buy me? Did you find me by chance?
MESSENGER: I came upon you in the woody vales of Kithairon.
OEDIPUS: And what were you doing there?
MESSENGER: Tending my flocks.   110
OEDIPUS: A wandering shepherd?
MESSENGER: But your savior, son, that day.
OEDIPUS: From what did you save me?
MESSENGER: Your ankles should tell you that.

OEDIPUS: Ah, stranger, why do you speak of that childhood pain?
MESSENGER: I pulled the skewer that pinned your feet together.
OEDIPUS: I have had the mark as long as I can remember.   115
MESSENGER: That was why you were given the name you bear.°
OEDIPUS: God! Was it my father or my mother who did it?
   Tell me!
MESSENGER: I do not know. The man who gave you to me
   Can tell you better than I.
OEDIPUS: It was not you that found me, but another?   120
MESSENGER: It was another shepherd gave you to me.
OEDIPUS: Who was he? Can you tell me who he was?
MESSENGER: I think he was said to be one of Laios' people.
OEDIPUS: You mean the Laios who was king here years ago?
MESSENGER: Yes; King Laios; and the man was one of his herdsmen.   125
OEDIPUS: Is he still alive? Can I see him?
MESSENGER: These men here
   Know best about such things.
OEDIPUS: ·   Does anyone here
   Know this shepherd that he is talking about?
   Have you seen him in the fields, or in the town?
   If you have, tell me. It is time things were made plain.   130
CHORAGOS: I think the man he means is that same shepherd
   You have already asked to see. Iokaste perhaps
   Could tell you something.
OEDIPUS: Do you know anything
   About him, Lady? Is he the man we have summoned?
   Is that the man this shepherd means?
IOKASTE: Why think of him?   135
   Forget this herdsman. Forget it all.
   This talk is a waste of time.
OEDIPUS: How can you say that,
   When the clues to my true birth are in my hands?
IOKASTE: For God's love, let us have no more questioning!
   Is your life nothing to you?   140
   My own is pain enough for me to bear.
OEDIPUS: You need not worry. Suppose my mother a slave,
   And born of slaves: no baseness can touch you.
IOKASTE: Listen to me, I beg you: do not do this thing!
OEDIPUS: I will not listen; the truth must be made known.   145
IOKASTE: Everything that I say is for your own good!

---

116. name you bear: "Oedipus" literally means swollen foot.

OEDIPUS: My own good
   Snaps my patience, then; I want none of it.
IOKASTE: You are fatally wrong! May you never learn who you are!
OEDIPUS: Go, one of you, and bring the shepherd here.
   Let us leave this woman to brag of her royal name.   150
IOKASTE: Ah, miserable!
   That is the only word I have for you now.
   That is the only word I can ever have.   (*Exit into the palace.*)
CHORAGOS: Why has she left us, Oedipus? Why has she gone
   In such a passion of sorrow? I fear this silence: 155
   Something dreadful may come of it.
OEDIPUS: Let it come!
   However base my birth, I must know about it.
   The Queen, like a woman, is perhaps ashamed
   To think of my low origin. But I
   Am a child of Luck, I can not be dishonored.   160
   Luck is my mother; the passing months, my brothers,
   Have seen me rich and poor.
                If this is so,
   How could I wish that I were someone else?
   How could I not be glad to know my birth?

ODE 3   *Strophe*

CHORUS: If ever the coming time were known
   To my heart's pondering,
   Kithairon, now by Heaven I see the torches
   At the festival of the next full moon
   And see the dance, and hear the choir sing   5
   A grace to your gentle shade:
   Mountain where Oedipus was found,
   O mountain guard of a noble race!
   May the god° who heals us lend his aid,
   And let that glory come to pass   10
   For our king's cradling-ground.

Antistrophe

Of the nymphs that flower beyond the years,
   Who bore you, royal child,

9. **god:** Apollo.

288

To Pan° of the hills or the timberline Apollo,
Cold in delight where the upland clears,   15
Or Hermes° for whom Kyllene's° heights are piled?
Or flushed as evening cloud,
Great Dionysos, roamer of mountains,
He—was it he who found you there,
And caught you up in his own proud   20
Arms from the sweet god-ravisher
Who laughed by the Muses'° fountains?

SCENE 4

OEDIPUS: Sirs: though I do not know the man,
I think I see him coming, this shepherd we want:
He is old, like our friend here, and the men
Bringing him seem to be servants of my house.
But you can tell, if you have ever seen him.   5

(*Enter Shepherd escorted by Servants.*)

CHORAGOS: I know him, he was Laios' man. You can trust him.
OEDIPUS: Tell me first, you from Corinth: is this the shepherd
We were discussing?
MESSENGER: This is the very man.
OEDIPUS (*to Shepherd*): Come here. No, look at me. You must answer
Everything I ask.—You belonged to Laios?   10
SHEPHERD: Yes: born his slave, brought up in his house.
OEDIPUS: Tell me: what kind of work did you do for him?
SHEPHERD: I was a shepherd of his, most of my life.
OEDIPUS: Where mainly did you go for pasturage?
SHEPHERD: Sometimes Kithairon, sometimes the hills near-by.   15
OEDIPUS: Do you remember ever seeing this man out there?
SHEPHERD: What would he be doing there? This man?
OEDIPUS: This man standing here. Have you ever seen him before?
SHEPHERD: No. At least, not to my recollection.
MESSENGER: And that is not strange, my lord. But I'll refresh   20
His memory: he must remember when we two
Spent three whole seasons together, March to September,

14. **Pan:** God of nature and fertility, depicted as an ugly man with the horns and legs of a goat. Pan was considered playful and amorous. 16. **Hermes:** Son of Zeus, messenger of the gods. **Kyllene:** Hermes' birthplace. 22. **Muses:** Nine sister goddesses of poetry, music, art, and sciences.

On Kithairon or thereabouts. He had two flocks;
I had one. Each autumn I'd drive mine home
And he would go back with his to Laios' sheepfold. —   25
Is this not true, just as I have described it?
SHEPHERD: True, yes; but it was all so long ago.
MESSENGER: Well, then: do you remember, back in those days,
That you gave me a baby boy to bring up as my own?
SHEPHERD: What if I did? What are you trying to say?   30
MESSENGER: King Oedipus was once that little child.
SHEPHERD: Damn you, hold your tongue!
OEDIPUS: No more of that!
It is your tongue needs watching, not this man's.
SHEPHERD: My king, my master, what is it I have done wrong?
OEDIPUS: You have not answered his question about the boy.   35
SHEPHERD: He does not know . . . He is only making trouble . . .
OEDIPUS: Come, speak plainly, or it will go hard with you.
SHEPHERD: In God's name, do not torture an old man!
OEDIPUS: Come here, one of you; bind his arms behind him.
SHEPHERD: Unhappy king! What more do you wish to learn?   40
OEDIPUS: Did you give this man the child he speaks of?
SHEPHERD: I did.
And I would to God I had died that very day.
OEDIPUS: You will die now unless you speak the truth.
SHEPHERD: Yet if I speak the truth, I am worse than dead.
OEDIPUS (*to Attendant*): He intends to draw it out, apparently —   45
SHEPHERD: No! I have told you already that I gave him the boy.
OEDIPUS: Where did you get him? From your house? From somewhere
else?
SHEPHERD: Not from mine, no. A man gave him to me.
OEDIPUS: Is that man here? Whose house did he belong to?
SHEPHERD: For God's love, my king, do not ask me any more!   50
OEDIPUS: You are a dead man if I have to ask you again.
SHEPHERD: Then . . . Then the child was from the palace of Laios.
OEDIPUS: A slave child? or a child of his own line?
SHEPHERD: Ah, I am on the brink of dreadful speech!
OEDIPUS: And I of dreadful hearing. Yet I must hear.   55
SHEPHERD: If you must be told, then . . .
                              They said it was Laios' child;
But it is your wife who can tell you about that.
OEDIPUS: My wife — Did she give it to you?
SHEPHERD: My lord, she did.
OEDIPUS: Do you know why?
SHEPHERD: I was told to get rid of it.

290

OEDIPUS: Oh heartless mother!
SHEPHERD: But in dread of prophecies . . .   60
OEDIPUS: Tell me.
SHEPHERD: It was said that the boy would kill his own father.
OEDIPUS: Then why did you give him over to this old man?
SHEPHERD: I pitied the baby, my king,
    And I thought that this man would take him far away
    To his own country.
                            He saved him—but for what a fate!   65
    For if you are what this man says you are,
    No man living is more wretched than Oedipus.
OEDIPUS: Ah God!
    It was true!
                    All the prophecies!
                                —Now,
    O Light, may I look on you for the last time!   70
    I, Oedipus,
    Oedipus, damned in his birth, in his marriage damned,
    Damned in the blood he shed with his own hand!

(*He rushes into the palace.*)

ODE 4   *Strophe 1*

CHORUS: Alas for the seed of men.
    What measure shall I give these generations
    That breathe on the void and are void
    And exist and do not exist?
    Who bears more weight of joy   5
    Than mass of sunlight shifting in images,
    Or who shall make his thought stay on
    That down time drifts away?
    Your splendor is all fallen.
    O naked brow of wrath and tears,   10
    O change of Oedipus!
    I who saw your days call no man blest—
    Your great days like ghosts gone.

Antistrophe 1

That mind was a strong bow.
    Deep, how deep you drew it then, hard archer,   15

291

At a dim fearful range,
And brought dear glory down!
You overcame the stranger°—
The virgin with her hooking lion claws—
And though death sang, stood like a tower   20
To make pale Thebes take heart.
Fortress against our sorrow!
True king, giver of laws,
Majestic Oedipus!
No prince in Thebes had ever such renown,   25
No prince won such grace of power.

Strophe 2

And now of all men ever known
Most pitiful is this man's story:
His fortunes are most changed; his state
Fallen to a low slave's   30
Ground under bitter fate.
O Oedipus, most royal one!
The great door° that expelled you to the light
Gave at night—ah, gave night to your glory:
As to the father, to the fathering son.   35
All understood too late.
How could that queen whom Laios won,
The garden that he harrowed at his height,
Be silent when that act was done?

Antistrophe 2

But all eyes fail before time's eye,   40
All actions come to justice there.
Though never willed, though far down the deep past,
Your bed, your dread sirings,
Are brought to book at last.
Child by Laios doomed to die,   45
Then doomed to lose that fortunate little death,
Would God you never took breath in this air
That with my wailing lips I take to cry:
For I weep the world's outcast.

18. stranger: The Sphinx.   33. door: Iokaste's womb.

I was blind, and now I can tell why: 50
Asleep, for you had given ease of breath
To Thebes, while the false years went by.

EXODOS°

(Enter, from the palace, Second Messenger.)

SECOND MESSENGER: Elders of Thebes, most honored in this land,
   What horrors are yours to see and hear, what weight
   Of sorrow to be endured, if, true to your birth,
   You venerate the line of Labdakos!
   I think neither Istros nor Phasis, those great rivers,   5
   Could purify this place of all the evil
   It shelters now, or soon must bring to light—
   Evil not done unconsciously, but willed.

   The greatest griefs are those we cause ourselves.
CHORAGOS: Surely, friend, we have grief enough already;   10
   What new sorrow do you mean?
SECOND MESSENGER: The queen is dead.
CHORAGOS: O miserable queen! But at whose hand?
SECOND MESSENGER: Her own.
   The full horror of what happened you can not know,
   For you did not see it; but I, who did, will tell you
   As clearly as I can how she met her death.   15

   When she had left us,
   In passionate silence, passing through the court,
   She ran to her apartment in the house,
   Her hair clutched by the fingers of both hands.
   She closed the doors behind her; then, by that bed   20
   Where long ago the fatal son was conceived—
   That son who should bring about his father's death—
   We heard her call upon Laios, dead so many years,
   And heard her wail for the double fruit of her marriage,
   A husband by her husband, children by her child.   25

   Exactly how she died I do not know:
   For Oedipus burst in moaning and would not let us

Exodos: Final scene.

293

Keep vigil to the end: it was by him
As he stormed about the room that our eyes were caught.
From one to another of us he went, begging a sword,   30
Hunting the wife who was not his wife, the mother
Whose womb had carried his own children and himself.
I do not know: it was none of us aided him,
But surely one of the gods was in control!
For with a dreadful cry   35
He hurled his weight, as though wrenched out of himself,
At the twin doors: the bolts gave, and he rushed in.
And there we saw her hanging, her body swaying
From the cruel cord she had noosed about her neck.
A great sob broke from him, heartbreaking to hear,   40
As he loosed the rope and lowered her to the ground.

I would blot out from my mind what happened next!
For the king ripped from her gown the golden brooches
That were her ornament, and raised them, and plunged them down
Straight into his own eyeballs, crying, "No more,   45
No more shall you look on the misery about me,
The horrors of my own doing! Too long you have known
The faces of those whom I should never have seen,
Too long been blind to those for whom I was searching!
From this hour, go in darkness!" And as he spoke,   50
He struck at his eyes—not once, but many times;
And the blood spattered his beard,
Bursting from his ruined sockets like red hail.

So from the unhappiness of two this evil has sprung,
A curse on the man and woman alike. The old   55
Happiness of the house of Labdakos
Was happiness enough: where is it today?
It is all wailing and ruin, disgrace, death—all
The misery of mankind that has a name—
And it is wholly and for ever theirs.   60
CHORAGOS: Is he in agony still? Is there no rest for him?
SECOND MESSENGER: He is calling for someone to open the
    doors wide
So that all the children of Kadmos may look upon
His father's murderer, his mother's—no,
I can not say it!
                        And then he will leave Thebes,   65
    Self-exiled, in order that the curse

294

Which he himself pronounced may depart from the house.
He is weak, and there is none to lead him,
So terrible is his suffering.
                              But you will see:
Look, the doors are opening; in a moment   70
You will see a thing that would crush a heart of stone.

(The central door is opened; Oedipus, blinded, is led in.)

CHORAGOS: Dreadful indeed for men to see.
   Never have my own eyes
   Looked on a sight so full of fear.

   Oedipus!   75
   What madness came upon you, what demon
   Leaped on your life with heavier
   Punishment than a mortal man can bear?
   No: I can not even
   Look at you, poor ruined one.   80
   And I would speak, question, ponder,
   If I were able. No.
   You make me shudder.
OEDIPUS: God. God.
   Is there a sorrow greater?   85
   Where shall I find harbor in this world?
   My voice is hurled far on a dark wind.
   What has God done to me?
CHORAGOS: Too terrible to think of, or to see.

                         Strophe 1

OEDIPUS: O cloud of night,   90
   Never to be turned away: night coming on,
   I can not tell how: night like a shroud!
   My fair winds brought me here.
                              O God. Again
   The pain of the spikes where I had sight,
   The flooding pain   95
   Of memory, never to be gouged out.
CHORAGOS: This is not strange.
   You suffer it all twice over, remorse in pain,
   Pain in remorse.

Antistrophe 1

OEDIPUS: Ah dear friend   100
　Are you faithful even yet, you alone?
　Are you still standing near me, will you stay here,
　Patient, to care for the blind?
　　　　　　　　　The blind man!
　Yet even blind I know who it is attends me,
　By the voice's tone —   105
　Though my new darkness hide the comforter.
CHORAGOS: Oh fearful act!
　What god was it drove you to rake black
　Night across your eyes?

Strophe 2

OEDIPUS: Apollo. Apollo. Dear   110
　Children, the god was Apollo.
　He brought my sick, sick fate upon me.
　But the blinding hand was my own!
　How could I bear to see
　When all my sight was horror everywhere?   115
CHORAGOS: Everywhere; that is true.
OEDIPUS: And now what is left?
　Images? Love? A greeting even,
　Sweet to the senses? Is there anything?
　Ah, no, friends: lead me away.   120
　Lead me away from Thebes.
　　　　　　　　　Lead the great wreck
　And hell of Oedipus, whom the gods hate.
CHORAGOS: Your misery, you are not blind to that.
　Would God you had never found it out!

Antistrophe 2

OEDIPUS: Death take the man who unbound   125
　My feet on that hillside
　And delivered me from death to life! What life?
　If only I had died,
　This weight of monstrous doom
　Could not have dragged me and my darlings down.   130
CHORAGOS: I would have wished the same.

OEDIPUS: Oh never to have come here
  With my father's blood upon me! Never
  To have been the man they call his mother's husband!
  Oh accurst! Oh child of evil,   135
  To have entered that wretched bed—
                          the selfsame one!
  More primal than sin itself, this fell to me.
CHORAGOS: I do not know what words to offer you.
  You were better dead than alive and blind.
OEDIPUS: Do not counsel me any more. This punishment   140
  That I have laid upon myself is just.
  If I had eyes,
  I do not know how I could bear the sight
  Of my father, when I came to the house of Death,
  Or my mother: for I have sinned against them both   145
  So vilely that I could not make my peace
  By strangling my own life.
                          Or do you think my children,
  Born as they were born, would be sweet to my eyes?
  Ah never, never! Nor this town with its high walls,
  Nor the holy images of the gods.
                          For I,   150
  Thrice miserable!—Oedipus, noblest of all the line
  Of Kadmos, have condemned myself to enjoy
  These things no more, by my own malediction
  Expelling that man whom the gods declared
  To be a defilement in the house of Laios.   155
  After exposing the rankness of my own guilt,
  How could I look men frankly in the eyes?
  No, I swear it,
  If I could have stifled my hearing at its source,
  I would have done it and made all this body   160
  A tight cell of misery, blank to light and sound:
  So I should have been safe in my dark mind
  Beyond external evil.
                          Ah Kithairon!
  Why did you shelter me? When I was cast upon you,
  Why did I not die? Then I should never   165
  Have shown the world my execrable birth.

  Ah Polybos! Corinth, city that I believed
  The ancient seat of my ancestors: how fair
  I seemed, your child! And all the while this evil

297

Was cancerous within me!
                              For I am sick   170
In my own being, sick in my origin.
O three roads, dark ravine, woodland and way
Where three roads met; you, drinking my father's blood,
My own blood, spilled by my own hand: can you remember
The unspeakable things I did there, and the things   175
I went on from there to do?
                              O marriage, marriage!
The act that engendered me, and again the act
Performed by the son in the same bed—
                              Ah, the net
Of incest, mingling fathers, brothers, sons,
With brides, wives, mothers: the last evil   180
That can be known by men: no tongue can say
How evil!
            No. For the love of God, conceal me
Somewhere far from Thebes; or kill me; or hurl me
Into the sea, away from men's eyes for ever.

Come, lead me. You need not fear to touch me.   185
Of all men, I alone can bear this guilt.

(*Enter Kreon.*)

CHORAGOS: Kreon is here now. As to what you ask,
  He may decide the course to take. He only
  Is left to protect the city in your place.
OEDIPUS: Alas, how can I speak to him? What right have I   · 190
  To beg his courtesy whom I have deeply wronged?
KREON: I have not come to mock you, Oedipus,
  Or to reproach you, either.
  (*To Attendants.*)   —You, standing there:
  If you have lost all respect for man's dignity,
  At least respect the flame of Lord Helios:°   195
  Do not allow this pollution to show itself
  Openly here, an affront to the earth
  And Heaven's rain and the light of day. No, take him
  Into the house as quickly as you can.
  For it is proper   200
  That only the close kindred see his grief.

195. **Lord Helios:** The sun god.

298

OEDIPUS: I pray you in God's name, since your courtesy
  Ignores my dark expectation, visiting
  With mercy this man of all men most execrable:
  Give me what I ask—for your good, not for mine.   205
KREON: And what is it that you turn to me begging for?
OEDIPUS: Drive me out of this country as quickly as may be
  To a place where no human voice can ever greet me.
KREON: I should have done that before now—only,
  God's will had not been wholly revealed to me.   210
OEDIPUS: But his command is plain: the parricide
  Must be destroyed. I am that evil man.
KREON: That is the sense of it, yes; but as things are,
  We had best discover clearly what is to be done.
OEDIPUS: You would learn more about a man like me?   215
KREON: You are ready now to listen to the god.
OEDIPUS: I will listen. But it is to you
  That I must turn for help. I beg you, hear me.

  The woman is there—
  Give her whatever funeral you think proper: 220
  She is your sister.
                    —But let me go, Kreon!
  Let me purge my father's Thebes of the pollution
  Of my living here, and go out to the wild hills,
  To Kithairon, that has won such fame with me,
  The tomb my mother and father appointed for me,   225
  And let me die there, as they willed I should.
  And yet I know
  Death will not ever come to me through sickness
  Or in any natural way: I have been preserved
  For some unthinkable fate. But let that be.   230

  As for my sons, you need not care for them.
  They are men, they will find some way to live.
  But my poor daughters, who have shared my table,
  Who never before have been parted from their father—
  Take care of them, Kreon; do this for me.   235

  And will you let me touch them with my hands
  A last time, and let us weep together?
  Be kind, my lord,
  Great prince, be kind!
                      Could I but touch them,
  They would be mine again, as when I had my eyes.   240

(Enter Antigone and Ismene, attended.)

Ah, God!
Is it my dearest children I hear weeping?
Has Kreon pitied me and sent my daughters?
KREON: Yes, Oedipus: I knew that they were dear to you
In the old days, and know you must love them still.   245
OEDIPUS: May God bless you for this—and be a friendlier
Guardian to you than he has been to me!

Children, where are you?
Come quickly to my hands: they are your brother's—
Hands that have brought your father's once clear eyes   250
To this way of seeing—
                              Ah dearest ones,
I had neither sight nor knowledge then, your father
By the woman who was the source of his own life!
And I weep for you—having no strength to see you—,
I weep for you when I think of the bitterness   255
That men will visit upon you all your lives.
What homes, what festivals can you attend
Without being forced to depart again in tears?
And when you come to marriageable age,
Where is the man, my daughters, who would dare   260
Risk the bane that lies on all my children?
Is there any evil wanting? Your father killed
His father; sowed the womb of her who bore him;
Engendered you at the fount of his own existence!
That is what they will say of you.

                              Then, whom   265
Can you ever marry? There are no bridegrooms for you,
And your lives must wither away in sterile dreaming.

O Kreon, son of Menoikeus!
You are the only father my daughters have,
Since we, their parents, are both of us gone for ever.   270
They are your own blood: you will not let them
Fall into beggary and loneliness;
You will keep them from the miseries that are mine!
Take pity on them; see, they are only children,
Friendless except for you. Promise me this,   275
Great prince, and give me your hand in token of it.

(*Kreon clasps his right hand.*)

Children:
I could say much, if you could understand me,
But as it is, I have only this prayer for you:
Live where you can, be as happy as you can —   280
Happier, please God, than God has made your father.
KREON: Enough. You have wept enough. Now go within.
OEDIPUS: I must, but it is hard.
KREON: Time eases all things.
OEDIPUS: You know my mind, then?
KREON: Say what you desire.
OEDIPUS: Send me from Thebes!
KREON: God grant that I may!   285
OEDIPUS: But since God hates me . . .
KREON: No, he will grant your wish.
OEDIPUS: You promise?
KREON: I can not speak beyond my knowledge.
OEDIPUS: Then lead me in.
KREON: Come now, and leave your children.   290
OEDIPUS: No! Do not take them from me!
KREON: Think no longer
That you are in command here, but rather think
How, when you were, you served your own destruction.

(*Exeunt into the house all but the Chorus; the Choragos chants directly to the audience.*)

CHORAGOS: Men of Thebes: look upon Oedipus.

This is the king who solved the famous riddle   295
And towered up, most powerful of men.
No mortal eyes but looked on him with envy,
Yet in the end ruin swept over him.

Let every man in mankind's frailty
Consider his last day; and let none   300
Presume on his good fortune until he find
Life, at his death, a memory without pain.

[c. 430 B.C.E.]

301

ALFRED, LORD TENNYSON [1809–1892]

Ulysses°

Born in Somersby, Lincolnshire, **Alfred, Lord Tennyson** (1809–1892), grew up in the tense atmosphere of his unhappy father's rectory. He went to Trinity College, Cambridge, but when he was forced to leave because of family and financial problems, he returned home to study and practice the craft of poetry. His early volumes, published in 1830 and 1832, received bad reviews, but his *In Memoriam* (1850), an elegy on his close friend Arthur Hallam, who died of a brain seizure, won acclaim. He was unquestionably the most popular poet of his time (the "poet of the people") and arguably the greatest of the Victorian poets. He succeeded William Wordsworth as poet laureate, a position he held from 1850 until his death.

It little profits that an idle king,
By this still hearth, among these barren crags,
Matched with an agèd wife, I mete and dole
Unequal laws unto a savage race,°   5
That hoard, and sleep, and feed, and know not me.

   I cannot rest from travel; I will drink
Life to the lees. All times I have enjoyed
Greatly, have suffered greatly, both with those
That loved me, and alone; on shore, and when

Ulysses (the Roman form of Odysseus): The hero of Homer's epic *The Odyssey*, which tells the story of Odysseus's adventures on his voyage back to his home, the little island of Ithaca, after he and the other Greek heroes defeated Troy. It took Odysseus ten years to reach Ithaca, the small, rocky island of which he was king, where his wife (Penelope) and son (Telemachus) were waiting for him. Upon his return he defeated the suitors who had been trying to marry the faithful Penelope, and he resumed the kingship and his old ways of life. Here Homer's story ends, but in Canto 26 of the *Inferno*, Dante extended the story: Odysseus eventually became restless and dissatisfied with his settled life and decided to return to the sea and sail west, into the unknown sea, and seek whatever adventures he might find there. Tennyson's poem amplifies the speech delivered in Dante's poem as Ulysses challenges his men to accompany him on this new voyage.
3–4. mete . . . race: Administer inadequate (unequal to what is needed) laws to a still somewhat lawless race.

Through scudding drifts° the rainy Hyades°   10
Vexed the dim sea. I am become a name;
For always roaming with a hungry heart
Much have I seen and known—cities of men
And manners, climates, councils, governments,
Myself not least, but honored of them all—   15
And drunk delight of battle with my peers,
Far on the ringing plains of windy Troy.
I am a part of all that I have met;
Yet all experience is an arch wherethrough
Gleams that untraveled world whose margin fades   20
Forever and forever when I move.
How dull it is to pause, to make an end,
To rust unburnished, not to shine in use!
As though to breathe were life! Life piled on life
Were all too little, and of one to me   25
Little remains; but every hour is saved
From that eternal silence, something more,
A bringer of new things; and vile it were
For some three suns° to store and hoard myself,   *years*
And this gray spirit yearning in desire   30
To follow knowledge like a sinking star,
Beyond the utmost bound of human thought.

    This is my son, mine own Telemachus,
To whom I leave the scepter and the isle—
Well-loved of me, discerning to fulfill   35
This labor, by slow prudence to make mild
A rugged people, and through soft degrees
Subdue them to the useful and the good.
Most blameless is he, centered in the sphere
Of common duties, decent not to fail   40
In offices of tenderness, and pay
Meet adoration to my household gods,
When I am gone. He works his work, I mine.

    There lies the port; the vessel puffs her sail;
There gloom the dark, broad seas. My mariners,   45
Souls that have toiled, and wrought, and thought with me—
That ever with a frolic welcome took
The thunder and the sunshine, and opposed

10. scudding drifts: Wind-driven spray; **Hyades:** Five stars in the constellation Taurus whose rising was assumed would be followed by rain.

Free hearts, free foreheads—you and I are old;
Old age hath yet his honor and his toil. 50
Death closes all; but something ere the end,
Some work of noble note, may yet be done,
Not unbecoming men that strove with Gods.
The lights begin to twinkle from the rocks;
The long day wanes; the slow moon climbs; the deep 55
Moans round with many voices. Come, my friends,
'Tis not too late to seek a newer world.
Push off, and sitting well in order smite
The sounding furrows; for my purpose holds
To sail beyond the sunset, and the baths° 60
Of all the western stars, until I die.
It may be that the gulfs will wash us down;
It may be we shall touch the Happy Isles,°
And see the great Achilles,° whom we knew.
Though much is taken, much abides; and though 65
We are not now that strength which in old days
Moved earth and heaven, that which we are, we are—
One equal temper of heroic hearts,
Made weak by time and fate, but strong in will
To strive, to seek, to find, and not to yield. 70

[1833]

60. **baths:** The outer river or ocean surrounding the flat earth, in Greek cosmology, into which the stars descended upon setting.
63. **Happy Isles:** The Islands of the Blessed, or Elysian Fields, in Greek myth, which lay in the western seas beyond the Strait of Gibraltar and were the abode of heroes after death.
64. **Achilles:** The hero of the Greeks, and Odysseus's comrade, in Homer's *Iliad*.

WILLIAM WORDSWORTH [1770–1850]

Lines

Composed a Few Miles above Tintern Abbey°
on Revisiting the Banks of the Wye
During a Tour. July 13, 1798

William Wordsworth (1770–1850) was born and raised in the Lake District of England. Both his parents died by the time he was thirteen. He studied at Cambridge, toured Europe on foot, and lived in France for a year during the first part of the French Revolution. He returned to England, leaving behind a lover, Annette Vallon, and their daughter, Caroline, from whom he was soon cut off by war between England and France. He met Samuel Taylor Coleridge, and in 1798 they published *Lyrical Ballads,* the first great work of the English Romantic movement. He changed poetry forever by his decision to use common language in his poetry instead of heightened poetic diction. In 1799 he and his sister Dorothy moved to Grasmere, in the Lake District, where he married Mary Hutchinson, a childhood friend. His greatest works were produced between 1797 and 1808. He continued to write for the next forty years but his work never regained the heights of his earlier verse. In 1843 he was named poet laureate, a position he held until his death in 1850.

Five years have passed; five summers, with the length
Of five long winters! and again I hear
These waters, rolling from their mountain-springs
With a soft inland murmur. Once again
Do I behold these steep and lofty cliffs,   5
That on a wild secluded scene impress
Thoughts of more deep seclusion; and connect
The landscape with the quiet of the sky.
The day is come when I again repose
Here, under this dark sycamore, and view   10

Tintern Abbey: The ruins of a medieval abbey that Wordsworth had visited in August 1793. Wordsworth says that he composed the poem in his head in four or five hours as he walked from Tintern to Bristol in 1798, and then wrote it down without revisions.

These plots of cottage ground, these orchard tufts,
Which at this season, with their unripe fruits,
Are clad in one green hue, and lose themselves
'Mid groves and copses. Once again I see
These hedgerows, hardly hedgerows, little lines   15
Of sportive wood run wild; these pastoral farms,
Green to the very door; and wreaths of smoke
Sent up, in silence, from among the trees!
With some uncertain notice, as might seem
Of vagrant dwellers in the houseless woods,   20
Or of some Hermit's cave, where by his fire
The Hermit sits alone.

          These beauteous forms,
Through a long absence, have not been to me
As is a landscape to a blind man's eye;
But oft, in lonely rooms, and 'mid the din   25
Of towns and cities, I have owed to them,
In hours of weariness, sensations sweet,
Felt in the blood, and felt along the heart;
And passing even into my purer mind,
With tranquil restoration—feelings too   30
Of unremembered pleasure; such, perhaps,
As have no slight or trivial influence
On that best portion of a good man's life,
His little, nameless, unremembered, acts
Of kindness and of love. Nor less, I trust,   35
To them I may have owed another gift,
Of aspect more sublime; that blessed mood,
In which the burthen of the mystery,
In which the heavy and the weary weight
Of all this unintelligible world,   40
Is lightened—that serene and blessed mood,
In which the affections gently lead us on—
Until, the breath of this corporeal frame
And even the motion of our human blood
Almost suspended, we are laid asleep   45
In body, and become a living soul;
While with an eye made quiet by the power
Of harmony, and the deep power of joy,
We see into the life of things.

          If this
Be but a vain belief, yet, oh! how oft—   50

306

In darkness and amid the many shapes
Of joyless daylight; when the fretful stir
Unprofitable, and the fever of the world,
Have hung upon the beatings of my heart—
How oft, in spirit, have I turned to thee,   55
O sylvan° Wye! thou wanderer through the woods,   *wooded*
How often has my spirit turned to thee!

   An now, with gleams of half-extinguished thought,
With many recognitions dim and faint,
And somewhat of a sad perplexity,   60
The picture of the mind revives again;
While here I stand, not only with the sense
Of present pleasure, but with pleasing thoughts
That in this moment there is life and food
For future years. And so I dare to hope,   65
Though changed, no doubt, from what I was when first
I came among these hills; when like a roe
I bounded o'er the mountains, by the sides
Of the deep rivers, and the lonely streams,
Wherever nature led—more like a man   70
Flying from something that he dreads than one
Who sought the thing he loved. For nature then
(The coarser pleasures of my boyish days,
And their glad animal movements all gone by)
To me was all in all.—I cannot paint   75
What then I was. The sounding cataract
Haunted me like a passion; the tall rock,
The mountain, and the deep and gloomy wood,
Their colors and their forms, were then to me
An appetite; a feeling and a love,   80
That had no need of a remoter charm,
By thought supplied, nor any interest
Unborrowed from the eye.—That time is past,
And all its aching joys are now no more,
And all its dizzy raptures. Not for this   85
Faint° I, nor mourn nor murmur; other gifts   *become discouraged*
Have followed; for such loss, I would believe,
Abundant recompense. For I have learned
To look on nature, not as in the hour
Of thoughtless youth; but hearing oftentimes   90
The still, sad music of humanity,
Nor harsh nor grating, though of ample power

To chasten and subdue. And I have felt
A presence that disturbs me with the joy
Of elevated thoughts; a sense sublime   95
Of something far more deeply interfused,
Whose dwelling is the light of setting suns,
And the round ocean and the living air,
And the blue sky, and in the mind of man:
A motion and a spirit, that impels   100
All thinking things, all objects of all thought,
And rolls through all things. Therefore am I still
A lover of the meadows and the woods,
And mountains; and of all that we behold
From this green earth; of all the mighty world   105
Of eye, and ear—both what they half create,
And what perceive; well pleased to recognize
In nature and the language of the sense
The anchor of my purest thoughts, the nurse,
The guide, the guardian of my heart, and soul   110
Of all my moral being.

           Nor perchance,
If I were not thus taught, should I the more
Suffer my genial spirits° to decay: *creative powers*
For thou art with me here upon the banks
Of this fair river; thou my dearest Friend,°   115
My dear, dear Friend; and in thy voice I catch
The language of my former heart, and read
My former pleasures in the shooting lights
Of thy wild eyes. Oh! yet a little while
May I behold in thee what I was once,   120
My dear, dear Sister! and this prayer I make,
Knowing that Nature never did betray
The heart that loved her; 'tis her privilege,
Through all the years of this our life, to lead
From joy to joy: for she can so inform   125
The mind that is within us, so impress
With quietness and beauty, and so feed
With lofty thoughts, that neither evil tongues,
Rash judgments, nor the sneers of selfish men,
Nor greetings where no kindness is, nor all   130

115. **Friend:** Wordsworth's sister Dorothy, who is made to sound younger by more than the year and a half that separated them.

The dreary intercourse of daily life,
Shall e'er prevail against us, or disturb
Our cheerful faith, that all which we behold
Is full of blessings. Therefore let the moon
Shine on thee in thy solitary walk;   135
And let the misty mountain winds be free
To blow against thee: and, in after years,
When these wild ecstasies shall be matured
Into a sober pleasure; when thy mind
Shall be a mansion for all lovely forms,   140
Thy memory be as a dwelling place
For all sweet sounds and harmonies; oh! then,
If solitude, or fear, or pain, or grief
Should be thy portion, with what healing thoughts
Of tender joy wilt thou remember me,   145
And these my exhortations! Nor, perchance—
If I should be where I no more can hear
Thy voice, nor catch from thy wild eyes these gleams
Of past existence—wilt thou then forget
That on the banks of this delightful stream   150
We stood together; and that I, so long
A worshiper of Nature, hither came
Unwearied in that service; rather say
With warmer love—oh! with far deeper zeal
Of holier love. Nor wilt thou then forget,   155
That after many wanderings, many years
Of absence, these steep woods and lofty cliffs,
And this green pastoral landscape, were to me
More dear, both for themselves and for thy sake!

                                                          [1798]

309